Y0-AAB-269

THE UNITED STATES AIR FORCE REPORT ON THE BALLISTIC MISSILE

THE UNITED STATES AIR FORCE REPORT ON THE BALLISTIC MISSILE

Its Technology, Logistics and Strategy

Edited by

LT. COL. KENNETH F. GANTZ

With a Preface by

GENERAL THOMAS D. WHITE,

Chief of Staff, USAF

Introduction by

MAJOR GENERAL BERNARD A. SCHRIEVER

1958

DOUBLEDAY & COMPANY, INC., GARDEN CITY, NEW YORK

Library of Congress Catalog Card Number 58-7795
Printed in the United States of America

EDITOR'S INTRODUCTION

On 9 January 1958 Major General Bernard Schriever, in charge of developing the long-range rocket missiles of the United States, appeared before a committee of Congress. During his testimony he said that the United States Air Force could, within a matter of five years or less, put space probes out to Venus and Mars and shortly thereafter make manned reconnaissance of the moon.

This capability, General Schriever made clear, did not depend upon a breakthrough yet to be made. He was describing the capabilities of current Air Force missiles: Thor, the intermediate-range ballistic missile now in quantity production; Atlas, the intercontinental ballistic missile now in flight testing; and Titan, another ICBM only a few months behind Atlas.

Thor, Atlas, and Titan are military weapons which have their counterparts in Soviet Russia. With their coming, the concepts, tactics, and techniques of air warfare broaden into forms of space warfare. They add a new family of weapon systems to supplement and increase the effectiveness of manned bomber systems. They already are blending into the forces of the Strategic Air Command, America's major striking arm in support of the hope to deter aggression by mounting a massive strength for retaliation.

This book is a professional review of the program of the United States Air Force that has developed the current long-range ballistic missile and is organizing missile forces and fitting them into the SAC line. Its chapters are written by top Air Force missilemen and technical experts, and it is as authentic and complete as security permits. The chapters were composed for publication in a special missile issue and in other current issues of the *Air University Quarterly Review*, which is the professional journal of the United States

Air Force in strategy, tactics, and techniques. At the request of the publisher the material of greatest interest was selected by the Editor of *Air University Quarterly Review* and integrated to make a comprehensive report from those actually involved in design and manufacture, in engineering development and testing, in the activation of operational squadrons and wings to make up the 1st Missile Division, and in all the technical, doctrinal, and logistical problems involved.

The book which has resulted is due to the inspiration of Mr. John McDonald of the staff of *Fortune* magazine, who engaged himself during a siege of influenza in reading the Ballistic Missile issue of the *Quarterly Review*. Struck by the important contribution the material might make to public understanding of the nation's status in the missile race with the U. S. S. R. after Sputnik, he immediately brought it to the enthusiastic attention of the editors of Doubleday and Company and won the interest and cooperation of the United States Air Force in response to Doubleday's desire to publish it. Thereafter Mr. McDonald gave freely of his counsel to the publisher in shaping the scope of the book and in planning its publication. The addition of the important chapter by General Power of Strategic Air Command was at Mr. McDonald's suggestion, which help the Editor gratefully acknowledges.

The book is introduced by General Thomas White, Chief of Staff of the United States Air Force, who describes the Air Force plans for space operations and sums up the basic doctrine for the Air Force in the decade ahead.

Major General Bernard Schriever, Commander of the Ballistic Missile Division, Hq. Air Research and Development Command, reviews the Air Force missile development program in his charge, which has developed Thor, Atlas, and Titan, and he looks ahead into the second generation of missiles to follow them. He gives special attention to the Air Force development-management concept and to development procedures. These procedures, which undertook the calculated risk of developing manufacturing and operational capabilities simultaneously with the engineering design and testing of the missile itself, have led to the outstanding success of creating a weapon system, its crewing, and its support in being, as the testing phase for the weapon draws to a close.

General Thomas Power, Commander in Chief, Strategic Air Command, contributes a chapter of first importance on the entrance of the missile into the SAC line, the marriage of a new and yet untried weapon system to a long-established and well-tried operational force. What are the qualifications of the ballistic missile as a strategic weapon system? How does the missile relate to the other elements that must combine with a weapon system to offer strategic capability?

Major General Ben I. Funk, Director of the Ballistic Missile Office, Air Materiel Command, explains the logistic systems and controls for missile employment and the enormous demands the missile weapon systems and their development make upon the industry of the nation. These demands, he shows, have led to the organization of "industry systems" and subsystems of vast scientific, engineering, and production resources. Major General Charles McCorkle, Assistant Chief of Staff for Guided Missiles, Headquarters USAF, deals with the knotty problem of the command of the missile, posing the closest control by the highest national authorities and sure response in minutes to aggressive attack. Colonels Alexander Sheridan and Harvey Shelton of the Air War College also enter the doctrinal areas of command, control, and employment of missiles to discuss the problems they impose on the art of warfare and on the defense of the United States.

Rocket-engine expert Colonel Edward Hall gives a close look at the cumulated experience of the Air Force in missile design and development that put aside the German approach with the wartime V-2 and started postwar from first principles. The result was the major rocket engines of today and the systems-engineered missile. The impressiveness of this achievement is underscored by a detailed section of "Notes on Technical Aspects of Ballistic Missiles," which was prepared by a group of experts in the Space Technology Laboratories of the Ramo-Wooldridge Corporation to explain the technical and engineering concepts underlying the intercontinental ballistic missile and its path to target. Many readers will find this section of the Appendix of outstanding interest and usefulness in illuminating the other parts of the book.

Colonel Claude E. Putnam, Chief of the Evaluation Staff of the Air War College, examines the experienced environment of the

United States Air Force as a "home" for ballistic missile and manned spacecraft weapon systems. The generations of experience with guidance, power plants, airframes, reconnaissance, strategic intelligence, strategic warfare, and survival in the upper air now move naturally into the space age.

In Appendix IV the reader will find "The USAF Reports to Congress," an integrated summary of the views expressed and positions taken by such Air Force leaders as General White, General Schriever, General Putt, General Irvine, and Secretary Douglas before the Preparedness Investigating Sub-committee of the Committee on Armed Services of the U. S. Senate. Generous selections from their verbatim testimony show how these airmen with major responsibilities for the missile and the era of space operations view (1) the status of the U.S. missile program, (2) the relative status and quality of U.S. missiles, and (3) the capabilities of the USAF for space operations. Included is a classic statement by General Schriever that marks the opening of the era of the spacecraft.

A number of other chapters deal with testing, targeting, and manning, and a comprehensive glossary of the terms related to the ballistic missile and its Air Force environment has been included as Appendix V.

It is hoped that man will go into space in peaceful competition for understanding of the universe. But Americans dare not neglect the implications of the missile and spacecraft for their security. These implications, together with presently known facts, are explored and described in the chapters that follow. The attention of the reader is invited to the fact that they reflect the understanding and opinion of their authors and the selection of the Editor and do not necessarily carry the official sanction of the Department of the Air Force.

CONTENTS

LIST OF ILLUSTRATIONS

These illustrations portray the development and testing of the Air Force missiles. They were selected from official Air Force photographs and will be found in the section following page 170.

CHRONOLOGY OF MAJOR EVENTS IN THE DEVELOPMENT OF AIR FORCE BALLISTIC MISSILES

The discussion of The United States Ballistic Missile *Report* is primarily concerned with current developments. The reader may therefore find the following chronology a helpful preview in relating the discussions to what has occurred since the advent of the hydrogen warhead signaled the accelerated development of the long-range ballistic missile.

1953		The thermonuclear breakthrough led to a recommendation by the Air Force Strategic Missiles Evaluation Committee that the program for the Atlas intercontinental ballistic missile, which had been proceeding with limited funds since 1951, be redirected, expanded, and accelerated.
1954	Aug	The Western Development Division, now Air Force Ballistic Missile Division, was activated under Air Research and Development Command to manage Atlas research, development, and testing. The program was given highest Air Force research and development priority.
1955	May	Development of the Titan intercontinental ballistic missile was assigned to Air Force Ballistic Missile Division.
	Sept	The ICBM programs were given highest national priority by the President.
	Dec	Development of the Thor intermediate-range ballistic missile was charged to AFBMD.

1956 March Under the added responsibility for initial operational capability (IOC) of both the intercontinental ballistic missile and the intermediate-range ballistic missile, AFBMD proceeded with plans for construction of bases, production of operational missiles and supporting equipment, and activation, equipping, and training of IOC units.

1957 Jan Thor flight-test program was started 13 months after awarding of contract.

June Atlas had its initial flight test.

July The first operational missile training base was activated at Cooke Air Force Base, California.

Sept Thor met complete success on its fourth test firing. The 1st Missile Division was activated at Cooke.

Nov Thor and Jupiter deployment was charged to the Air Force, the first IOC units to be ready by December 1958.

Warren Air Force Base, Wyoming, was selected as a missile launching site.

General Thomas D. White, USAF Chief of Staff, announced actions designed to provide an earlier operational capability in missile weapons:

(1) Transfer of the 1st Missile Division from AFBMD (ARDC) to Strategic Air Command, United States Air Force.

(2) Transfer of the IOC responsibility for the IRBM and the ICBM to Strategic Air Command.

Dec Thor made the first U.S. IRBM fully guided flight, using an all-inertial guidance system.

The ICBM Atlas was successfully fired. All test objectives were achieved.

PREFACE

Missiles and the Race Toward Space

GENERAL THOMAS D. WHITE, USAF

In little more than a decade the nature of international relations has been radically altered by the concurrent development of thermonuclear weapons, intercontinental bombers, and missiles. International relations soon will be further complicated by man's capability to travel in the far reaches of space. This era of rapid technological progress could benefit all mankind, or it could result in a holocaust which might destroy the civilized world. The United States Air Force intends to do everything within its power to prevent war and to enhance the peaceful benefits that knowledge of space could bring.

To ensure peace, the United States has no current alternative but to maintain powerful military forces in a state of constant readiness for war. Since the prime purpose of our military forces is to deter war, our deterrent forces will have accomplished their purpose if they never have to be used in battle. Should the United States be required to use its military forces, however, they must be strong enough to achieve victory.

The basic philosophy of the United States Air Force as concerns military air power is the requirement for flexible offensive forces second to none. These forces must be capable of *selective* operations anywhere in the world in support of our national objectives. Possession of a strong defense, particularly a strong air defense, is important, but our possession of first-rate offensive forces is the principal deterrent to enemy attack.

The idea of deterrence through possession of strong military strength is not new. In years past the deterrent stature of the United States existed in its reserve and mobilization potentials and in the protection afforded by its oceans—as well as in the size and quality of its forces in being. But this has changed. Deterrence can no longer be measured in terms of distance or mobilization potential. The potency and flexibility of powerful striking forces which can retaliate on a moment's notice compose the only real deterrent today. This deterrent power can be sufficient only so long as it convinces potential enemies that aggression against the United States and its allies would not pay. The most important responsibility of the United States Air Force is to maintain its deterrent power strong and modern, with forces that are sufficiently flexible to meet all situations in which they are likely to be needed.

Missiles

Air Force capabilities have always been developed in accordance with assigned responsibilities and are always projected into the future on the same basis. The reason the Air Force builds weapon systems of any type is to produce better combat capabilities. As the state of the art has improved, so have the weapon systems of the Air Force improved. The technological progress evidenced in a comparison between the B-29 atomic bomber of 1945 and the global B-52 jet nuclear bomber of 1958 is obvious. The sciences of aeronautics and astronautics will combine to bring progress that is even more significant and astounding in the years to come.

The Air Force embarked on the intermediate- and long-range missile programs because the combat potentialities of missiles offered certain advantages in comparison with manned systems. This is true even with early models of missiles, which will be much less efficient than those we expect to obtain later on. The Air Force has made considerable progress in the research and development of missiles, in detailed planning for their operational use, and in the provision of logistic support of missile systems when they become operational. Building a missile capability has been the number-one priority project of the Air Force in recent years.

There are many reasons why ballistic and guided missiles are compatible and complementary systems to manned aircraft. The alert potential, quick reaction time, and reduced vulnerability to enemy attack of operationally reliable missile systems will result in more effective and economical performance of many Air Force missions. However, weapon selection and the determination of proper force structure will also depend on many other factors, such as reliability, accuracy, warhead weight, carrying capability, range, cost, and the type of targets to be attacked.

Although there are many advantages to be gained from exploitation of missiles, care must and will be taken to avoid the danger of going overboard on missiles or, for that matter, on any single weapon system or weapon. USAF studies indicate that even with vastly improved missiles the strongest force structure, the one providing the best survival insurance, will be one in which missiles and high-performance manned systems are used together in complementary roles. Aircraft, missiles, and spacecraft are mutually supporting systems. They are compatible in development and in operational strategies designed to gain and hold a superior advantage in air and space. They are a functionally complete system.

This factor of system completeness must be kept in perspective if the future patterns of air power are to be seen clearly. Manned aircraft, missiles, and piloted spacecraft are parts of a continuing, integrated system. From an operational viewpoint they are a single instrument. Operating under the same control structure, missiles, manned aircraft, and spacecraft will provide great flexibility. If circumstances should rule out mission accomplishment with one method, another method will be responsive to the mission. If more than one method is required, they can be applied simultaneously to the target objective.

Astronautics

Ballistic missiles have sometimes been erroneously referred to as the ultimate weapon. It is extremely doubtful whether there ever can be an ultimate weapon, although experience has shown that a single weapon or weapon system can be decisive at a certain time or place. Missiles should be considered but another step, albeit a very important step, in the evolution from manned aircraft to true piloted spacecraft.

In discussing air and space it should be recognized that there is no division, per se, between the two. For all practical purposes air and space merge, forming a continuous and indivisible field of operations. Just as in the past when our capability to control the air permitted our freedom of movement on the land and seas beneath, so in the future will the capability to control space permit our freedom of movement on the surface of the earth and through the earth's atmosphere.

The Air Force has been pioneering in the fringes of space for several years with manned aircraft. The Bell X-2, a rocket research plane, carried Captain Iven Kincheloe up to approximately 25 miles above the earth at 1900 miles per hour. The X-15, which is now in the development stage, is designed for speeds and altitudes much greater than those of the X-2. The next step is the Air Force program to fly at hypersonic speeds, circumnavigating the globe many times before re-entering the earth's atmosphere. As a weapon system, this program will represent the first major breakthrough in sustained piloted space flight. With this system it will be possible to resolve many of the problems involved in either placing man on a continuous orbit around the earth or sending him soaring into outer space and to nearby planets. At the rate things are going, it is technically feasible for manned space flight to become routine in a very few years. The current technological race is producing scientific advances at an unprecedented rate. Engine thrust has been increased many times over what was available a few years ago; and personal equipment has been improved to a point where it will be adequate for manned space flight to the moon.

Air Force experience factor

It is natural for the Air Force to have a major operational interest in the integration of air and space capabilities. Since the beginning of controlled flight in a heavier-than-air machine over fifty years ago, the Air Force has used the airplane as its basic system. During these years it has accumulated a vast amount of development knowledge, operational experience, and practical skills. Today, as the United States Air Force stands on the threshold of the space age, this know-how—the Air Force maturity in the science of flight—is a tremendously valuable and important asset. Through constant exploitation of the range, speed, altitude characteristics, and carrying capacity of aircraft, the Air Force has developed techniques of air warfare which were brought to a high state of perfection in World War II and which were improved even more during the Korean War. Strategic air warfare, the capability to penetrate deep within an enemy's defenses and attack his vital sources of power, is but one product of Air Force imagination, skill, and experience.

Today the operational structure of the Air Force reflects this intensive experience in excellent equipment and a dedicated body of professional airmen. Predominant characteristics of this structure are quick reaction, flexibility, firepower selectivity, mobility, and penetrative ability. With an infinite number of combinations of range, speed, routes, altitudes, and tactics and operating in a medium that is undivided, unobstructed, and unlimited, the United States Air Force can accomplish an infinite number of tasks. The forces can be shifted rapidly from task to task or from one locality to another. They can be adapted quickly to various requirements for firepower in war and to employment for humanitarian, political, and psychological purposes in peace. Missiles can be exploited most efficiently and effectively when combined with this extensive operational experience.

Missile development and the probing of piloted craft into the fringes of space have been tremendous undertakings, surpassing even the Manhattan Project in scope and goals. In the not-too-distant future, efficient ballistic missiles and true piloted spacecraft will enter our forces as operational weapons. The Air Force will be ready to receive them and use them effectively, although new problems and challenges can be expected.

The United States and its allies must maintain the capability to exert a steady, unremitting pressure against war in the years ahead. This can be done if United States air power is the best air power. To be the best, it must be ready night and day, for every day of every year, to execute a counterstroke which is powerful, swift, and deadly.

Such a force will make an aggressor reluctant to attack. The Air Force is dedicated to creating for our country the best air power it is possible to produce.

Headquarters United States Air Force

INTRODUCTION

The USAF Ballistic Missile Program

MAJOR GENERAL BERNARD A. SCHRIEVER, USAF

The USAF ballistic missile program is the largest military development program ever undertaken by this nation in peacetime. Compared to previous programs, it involves many simultaneous technical advances in the state of the missile art. Among these are development of equipment to produce high engine thrusts, great accuracy of guidance, and equipment to resist high speeds and temperatures. It also requires greater expansion of production and test facilities than has been true of any other Air Force program. It is a single, integrated program, based upon years of Air Force missile and aircraft experience. From it operational weapon systems will emerge for the intercontinental mission and the intermediate-range mission. The Air Force with its firm belief in utilizing all elements of science and industry has assembled the strongest scientific-industrial-military development team that it could to perform the complex and vital development-operational task for these missiles.

Program origins

The Air Force has been actively interested in ballistic missiles since the closing days of World War II, beginning with our knowledge of the German V-2 program. The V-2, remarkable rocket development that it was in view of the time allotted for development and operations, had notable shortcomings. Its payload was small and its accuracy questionable. Economically, as a military weapon, it was costly. Its range was far less than that of aircraft, which could deliver more payload with greater accuracy. It was only resorted to when the Allied air forces drove the Germans from the skies.

These facts were well known to us. Consequently Air Force ballistic missile development work following World War II concentrated on first extending the state of the missile art, particularly in propulsion and guidance.

In 1946 the Air Force began an orderly and systematic missile development program. Contracts were negotiated with North American Aviation for rocket propulsion and long-range missile (Navaho) development, and with Consolidated-Vultee Aircraft (now the Convair Division of General Dynamics Corporation) for study and investigation of missile guidance and control, rocket engine swiveling, and lightweight missile structures.

Our most advanced rocket power plant today is a direct result of this North American contract. Similarly our current ballistic missile program profited heavily from Consolidated-Vultee design and testing under Project MX-774.

The Air Force ballistic missile program benefited during the postwar years from other Air Force long-range guided missile programs such as Matador, Snark, and Navaho, and from air defense missile developments. All contributed to the solution of ballistic missile propulsion, guidance and control, and structural problems. Also aircraft and engine programs contributed advances in turbopumps, heat-resistant materials, combustion theory, autopilots, radio-inertial and all-inertial guidance, and so forth. Such progress was cumulative and did much to solve outstanding technical problems of long-range missiles.

The Air Force ballistic missile development program was kept at a relatively low level until 1950, because more conventional guided missiles appeared to offer the best and easiest solution to the range/payload/accuracy problem which faced long-range strategic missile designers. Economic factors related to the cost of development also played a part in this situation. In particular, two inhibiting factors were the lack of an attractive payload in terms of weight versus yield, and concern over how to protect this payload on re-entry. The re-entry problem was considered to be a particularly knotty one.

By 1950 Air Force development agencies felt that enough progress had been made in these areas to warrant study and limited design of an ICBM, the intercontinental ballistic missile. A contract was awarded to Convair* in early 1951 for the development of an ICBM. This was the original Atlas program, on which conservative development policies were followed because of the technical problems still to be solved. By 1953 impending solution of most of these problems allowed design and initial construction of Atlas vehicles.

The "thermonuclear breakthrough"

This was the status of the program when several new factors altered the development picture. The first was the "thermonuclear breakthrough" of 1952–53, when Atomic Energy Commission advances in nuclear weapon technology pointed the way to the design and production of small, high-yield warheads, that is, small warheads with great explosive power.

To this factor, tremendous in its implications as it was, must be added a second. In 1953 the Department of Defense conducted a vigorous examination of all long-range missile programs. In its report the Department of Defense guided missiles study group of the Armed Forces Policy Council recommended that strategic missile programs could best be evaluated by a special group of the nation's leading scientists. To perform this evaluation, Mr. Trevor Gardner, then Air Force Special Assistant for Research and Development, established the Air Force Strategic Missiles Evaluation Committee, also known as the "Teapot" Committee. It was composed of outstanding scientists and engineers and chaired by the late Professor John von Neumann,** then of the Princeton Institute for Advanced Study and later an AEC Commissioner.

* Convair had carried on studies of its own in ICBM areas after completion of its original ballistic missile contract in 1948.

** Other members of the Committee were Professor Clark B. Millikan, California Institute of Technology; Professor Charles C. Lauritsen, California Institute

Thoroughly aware of the implications of the thermonuclear breakthrough, and supported by independent studies made by organizations such as the RAND Corporation, Mr. Gardner and his group made positive recommendations that a redirected, expanded, and accelerated Atlas program be established. In its report the Committee concluded that if the program was given increased priority and funding, and if direction of the program was placed under the control of a strong development-management organization, an operational ICBM could be achieved years sooner than might otherwise be possible.

The Air Force approved the "Teapot" Committee's recommendations in May 1954. Directives were issued assigning the program the highest priority in the Air Force. The Air Research and Development Command was directed to establish a field organization with a general officer in command to exercise complete authority and control over all aspects of the program. Directives were issued that the program was to be reoriented and accelerated to the maximum extent that technology would permit.

In August 1954 the Western Development Division (now the Air Force Ballistic Missile Division of Headquarters Air Research and Development Command) was established in Inglewood, California, to perform these tasks. At the same time, to perform procurement and contracting functions for the new program, the Air Materiel Command established the Special Aircraft Project Office (now the Ballistic Missiles Office, Directorate of Procurement and Production, Headquarters Air Materiel Command), at the Inglewood location. This organization, under Major General Ben I. Funk, performs the normal range of AMC functions on an expedited basis.

In early studies of what type of organization should be set up to manage and direct the program, all advisers were insistent that centralized management control of the project was necessary. The task of technical direction and systems engineering was considered more complex than that encountered on the original Manhattan

---

of Technology; Dr. Louis G. Dunn, California Institute of Technology; Dr. Hendrik W. Bode, Bell Telephone Laboratories; Dr. Allen E. Puckett, Hughes Aircraft Company; Dr. George B. Kistiakowsky, Harvard University; Professor J. B. Wiesner, Massachusetts Institute of Technology; Mr. Lawrence A. Hyland, Bendix Aviation Corporation; Dr. Simon Ramo, Ramo-Wooldridge Corporation; and Dr. Dean Wooldridge, Ramo-Wooldridge Corporation.

atom bomb project. After study, the decision was made that the Air Force would retain over-all system responsibility and contract for a technical and scientific staff. Obviously a strong team of scientists and engineers was required to perform these functions. After thorough consideration of this need, the Ramo-Wooldridge Corporation was selected to provide the important systems engineering and tech-

Management Structure
AF Ballistic Missile Program

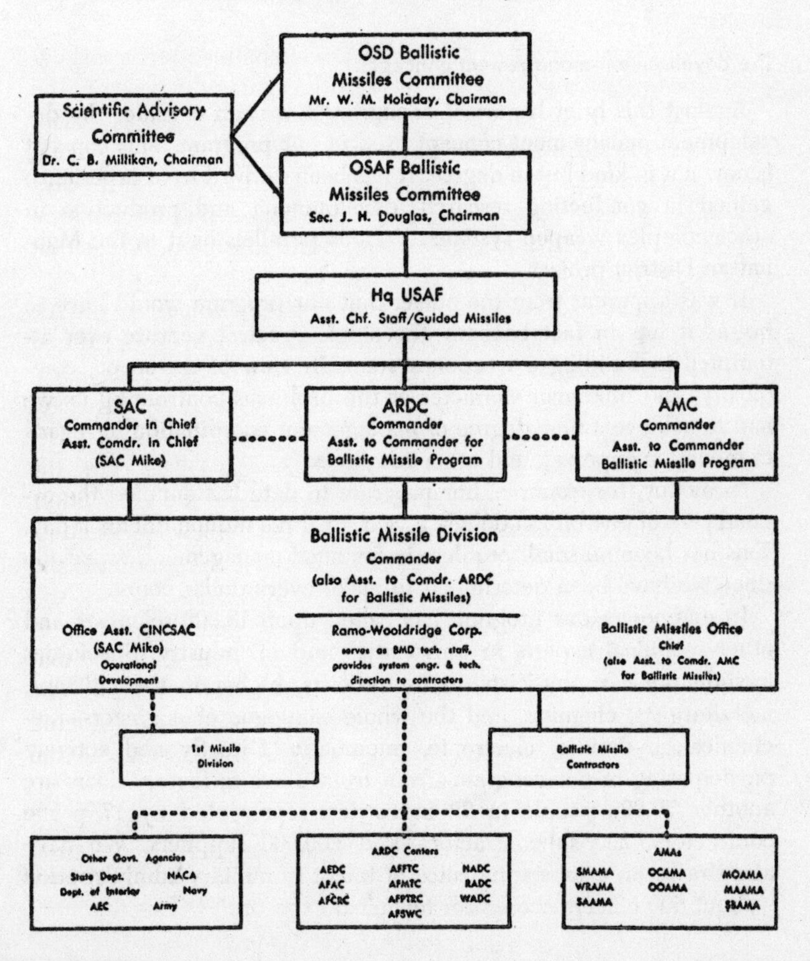

nical direction of the associate contractors who made up the development team. They provide the scientists and engineers needed to perform the complex technical and scientific analysis and systems engineering. Together with their counterparts of the Air Force Ballistic Missile Division, the R-W technical and scientific personnel were integrated into a development-management team, with all the elements working on a side-by-side, counterpart basis. This organizational integration permitted close working relationships and saved time in getting on with the job.

The development-management concept

Against this brief historical background we can consider the development-management concept used in our program. This concept is new not in kind but in degree. It has been derived from experience gained in conducting research, development, and production in other complex weapon systems. Various parallels exist in the Manhattan District project.

It was apparent from the outset that our program would have to be—as it has in fact become—the single greatest venture ever attempted in building a weapon system. In view of the scope, complexity, and unknown character of the problems confronting us we had to achieve a new degree of management coordination in regard to money, manpower, and other resources.

In money, for example, our program to date has entailed the expenditure of one billion dollars a year, or three million dollars a day. This has been no small problem in financial management, especially since we have been determined to make every dollar count.

In manpower our program has called upon 18,000 scientists and other technical experts in universities and in industry. Specialties include nuclear physicists, astrophysicists, higher mathematicians, metallurgists, chemists, and the whole catalogue of engineers—mechanical, hydraulic, electronic, pneumatic. Directly and actively participating in our program—from front office to factory floor—are another 70,000 people in 22 industries, represented by 17 prime contractors, 200 subcontractors, and 200,000 suppliers. We have also drawn on a substantial slice of talent in military administration —about 500 officers chosen for technical expertise.

In short, we had first of all to bring into being what various observers have described as the most efficient science-government-industry team ever put together. It has been this cross-fertilization of all these minds and disciplines and skills—the interlocking of the abstruse calculations of physicists with the driving competence of industrial executives—which has enabled us to accomplish in three and a half years what it took the Soviets seven years to do in developing the missile art.

From the earliest days we saw that our assignment would demand a new kind of specialized planning to coordinate the myriad elements involved in our program. This specialized planning provided us with the foundation of our newer management concept, the concept of concurrency. This may be defined as moving ahead with everything and everybody, altogether and all at once, toward a specific goal. It was this management concept of concurrency that enabled us to take a tremendous calculated risk to compress the time required to obtain operational capability of our ballistic missiles.

We decided to break with tradition—to discard the usual procedure. That procedure is to build a new weapon, part by part, in a series of consecutive steps—to fashion hand-wrought prototypes before venturing into production tooling. But to reduce the time cycle we decided to attack all areas of our assignment concurrently. In short, we took the calculated risk of planning, programing, and spending our funds concurrently on research, development, testing, production, manpower training, base construction, and other phases of our program.

Our aim was to bring all elements of our program along so that they all would be ready, at each successive stage, to be dovetailed into each other. Thus, for example, at the same time we were converting the formulas of thermodynamics into blueprints for rocket engines, we were designing the equipment to produce them. And while we were pressing ahead with blueprints and equipment for the rocket engines, we were converting the formulas of aerodynamics into the contours of the nose cone and preparing to fit that into the casing of the airframe which was engineered around the rocket—and so on up and down the line.

At the same time all this was going forward, we were preparing our ground equipment and logistical support structure from the gantry crane at the launching pad to assembly line—including transportation, maintenance and repair, storage, and supply. We were pouring concrete for our missile training base at Cooke Air Force Base, California, and selecting an operational base, now under way at Cheyenne, Wyoming. We are now in the process of selecting still another operational ICBM base. And in accord with a prearranged plan to hasten the availability of IRBM squadrons for overseas duty, the task of putting into shape these first missile squadrons has been transferred to the Strategic Air Command.

At the same time that Air Force training specialists were writing the first missile manuals, the first batches of ICBM and IRBM missile instructors were taking intensive courses in the strategy and handling of the ballistic missile as a weapon system and in the human psychology involved.

Development concepts and policies used in the past have changed considerably from one weapon system to the next as systems have become more complex and costly. For the past few years we have tended to rely more and more on the "prime contractor" approach to weapon system development in order to speed system development and integration. Studies of the classic development cycle (broadly, the time it takes to translate an idea into an operational weapon system), in which study, development, test, production, and introduction into the military force take place more or less discretely and in series, indicate that this process averages about seven years. This is a long time, especially in view of limited in-service life and rapid technological advances which today quickly outmode many weapon systems. One possible solution to this situation is to shorten the development cycle by taking concurrent development, production, and operational actions. Obviously this can be done only when a weapon system has such promise of success and great potential that it is worth taking risks. Long-range ballistic missiles are such weapons. Viewed from this light, the ballistic missile program is engaged in shortening the normal development-to-operational cycle for a weapon system.

It should be clearly understood that no criticism is implied of our normal development policies. They have been carefully evolved and appear to suit normal circumstances. Likewise it should not be implied that the development-management approach followed in the ballistic missile program can be applied to just any program. This

AF Development-Operational Cycle

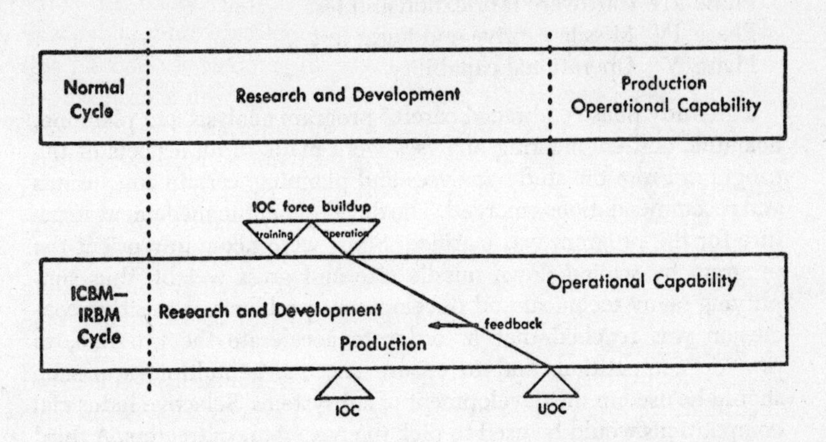

Comparison of the normal sequence of research and development and operational capability with the sequence of the accelerated ballistic missile program. In an aircraft program the operational capability is not achieved until research and development have been virtually completed. In the ballistic missile program these events had to be considerably overlapped, primarily to save time. Also the characteristics of the weapon required that data from experience with the initial operational capability (IOC) be fed back into the development cycle as soon as possible.

system appears to be best applied only to large-scale, especially important programs where it offers a means of developing and producing complex systems, where things must be done on a large scale, where many industrial concerns, many Government agencies, new and expensive facilities, and large funds are involved.

Basically, then, the development-management approach for the project is geared to a strong management team composed of the Air Force Ballistic Missile Division, the Ballistic Missiles Office of AMC, and the Space Technology Laboratories of the Ramo-Wooldridge Corporation. This team took over the job of centralized direction and proceeded to devise and manage a reoriented and accelerated program. This process was carefully scheduled in phases in order to meet projected time scales:

Phase I Program study and reorientation
Phase II Contractor selection
Phase III Hardware fabrication and test
Phase IV Missile captive and flight test
Phase V Operational capability

The study phase embraced careful program analysis and planning. Scientific and engineering analyses were made of all aspects of the program. From the study analyses and planning, certain conclusions and recommendations emerged. The development-management structure for the program was clarified. Steps were taken to reorient the program by scaling down missile size and gross weight, thus simplifying many technical and development problems. A positive conclusion was reached that in order to accelerate the program, to provide competition, and to ensure success, a multiple approach should be used in the development of subsystems. Selective industrial competitions would be used to pick the associate contractors. A third result of the study analysis and planning was an integrated development-test facility plan.

The selection of contractors marked an important phase of the ballistic missile program. Contractors were carefully chosen, through a highly selective, competitive method that identified the contractors with the highest capability. In this process, the Division management team prepared a statement of the job requirements. After study of these requirements, an AMC/ARDC team prepared a recommended list of the best qualified contractors. Then these contractors were given a preproposal briefing, after which they prepared their technical proposals. Concurrently with the contractor preparation of technical proposals, a joint evaluation board with members from ARDC, AMC, and independent agencies was established. This evaluation board prepared suitably weighted proposal evaluation criteria. All contractor proposals were then reviewed and evaluated by board members and specialists. Following this review and evaluation, the board recommended a winner. This recommendation was forwarded to ARDC, AMC, and USAF for approval. By means of this selective competition method, the basic subsystem contractors for the program were chosen.

The outstanding feature of this method was the speed with which the selection of contractors was accomplished. In most cases the entire process from the statement of job requirements through to notification of contractor selection took place within ninety days. Immediately on notification of selection, contractors were put to work through the use of letter contracts. The letter contracts were used in order that no time be lost in definitization of contracts before getting the program under way.

Contractor selection by this process was completed by the end of 1955. The contractors themselves were grouped into teams for individual missile development. This was possible through the utilization of dual-source subsystem development efforts for each individual subsystem. These dual-source subsystem developments played an important role in the program: for example, the development of an intermediate-range ballistic missile was introduced into the Air Force ballistic missile program late in 1955 through the simple process of reorienting certain ICBM contractors and of adding Douglas Aircraft Corporation as the airframe contractor for the IRBM No. 1. Much time, effort, and cost were saved through this process.

Our procedures for selecting contractors and our development planning for the ballistic missile program have had important consequences for the nation from a long-range standpoint. In the past three years, as a result of our current program, we have produced a nationwide ballistic missile development-test-production capability, an extensive complex of men and facilities. Moreover our policy of developing Atlas, Titan, and Thor missiles making use of normal production fabrication techniques not only provides us with missiles for test but at the same time assures us that the contractors' production lines will be able to deliver missiles for our operational forces earlier than if the test missiles had been constructed on an individual basis. Such techniques will expedite our transition to the age of missiles and will ensure that ballistic missile technological advances can be rapidly translated into useful hardware. As a further byproduct of this rapid expansion of scientific, engineering, and production capability, we have opened the door to the space age and will be able to exploit developments in that area much faster than before.

A factor which has conditioned the ballistic missiles program from the very beginning has been the emphasis placed on the development-test concept. Unlike an aircraft test program, ballistic missiles, once launched, cannot be re-used. Moreover, test facilities of the size and scope required for the accelerated missile program were virtually nonexistent in 1954. Consequently a large-scale test facility program had to be laid down, as well as one for production facilities.

Before the test plan and facility requirements were prepared, we reviewed and analyzed all previous missile and aircraft programs so that we could prepare a rational test philosophy. This review was based on all previous missile testing experience, as well as the re-

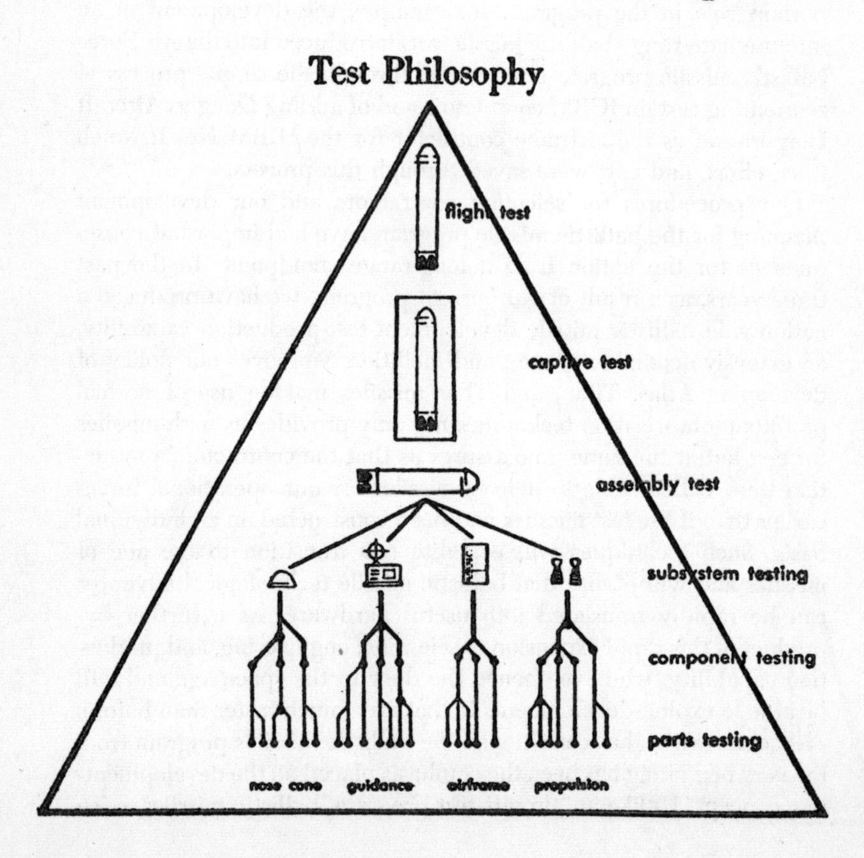

quirements of the accelerated program. A test program was planned
with the aim of reducing the number of costly "one way" missile
and costly systems tests will not fail because of failure of components
flight tests and of getting required information as early as possible.
Insofar as possible, components would be thoroughly tested on the
ground prior to flight tests. The method utilized provided a step
approach, beginning with component tests, then assembly tests, then
captive tests of propulsion and airframe, and captive tests of complete

Philosophy

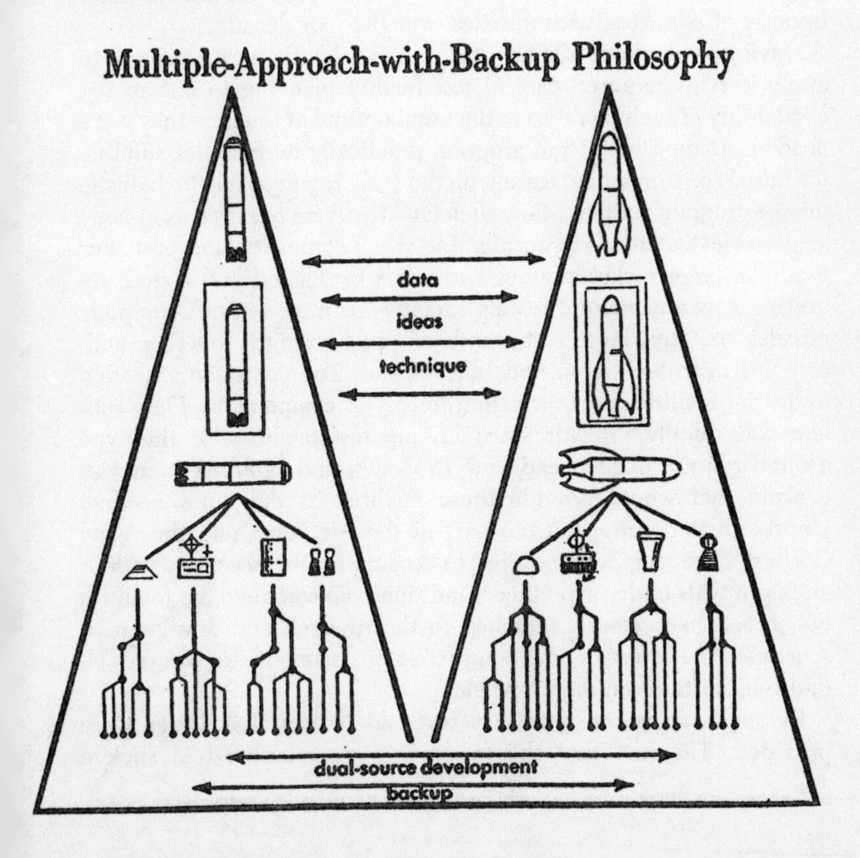

missiles prior to flight testing. In this way reliability could be checked at the lowest possible levels and systems interaction tests could be performed as subsystems were mated. This test philosophy was adopted and is in use in the program today.

This plan provides the maximum likelihood that the more advanced and costly systems tests will not fail because of failure of components or minor assemblies and that information on over-all systems interaction will be available before we embark on large-scale flight tests. Another important element of the test philosophy is that there are no special-purpose test vehicles.* In other words, no "dead-end" testing would take place. The ballistic missiles themselves will serve as data-collecting test vehicles. Thus development-test effort is all applied to the missiles themselves. Needless to say, such a plan was only possible because of our work with missiles over the past decade.

Having worked out a logical test philosophy, the next step was to apply it. This required careful test facility planning to ensure the availability of such facilities in the numbers and at the time they were needed. At the start of the program practically no facilities suitable for missile or component testing on the scale required for the ballistic missile program existed. Many such facilities were required as quickly as possible—facilities of considerable size, complexity, and cost. For example, large rocket engines had to be developed and tested, requiring new and unique testing facilities; captive tests of complete missiles required large test stands of great strength together with complex instrumentation and blockhouses. The contractors needed industrial facilities for fabrication testing of components. The problem was doubly difficult since unique test facilities of the type desired require a long lead-time to design and build. A plan was evolved that would provide these facilities at the times needed. Unprecedented action on the part of the Air Force and the Army Corps of Engineers was required to accomplish the necessary actions and approvals under expedited conditions. To complete the facilities which had been closely matched to the research and development schedule, the construction contractors in many cases worked on multiple shifts seven days a week.

By such means the necessary test and industrial facilities were provided. The fact that the facilities were completed in such a

* Except for the re-entry test vehicle to gather nose cone re-entry data.

relatively short time is indicative of the speed, diligence, and competence with which the Air Force installations personnel, the Army Corps of Engineers, and the construction contractors worked. As an indication of the size and importance of these facilities, to date nearly $500,000,000 of new development, test, and production facilities have been completed or are programed for the Air Force ballistic missile program. Of this total, approximately $400,000,000 has been provided by the Government and $100,000,000 by the participating contractors. This program has provided the nation with a base of missile-test and industrial facilities superior in quantity and quality to any in the world today.

One outstanding accomplishment of our test program is worth mentioning. This is the answer to one of our most difficult problems—that of re-entry. The problem was to design a re-entry body (nose cone) that would not burn up as it re-entered the earth's atmosphere at meteoric speeds. To solve the problem, many extensions into the regions of hypersonic research were required and empirical verification of this research was needed. An intense program was laid on: study contracts were let to conduct shock-tube tests, materials research, hypersonic wind tunnel and ballistics research, nose-cone drop tests, and hypersonic flight tests.

For the latter, the Division contracted with the Lockheed Aircraft Corporation to develop a re-entry test vehicle, called the X-17. Its job was to simulate re-entry conditions at high mach numbers—in excess of mach 14—in order to validate hypersonic theories. It is a three-stage missile. The first stage drives the missile to a high altitude where it falls over and starts its descent; then the second and third powered stages drive the nose cone to higher and higher hypersonic speeds as it descends through the atmosphere. Telemetered data derived from the flight provide the needed design information. This re-entry test vehicle proved to be a quick and accurate way to gain reliable data without flying a full-scale missile. It was successful in proving out the theories of heat transfer and design shapes of nose cones and it reassured us that our theoretical calculations on nose-cone design were valid.

The operational development program

After the missile development program was under way, the Division received additional directives to undertake operational development programs for the missiles. These directives rounded out the ballistic missile program by making the Division responsible for all actions necessary to achieve the initial operational capability (IOC) with these weapon systems. With this assignment, the Air Force ballistic missile program became an integral one. A single agency was now responsible for the entire weapon system development-operational program. Moreover, the two programs are concurrent rather than in series. While missile development and test are under way, so also are all the actions ensuring that when development is completed an operational force will be trained to handle the missiles and that the force will be ready for the Strategic Air Command. This is an unprecedented assignment for the Air Research and Development Command. It has absorbed a great deal of effort, particularly since we are dealing with new weapon systems with which we have little experience. Our operational experience must be gathered out of the development and test program. Again, through this combination of missions the development-operational cycle for the systems should be shortened, since the agency which is accumulating this experience will be able to put it to use quickly.

Integration of this responsibility was aided by the fact that from the beginning BMD had a staff to study system operational planning. With the addition of the responsibility for initial operational capability, the operational planning staff has expanded considerably in both size and mission. From it have come not only the operations, personnel, logistics, and installations concepts which furnish the guidelines for the organization and employment of the IOC force, but the actual detailed plans that are at the present time being put into effect.

Turning these concepts into practical, usable plans and then implementing them have required detailed work and coordination. Organizational structure and composition had to be planned. The facilities required for operations and training had to be identified and action had to be taken quickly to begin establishing and building these items that require a long lead time to obtain. A procedure for locating and assigning personnel with the abilities and experience necessary to man the units had to be worked out. Programs for training personnel had to be determined to the extent of writing course lesson plans, designing training aids and equipment, and determining training evaluation procedures. This latter process has already produced several changes in the missile and its test and handling equipment to adapt it more closely to the abilities of the airman who will do the job.

Logistics plans are being worked out in detail in coordination with the logistics and missile maintenance concepts. AMC is instituting an entirely new type of logistic system, based upon electronic data processing, for use with the ballistic missile forces. An explanation of this system appears elsewhere in this issue.

BMD could not develop all these details itself and expect them to be realistic. Active participation of other Air Force commands was mandatory. Therefore liaison offices were established at BMD by the Strategic Air Command, the Air Training Command, ARDC's Air Force Personnel and Training Research Center, and Air University. In addition coordination was accomplished with Headquarters USAF, the U. S. Army Corps of Engineers, Air Force Weapon System Phasing Groups, and others. The ballistic missile program is truly Air Force-wide.

Actions in the IOC area have taken place rapidly. Recently the field unit to command the initial operational capability force, the 1st Missile Division, was established. Under it will come the wings and squadrons, some of which are now being formed, as well as ballistic missile bases within the United States. Cooke Air Force Base, California, is the first of these bases, where training will be performed. Facilities are under construction and the base is being manned.

In November 1957 General Thomas D. White, Chief of Staff of the United States Air Force, directed that responsibility for attaining the initial operational capability with ballistic missiles be transferred from AFBMD to the Strategic Air Command. This transfer of responsibility did not affect the integrated development-operational program, since all it did was to add another partner, the Strategic Air Command, to the AFBMD ballistic missile management complex. General Thomas S. Power, Commander in Chief of the Strategic Air Command, took over that part of the AFBMD organization which had been conducting the operational-development program, and he assumed control of the former ARDC field units, the 1st Missile Division, and Cooke Air Force Base, where initial operational training for our ballistic missiles was under way. The new SAC operational organization located at AFBMD was named SAC Mike and its commander was added to the Strategic Air Command as Assistant Commander in Chief of SAC for SAC Mike.

This transfer of IOC responsibility from ARDC to SAC has had the beneficial effect of expanding the ballistic missile management complex to include participation of the ultimate using command as a full partner in creation of ballistic missile operational systems. This action will ensure that long-range ballistic missiles will be integrated into the SAC operational inventory at the earliest possible date. Such participation may well set examples that future weapon system development programs will follow.

Program control

The ballistic missile program is nationwide in all aspects. The work of seventeen major system contractors located in every part of the United States has to be coordinated and kept in phase. The magnitude of the program is such that if a slippage occurred in any area, the whole program could be delayed. To keep abreast of the entire program, the efforts of all the members of the management-development team are closely monitored in a central place in BMD—the Program Control Room. The joint BMD—BMO—Ramo-Wooldridge Program Control Room is the nerve center for the project. As a management tool it provides "management visibility" by displaying information on the status of every aspect of the project in graphic form.

This management information is provided through frequent visits with contractors, use of the extensive communications network between BMD and the contractors and field offices, written reports, and periodic meetings of BMD, BMO, and Ramo-Wooldridge personnel. The information is not displayed until it has been double-checked and coordinated by the offices concerned with that phase of the program. Any problems are spotted early and acted upon quickly. Those that may produce schedule slippages are identified with a "red flag" and carry that identification until they are solved. The "red flag" problems are given immediate treatment and their status is considered each time a review is made.

The program pulse is felt continuously. It is presented formally once a month to key members of the management team. In these presentations, the rule of "management by exception" is followed. There are hundreds of items that could be considered. It would take several days to treat them all. Instead, only progress and problem areas are noted and discussed.

Today we are in the fourth and fifth phases of the program—the captive and flight-test phase, and the establishment of an operational capability phase, respectively. The flight-test portion of Phase Four is the most critical phase of the entire development program. We have entered it with confidence that the missiles will indicate the results of the carefully structured test program. Realistically, we must recognize that this is the phase where troubles appear. We think that our careful planning will enable us to meet these troubles. We have already made substantial headway in overcoming such difficulties. Some setbacks are to be expected, since we are after all still in the "Model T" stage of long-range missilry. In fact, in ballistic missiles we stand today at about the place where our aircraft stood some forty years ago, except that our scientific knowledge of these new, complex "birds" is far superior to that possessed by the aviation pioneers about their craft.

The future

The application of modern technology to our program will ensure success in refining and improving our first comparatively primitive ballistic missiles, in producing them at less cost, and in making them more accurate, more reliable, and less complicated. At the same time we shall have to keep moving forward to design, develop, and produce the next generation of missiles. We must look beyond the achievement of parity or superiority vis-à-vis the Soviet Union in this whole field. It would be a colossal blunder if we ever sought to arrest or halt our forward strides at a point where we could match a ballistic missile against every one of the Soviets' or even have more of ours in stockpile. Any letting down at such a juncture would mean that we had fallen victim to a Maginot Line mentality.

On the clock of national security we must be able to tell time not just by the minute hand but also by the hour hand. This means long-term planning. This means that 1968 has to be as real in our thinking as 1958 or '59 or '60.

Equally important, we must keep moving forward with the science and military technology involved in space flight. The military requirements in this field are at present less clearly defined but are no less demanding of our country's sustained and vigorous efforts if we are to equal and surpass Soviet concepts and capabilities in the conquest of space. All who are familiar with this problem affirm the need for initiating our own space projects as swiftly and as boldly as possible.

If we are to achieve leadership in space technology in the 1965–70 period, we must have sufficient "lead time." Fortunately this lead time for leadership has been made available by the know-why and know-how accumulated in the Air Force ballistic missile program. This program has put us on the threshold of space travel. Ballistic missiles, whether Thor, Atlas, or Titan, are in fact primarily space vehicles traversing most of their flight distance in space. They are the forerunners of such projects as lunar rockets, space stations, and spaceships for carrying men and cargo.

In our Air Force ballistic missile program we have brought into being a vast military, scientific, and industrial organization staffed by personnel of the highest competence. This organization has mastered many new areas of knowledge which can be springboards to substantial short cuts in our conquest of astronautics. We have already provided for approximately $500 million worth of new facilities for the design, development, test, and production of ballistic missiles—facilities nonexistent only three years ago. These existing abilities and assets created by the Air Force ballistic missile program furnish some of our most promising steppingstones for further advances into the new age of space science and technology. Data from test flights of airframe, propulsion, and guidance subsystems, for example, illustrate the extent to which the ballistic missile is both portent and precursor of tomorrow's achievements in astronautics. From a practical standpoint the same propulsive unit that lifts a heavy nose cone with its warhead and accelerates it to 25,000 feet per second in outer space could also put a somewhat lighter body in the escape velocity of

35,000 feet per second, or in an orbital path around the earth. Similarly the guidance system which permits the warhead of a ballistic missile to reach its target with acceptable accuracy would also be sufficiently accurate to hit a target much smaller than the moon. Such propulsive and guidance components could also be used for experiments with surface-to-surface transport vehicles for carrying mail or materiel to critical sites. Perhaps 90 per cent of the unmanned follow-on space projects for the future can be undertaken with the propulsive, guidance, and structural techniques now under development in the Air Force ballistic missile program.

Recent studies have shown that use of our current rocket engines and missiles would make possible, at a very early date and with the greatest economy, both unmanned reconnaissance of the moon and a basic vehicle for manned space flight. Our present IRBM and ICBM booster engines possess the propulsive capacity required for important military and scientific space missions over the next ten years. The Atlas engines, for example, weigh less than a Cadillac, yet generate more than 6 million horsepower.

The booster engine of the Thor missile, when combined with a second-stage rocket now available, can place a satellite in orbit with a respectable payload. By adding third-stage rocket hardware, already at hand, to the present Thor, unmanned reconnaissance of the moon is possible within a comparatively short time. Although the current speed of our ballistic missiles is approximately 16,000 miles per hour, we are already developing engines that will provide 50 per cent more speed, or the 24,000 miles per hour we need to get to the moon. An added small step-up to 25,000 miles per hour would take us to Mars and Venus. A slightly modified Thor, plus a new high-energy fuel which is being perfected, can make possible the first unmanned reconnaissance of Mars and Venus.

Similarly the ICBM Titan booster engine, when completed, can—with the addition of high-energy second and third rocket stages—place much greater weights into orbit, satellites carrying men for a variety of space missions. This same propulsive power could send a man-carrying vehicle on a circumlunar flight—a journey around the moon and back to earth. Further in our future are the potentialities for thermonuclear propulsion and payloads of hundreds of tons.

It may well be that the most important contribution of the Air Force ballistic missile program will be found in the broad and solid bases it has laid for our future advances in astronautics. All Government agencies dealing with problems of the space age should be able to take full advantage of the lore, the experience, the hardware, the facilities, and the personnel of the Air Force ballistic missile program.

Meantime our development and test projects have yielded excellent results. Test launchings of both Atlas and Thor during 1957 and in early 1958 again validated the scientific assumptions upon which the entire Air Force ballistic missile program has been based. At the moment both missiles are satisfactorily meeting ever more complex testing requirements.

To date all major milestones for the Atlas, Titan, and Thor development programs have been passed essentially on schedule. This rate of progress inspires confidence that the program will soon bring to the United States and its allies the new deterrent power represented by long-range ballistic missile operational capability.

There is one final question: What will we have achieved when we reach our goal—when ICBMs and IRBMs have become reliable operational weapon systems produced in quantity? Paradoxically the best we can hope for is that we will never have to use these weapons, that our ballistic missile capability will be so highly respected by all potential aggressors as to indefinitely deter them from attacking us.

This should not imply that the ICBM and IRBM are "ultimate weapons," as they are frequently called, nor that the ballistic missile will replace the manned intercontinental bomber. But it will undoubtedly become one of the most potent and convincing arms in our arsenal of strategic weapon systems.

It is hard to believe that any one weapon, no matter how powerful, can by itself enforce peace in this uneasy world. But we are confident that weapons like the ICBM and IRBM will help the Air Force to enable the free world to maintain deterrent forces which no aggressor in his right mind would dare to challenge.

Air Force Ballistic Missile Division, Hq ARDC

CHAPTER 1

Air Force Missile Experience

COLONEL EDWARD N. HALL, USAF

It is probable that more misinformation has been generated on the subjects of guided missiles, long-range missiles, ballistic missiles, intermediate-range missiles, and intercontinental missiles than on almost any other conceivable subject. What are these devices, how do they differ from each other, why have they come into being, what has been their past history? The answers available to the general public have been fragmentary and frequently misleading, primarily because of their inevitable security restrictions. This had been a highly justifiable policy in the past, but at this time the American public and its high-ranking civil administrators are being confronted with crucial decisions concerning these weapons, their control, and their use and are possibly being forced to conclusions based upon a paltry smattering of factual background. This article is being written in an effort to dispel some of the mists of obfuscation that pervade this field.

Missiles may be divided into two categories: ballistic and airfoil controlled. Both categories have been somewhat arbitrarily further divided into guided and unguided species. The word arbitrary is employed here because it is hard to conceive of any justification today for a truly unguided missile, one deliberately designed to take off and capriciously land, "I know not where." Guided missiles follow trajectories that may be altered by signals from some guidance device well after the moment of launch; unguided missiles are those in which all guidance influence ceases within an extremely short time after launch.

Both ballistic and airfoil-controlled vehicles have been employed by mankind for a very long time. Ballistic weapons as rocks hand-cast by primitive man preceded their airfoil-controlled cousins, arrows launched from bows and controlled by tail feathers, by a significant period of time. A greater amount of effort through the years has gone into the ballistic-controlled vehicles than into the airfoil-controlled ones (e.g., rocks thrown by hand or catapult and gun-propelled slugs and shells). Only recently has serious consideration been given to the development of relatively long-range airfoil-controlled weapons. An essential ingredient in the development of relatively long-range ballistic devices was the creation of a basic science of ballistics. Similarly a sizable mass of data in the field of aerodynamics was a necessary precursor to the development of long-range airfoil-controlled vehicles.

Ballistic science is much the older of the two, stemming back pretty directly to Kepler's Laws of Motion, which have been constantly and repeatedly confirmed by such phenomena of celestial mechanics as the motions of the moon, planets, and comets. Aerodynamics could not support accelerated development of long-range devices until late in the 19th century. Exercising these two general sciences man has developed a series of missiles.

In the course of this activity, cross-pollinization in the two fields has occurred to such an extent that the course of individual developments has in many cases become obscure. For many years ballistic missiles, considered apart from their launching devices, were simple. The shell hurled from a big gun, although differing in degree of sophistication, had much in common with the rock launched from the hand of primitive man. Aerodynamic effects in both cases were small. The trajectories resulted largely from the interplay of gravity, conservation of momentum, and, in the case of extreme ranges, centrifugal force. Extremely strong, lightweight structures were not needed.

Significantly the method of propulsion employed in the gun involved the use of very heavy launching devices of a relatively declining effectiveness as muzzle velocities in excess of about 4000 feet per second were reached. Projectiles were guided by accurately aligning the gun in the direction and elevation desired. No guidance signals were transmitted to the projectile after exit from the gun barrel. While stability was imparted by projectile spin, even at this relatively early level of missile sophistication a certain degree of hybridization occurred; fin-stabilized gun-launched projectiles were developed, in which a certain amount of aerodynamic science was drawn upon. The serious development of long-range, aerodynamic-controlled missiles had to await the development of the airplane.

Quite early in this saga attempts were made to apply this newer science to long-range missiles. Even during World War I efforts were made to load military airplanes with bombs and direct them without pilots to specified targets. Out of aerodynamic science grew automatic control devices such as autopilots, auto navigation equipment of both radio and inertial varieties, automatic bombing systems, and the advent of reliable, efficient propulsion systems. It became evident that a proper integration of these sophistications could make practical an unmanned, long-range, aerodynamically-controlled missile. During World War II several instances of the operation of such devices took place.

Up to this point a fairly distinct demarcation existed between ballistic and aerodynamic approaches. Ballistic vehicles were dense, unsophisticated structures, most of them propelled by expanding gases generated by combustion of solid propellants in gun barrels. No provisions were made for internal control, guidance, or propulsion equipment. Aerodynamic missiles, on the other hand, sprang directly from airplane experience. In these were automatic control systems, strong, lightweight airframes, sophisticated guidance systems, and advanced propulsion units.

Modern missile beginnings

Until the War the potential performance of long-range missiles was largely misunderstood. The barrier to be overcome was not of sound, or heat, but of the mind, which is really the only type that man is ever confronted with anyway. A traditional approach by the aerodynamic people to the problem of range versus speed had convinced them that an inverse relationship existed between these two parameters and that, consequently, truly long-range, airfoil-controlled vehicles would have to travel at relatively slow speeds. The ballistic advocates, also limited by mental blocks, thought in terms of thousands of yards rather than thousands of miles. Although the latter group had had rockets at its disposal for hundreds of years, it had employed them in a manner highly analogous to the gun. Thus aerodynamicists talked about relatively slow devices capable of ranges up to 10,000 miles or so, employing reciprocating or compound engines with conventional propellers and high-aspect-ratio airfoils. Military ballistic people were thinking in terms of rocket- and gun-propelled projectiles with unsophisticated structures and very limited guidance and control systems capable of ranges of hundreds of thousands of yards.

Between these two placid pools of specialized interest there were several small, disturbing anomalies. Dr. Robert Goddard in the United States and the Weapon Development Group of the German Army were pursuing programs of high-performance rocket development. Dr. Goddard was completely unsuccessful in his efforts to interest the United States armed forces in his work, and the German effort, until a time too late to be of any influence in deciding the outcome of World War II, was similarly ignored. The efforts of both of these groups were aimed at the development of a desirable hybrid in which the sophistication of the aerodynamic approach would be effectively applied to a ballistic vehicle. These efforts incorporated the subtle structural talents of the airframe industry and the highly sophisticated guidance and control mechanisms developed for imparting stability to modern airplanes, navigating them, and controlling bomb release from them—all this married to a high-performance rocket-propulsion system to produce an entirely new species of vehicle.

Except for the propulsion system all elements stemmed directly from the airplane development art. And the rocket propulsion systems employed on these devices, in the United States at any rate, have also stemmed from the propulsion development programs of the United States Air Force. The problems of heat transfer, turbine operation, combustion, and pumping are intrinsically the same as those that plagued the developers of reciprocating engines, turbojet engines, ramjet engines, and other aeronautical power plants. These rocket engines have been developed by the same U. S. Air Force and affiliated organizations that developed the preceding types of power plants mentioned, using the same basic philosophies. The result is that large liquid-rocket power plants are available today as reasonably reliable, producible items to provide the extreme propulsion requirements of the long-range guided ballistic missiles. The rapid advance of the Air Force ballistic missile program has been predicated upon this rich background of familiarity with, and development of, all the key elements required for success in its field.

The rate of development progress

The rate of progress achieved in ballistic missile development has been limited by two categories of factors: the operational and the technical. That ballistic missile development can only be carried out by the armed services is an accepted fact. Armed services, however, must always seek to justify their development activities in terms of the economic validity of the gains to be achieved. No new weapon, however spectacular, can really be justified unless it promises to perform military tasks at a lower gross cost than will any weapon system preceding it. A rocket-propelled, guided ballistic missile of short range would be questionable from an economic standpoint if compared to the operating cost of the manned bomber. Even a relatively long-range missile of this variety would be questionable until the detonation magnitude of its warhead and the accuracy with which it could be positioned would make it less costly per unit of effectiveness than the piloted bomber. Questions would still arise about the methods of reconnaissance and bomb-damage assessment that could be employed as a necessary adjunct to such a weapon system.

A limiting factor in the missile development drive until very recently was the questionable effectiveness of available warheads and guidance systems. Obviously the use of a TNT warhead on a ballistic missile with a range of more than a thousand miles would be extremely costly. With missiles dispersing several miles in the target areas, as they must with today's guidance systems, several thousand would be needed to destroy a specific target of limited size. As the accuracy of the guidance system improves and as the detonation effectiveness of the warhead increases, the numbers of missiles required to perform any specific military task drop—as do comparative costs.

The atomic bomb greatly improved the destructive potential of this type of missile, but even it, when coupled with available guidance accuracies, did not guarantee economies beyond the use of manned bombers. With the atomic warhead such economies could only be achieved by the development of extremely accurate guidance systems. It was the thermonuclear bomb that altered this picture radically. This weapon promised economical dividends in the destruction of military targets by means of long-range ballistic missiles. So it is that from the operational point of view the drive to develop these missiles was compromised by lack of clear-cut evidence that their employment was militarily justified until improvements in warhead and guidance techniques occurred.

A much more basic limitation to the development of long-range ballistic missiles existed up to 1950: adequate propulsion systems. The long-range ballistic missile consists of guidance, control, structure, warhead, and propulsion. Each of these must be adequate if there is to be a worthwhile military missile. The propulsion system is in a somewhat different category from the others. This is the one component without which the missile could not fly at all. In fact the long-range ballistic missiles are so intimately tied up with rocket propulsion systems that frequently the terms missile and rocket are used interchangeably.

A fallacious concept, formerly widely cherished by air power "experts," that the relationship between range and speed was an inverse one has already been mentioned. There was evidence upon which to base this false conclusion in the form of ranges and speeds of the aircraft developed prior to the 1950's. Some of this evidence centered on the assumption that lift for these long-range vehicles would inevitably be supplied aerodynamically.

As soon as one accepts the fact that centrifugal force is quite as reliable as aerodynamic lift—attested to by the degree of assurance man has developed that the moon will not fall down—the picture becomes greatly clarified. While the attainment of mach 1 speeds was always accompanied by very limited ranges in that era, this limitation was largely a product of the characteristics of air-breathing engines, available conventional fuels, and aerodynamic drag. It was always evident that if one could get out of the atmosphere and reach orbiting velocities, terrestrial range would become unlimited. The problem lay in the development of a power plant and structural system capable of attaining orbiting speeds outside the earth's atmosphere. What structures and what power plants can be used?

A survey of existing power-plant and structural concepts reveals that the choice is a narrow one. The reciprocating engine and propeller combination is only effective at relatively low altitudes and speeds. Propeller efficiencies drop very rapidly at great altitudes unless the blades are extremely large and heavy. The ratio of thrust to drag attainable with this type of propulsion system is very unfavorable for high-speed flight. The air-breathing turbojet and ramjet engines suffer the same general deficiencies, although the turbojet engine is greatly superior to its reciprocating brother in thrust-frontal area and thrust-weight ratios. But the value of the air-compressor element of the turbojet approaches zero as forward speeds rise above mach 3. This is so because the inevitable rise in stagnation temperature brought about by the forward speed of the aircraft, when coupled with the further temperature rise through the turbojet compressor, heats the incoming air to the no-thrust point in this speed range. This limitation is imposed by structural problems stemming from limitations in the strengths of available materials at high temperatures. Advanced cooling techniques and further development of high-strength, high-temperature-resistant materials may push this limit up but not to any useful degree when compared with the speed requirements necessary for orbiting the earth. The case for the ramjet, which employs no compressor, is similar to that of the turbojet, if slightly more favorable. Here we do not have to worry about structural loads on centrifugally stressed turbine and compressor elements. But the high stagnation temperature of the incoming atmosphere remains as a severe problem. The twin necessities of furnishing a reasonable static pressure to support combustion and a very high forward speed to sustain flight cause stagnation temperatures in the combustion chambers and discharge nozzles to become limiting at about mach 5. This is still very far from earth-orbiting velocity.

Only in the non-air-breathing rocket engine does none of these intrinsic limitations bar the way to earth-orbiting velocity. Since the rocket uses no air, high stagnation temperature of surrounding atmosphere is of no consequence to the power plant. Developing thrust more effectively in vacuum than in the atmosphere, rocket-propelled vehicles may approach and exceed orbiting velocities without the problems associated with atmospheric friction. Theoretically, therefore, the rocket power plant should be capable of attaining earth-orbiting speeds and unlimited terrestrial flight ranges at very high velocities. Development of rockets of sufficient specific impulse, structural lightness, and reliability for long-range ballistic application had to await the development of modern metallurgical techniques, of propellant chemistry, and of the thermodynamics required to determine what performance was available from the materials at hand.

Rocket engine development program

At the conclusion of World War II the Air Materiel Command of the Army Air Forces became interested in the further development of the German A-4 type rocket. As a result the rather battered components of three of these engines were shipped from Germany to North American Aviation, the contractor designated by the project office at Air Materiel Command. At this time no large-scale liquid-rocket development facilities existed in the United States. Two large test stands and associated equipment for the development testing of these engines were to be erected at Edwards Air Force Base. Shortly after this, agreements were reached between the Air Materiel Command and the Curtiss-Wright Corporation for the use of Dr. Robert Goddard's patents in the Army Air Forces' rocket development work. Additional work to establish the operational effectiveness of nitric acid as a rocket oxidant was contracted at Aerojet, Bell, and Kellogg.

It was the conviction at this time of the Army Air Forces, which became the United States Air Force in 1947, that the rocket development program should be handled in a manner like that of other engine development programs. Traditionally industry had always been regarded as a partner in these ventures. It was felt that a continuation of this policy would make available the most competent organizations and best brains for rapid exploitation of rocket art. The former Air Corps' engine development programs, dating back to the days of the

Hispano-Suiza and Liberty engines of World War I, had attempted to harness available sources of industry to development and production programs. The Air Force feels today that this was a wise decision. The fact that the only successful large liquid-rocket engine programs in the United States have been Air Force programs is in no small measure due to this manner of operation. This policy has greatly eased transition from applied research to development to production and has minimized scientific stagnation.

Since the inception of these rocket development programs the Air Force has spent large sums of money on the development of rocket engines. This expenditure was justified by the belief that only through the development of such power plants could high-speed, long-range guided ballistic and aerodynamic missiles be created. The men entrusted with the development of this device for the U. S. Air Force were experienced in developing successful reciprocating and turbojet engines. They had no delusions about the relationship between a demonstration of basic principles and the completed development of rocket engines adequate in reliability and simplicity for inclusion in the military inventory. The Air Force understood that preliminary design and demonstration of feasibility of basic principles amounted to less than five per cent of the costs of an engine-development program. Each rocket-development project, in the Air Force view, would be faced with a long period of component tests, engine shakedown, and redesign. This realistic attitude has meant that the activities have seemed unspectacular, and achievements have seemed to be attained at a relatively slow pace.

By 1949 the first large engines based on the recovered V-2 fragments had been fired at the new rocket facilities of North American Aviation. They developed thrusts and thrust-weight ratios considerably in excess of the German units. But the Air Force and its contractors, with a now respectable background of rocketry, realized that the basic German approach to the power plant was rather limited. During 1950 it was decided that this initial engine effort would no longer meet more ambitious Air Force requirements, and the entire program for large liquid-rocket engines was reoriented toward larger, lighter, higher-performance units. This enlarged program produced rocket engines useful not only to the Air Force but to the Army as well. When the U. S. Army Ordnance Corps, spon-

Air Force Experience in Missile Development

Project	Inception Date	Significant Dividends to the Ballistic Missile Programs
Navajo	1946	Large, lightweight thrust chambers, much design data for large liquid-oxygen-alcohol engines, large injector design techniques, much inertial guidance design data. Illustrated air-bearing gyro limitations, and provided first successful American large liquid rocket engine.
MX-774	1946	Control techniques employing swiveling engines, lightweight structures for tanks, and separation techniques.
Atlas	1951	Ultra lightweight tank structures, feasibility of very high expansion-ratio discharge nozzles, precision guidance and control, development of high specific impulse from conventional propellants, appreciation of propellant utilization problems and techniques of attacking them.
Rocket Engine Advancement Program	1951	Large hydrocarbon liquid oxygen rocket engines, advanced high suction specific pumps, very lightweight gimbaling systems, fluorine rocket technology, techniques leading to extension of stable combustion limits of rocket engines, practical methods of ignition and handling of starting transients, limitations and methods of throttling, very large turbo pumps and thrust chambers. This program has provided the basis for all the large oxygen hydrocarbon rocket engine work in the United States.
Nalar	1951	Extensive propellant performance and ignition work, short combustion chambers, rapid ignition at low temperatures, ingenious positive expulsion tanks.
Shrike	1947	First closely controlled series production of pressurized hydrocarbon nitric acid rocket.
Rascal	1947	Turbo-pump driven, two leveled-thrust engines, automatic control systems, practical acid hydrocarbon gas generators.
X-2	1947	High-ratio, continuous throttling of liquid-oxygen-alcohol engines, early employment of common propellants for thrust chamber and gas generator, tank pressurization by turbine discharge heat exchanger, direct-driven, high-speed propellant pumps, spark plug ignition.
LR-45	1949	Mechanical techniques leading to safe operation of nitric acid hydrocarbon rockets, automatic high-response-rate control systems, high-performance propellant pumps and specialized bearings and lubrication systems.
LR-63	1951	Safe, highly reliable, hydrocarbon acid, lightweight rocket system, effective use of refractory ceramics, highly compact components.
Bomarc	1951	Hot gas pressurization data, large engine application of refractory materials, design techniques for interaction of sloshing and controls, low cost practical low ignition energy propellants and combustion techniques, swiveling engine control system.
Falcon	1950	Quality control techniques for rubber-base propellants, design data for case-bonded grains, aging characteristics of rubber-base propellants.
16 NS 1000	1953	Large-scale exploitation of low-cost rocket potential of ammonium nitrate.
Ohio State Project	1949	Pumping, handling, and combustion of liquid hydrogen and liquid fluorine.
Sergeant*		Large, high-mass-ratio, solid rocket techniques.
Corporal*		Pressurized, nitric-acid rocket techniques.
Nike	1944	Initiated jointly by Ordnance and Air Force. Joint study program led Air Force to development of Gapa and Bomarc for improved performances.

* JPL programs jointly supervised by military services.

soring the Redstone Missile Development Program, had no adequate engine available within its own facilities, the Air Force made its engine available to Army Ordnance. It has since been successfully employed as the power plant for the Redstone missile.

During this same period, vigorous programs to develop a family of nitric acid–hydrocarbon rockets were being sponsored by the Air Force at various contractor plants. One of these development programs, intended for airplane application, involved subscale unit firings to establish the basic characteristics of this propellant pair. This subscale unit went through many metamorphoses of development and finally provided the basic device around which the current Nike engine is built.

Development philosophy

Although the bulk of Air Force development work is left to industrial contractors, the role played by Air Force engineers should not be overlooked. Air Force development procedures have been designed to receive the most from industry for the taxpayers' dollar—to develop power plants that are practical ventures yet press the current limits of the engineering art. A key element in this development is availability of Air Force officers of sufficient technical competence to recognize real potentials of scientific development, to discard pseudoscientific hogwash, and to apply, through good management techniques, lessons learned on previous engine programs. There is no way in which the responsibility for setting up weapon-development programs can be divorced from the military. If the objectives of such a development program are unreal, the contractor, regardless of his intrinsic competence, will fail. If proper guidance is not supplied by the military, the contractor's program will be so prolonged as to invite exceedingly high costs and produce very little of technical merit.

Because the Air Force was convinced that long-range rocket-propelled missiles would become necessary weapons and that the development of suitable rocket engines would be the pacing factor for these missiles, its rocket programs continued even through the years of lean appropriations prior to the Korean War. As a result when the ballistic missile designer's job was suddenly and dramatically eased by the advent of practical, lightweight thermonuclear warheads, the Air Force was ready to begin matching this development with a ballistic missile delivery vehicle. Rocket-propellant pairs had been selected as best for this job because of economy, availability, performance, and handling characteristics; engine components were in a realistically advanced state of development, and the means of estimating facility, manpower, and dollar requirements to meet accelerated programs had been developed. On the firm foundation of this continuous, vigorously prosecuted Air Force rocket development program, all the long-range and intermediate-range ballistic missiles now in development by the United States have been based. Again at this stage of the development of rocket engines, the Air Force has made available its rocket engines to the Army Ordnance Corps for use in the Jupiter program.

Structure and control

All the components of long-range ballistic and aerodynamic missiles, except for the rocket-engine power plants, are direct descendants of basic components in modern military aircraft. The Air Force and its contractors spent twenty-five years developing structural materials and manufacturing techniques that offer high strength and low weight. A high percentage of the cost of the development of lightweight alloys and high-temperature alloys in this country has been underwritten by the U. S. Air Force in one form or another.

In ballistic missiles, range is an especially sensitive function of the ratio of propellant weight to total weight. Two items essential to long ballistic ranges are high-performance rocket power plants and extremely low weights of structural elements. In recognition of this, shortly after World War II the Army Air Forces started a program with Convair for intensive studies of structure, control, and guidance of long-range ballistic missiles. This program eventually led to impressive advances in control of ballistic missiles through gimbaling of rocket engines, better understanding of the requirements of guidance components, and a lightweight structural concept now employed in the Air Force ICBM program. The basic structures of all the long-range and intermediate-range guided missiles, ballistic and aerodynamic, of the USAF are highly sophisticated and employ subtle techniques coupled with carefully chosen materials to attain strength-weight ratios of a very high order. Each of the Air Force missiles has developed a structure peculiarly suited to the specific purpose. That these structural approaches have produced superior results is indicated by the recent action of the Army Ordnance Corps. After it examined the basic structure of the Air Force Thor missile, Army Ordnance decided to alter its basic structural design of the Jupiter missile to permit employment of the materials and fabrication techniques utilized on Thor.

The extension of missile control systems beyond performance limits of piloted aircraft has not proved as difficult as extrapolations of other elements. In the operational employment of missiles themselves many other conventional Air Force elements must be brought into play. Thus a long-range or intermediate-range missile would be of limited use without Air Force target-system information, reconnaissance, and communication nets, all integrated under central control. Only with these can missile devices be efficiently meshed into the operations of present manned bombers so as to destroy with a minimum effort the most significant items of potential enemy resistance.

The Air Force missile program encompasses both ballistic and aerodynamic types of vehicles designed to cover many applications over both long and intermediate ranges. This program has been based upon a consistent philosophy systematically pursued over a long period of years. The Air Force mission in this field has been well understood, was reiterated in the Key West agreement reaffirming roles and missions of the three services, and further confirmed by the Secretary of Defense in his recent memorandum. This program has proceeded along lines of development demonstrated to be effective through past extensive experience with large airborne vehicles. This program has not been spectacular, but massive and sound. There is every reason for confidence that it will do the job well and on schedule.

Air Force Ballistic Missile Division, Hq ARDC

CHAPTER 2

Missiles In Perspective

COLONEL CLAUDE E. PUTNAM, USAF

Practically everyone has read and heard a great deal lately about missiles—both ballistic and aerodynamic—constituting the ultimate weapon systems, about fighters and bombers becoming obsolete, and even about the death of the flying Air Force. We must agree that missiles are welcome and compatible additions to the Air Force family of weapons, but it is incumbent on all airmen to keep them in perspective. The ballistic missile is not an "ultimate" weapon as General White, in the preface to this volume, points out. One useful way to keep this in mind is to consider factually and dispassionately the kinship between aircraft and missiles—where they came from and where we go from here—in the evolution of the military art.

It is incontrovertible that practically all important components of present-day sophisticated missiles had their genesis in the development of the airplane. These developments cover a span of fifty years and stem directly from the airman's insatiable demand to travel ever faster, higher, and farther with payloads appropriate to the mission at hand. A look at the evolution of the essential components of all modern missiles demonstrates the truth of this statement, and the fundamental missile problems thus frame themselves in familiar Air Force patterns of experience.

Air Force parentage of the missile

Guidance. The problem of guidance in flight is as old as the airplane. Instrument and automatic guidance techniques began to emerge shortly after powered flight was proved to be practical. A crude automatic pilot was tested by U.S. airmen at the North Island military aviation school before World War I. During the early 1930's Air Corps Major Bill Ocker pioneered the development of instruments that eventually made it possible for the airplane to fly through clouds. In 1929 Lieutenant Jimmy Doolittle had made the first all-instrument flight inside a completely covered cockpit, from take-off to landing. It was a logical development to tie the blind-flying instruments to a workable system for automatically manipulating the flight-control surfaces and to enable an airplane to fly a preset course largely independent of human hands and brains.

The Air Corps need for a highly stable platform for the Norden bombsight of the mid-1930's spurred development of more versatile automatic pilots, and the electronic autopilot provided a satisfactory solution to this problem. Parallel developments in radio-control techniques made possible remote control of this more sophisticated autopilot. The radio-controlled drone was born in the early 1940's, enabling airplanes for the first time to be maneuvered and landed without a human being aboard. These very same techniques were soon applied to Air Force guided bombs during World War II, e.g., the tarzon and razon. Thus we clearly see the emergence of the guidance and control systems employed in modern missiles. It is a little-known fact that "Boss" Kettering had a pilotless airplane, which could have been developed into a weapon carrier, flying at Muroc Lake at a time that preceded the development of the German V-1 by a very healthy margin. Higher priority programs resulted in the abandonment of the project at the outbreak of World War II, but the idea and essential components were demonstrated.

More recent developments include inertial-guidance techniques, which had their inception in the Air Force Navaho in 1946, and star-tracking techniques which were developed for the Air Force Snark in the late 1940's. Also in 1946 guidance techniques employing rocket engines which swiveled on gimbals were evolved for the MX-774, the forerunner of the Atlas missile. Advanced electromagnetic wave control techniques were conceived in 1947 for the air-to-surface missile Rascal. Advanced swiveling engine control systems were developed for the surface-to-air Bomarc in 1951. It is significant to note that all these developments sprang directly from the aircraft industry and its subcontractors to meet operational requirements laid down by the Air Force.

Propulsion. Here again the problem is as old as the airplane. The Wright brothers perfected the first practical airplane propulsion system, permitting their epic flight at Kitty Hawk, North Carolina, on 17 December 1903. More advanced engines emerged hand-in-hand with the development of airframes that could carry and utilize the increased powers. One need only cite the Liberty engine of World War I and the turbosupercharger of 1928 to demonstrate the Air Force's long history of experience with propulsion problems. Refinement of Englishman Frank Whittle's jet engine introduced the jet age to U.S. aviation. Rocket engines followed closely on the heels of World War II with our dramatic improvement in the design and thrust output of the German V-2 rocket engine. The development of the first successful American large liquid rocket engine was initiated for the Air Force Navaho in 1946. The Navaho also spurred the development of the first practical ramjet engines which, after painstaking improvement, found application as the sustainer power for the operational Bomarc.

Manned airplane applications for the rocket engine were not ignored. On 14 October 1947 USAF Captain Charles E. Yeager blasted the Bell X-1 rocket-powered research plane through the sound barrier for man's first attainment of supersonic speed. Major Arthur Murray in the X-1A sister ship attained the then unprecedented altitude of 94,000 feet in 1954. In September 1956 Captain Milburn G. Apt took the X-2 to a speed of 2178 miles per hour before structural failure cost him his life. This aircraft had previously established an altitude record of 126,000 feet. The X-2 provided the first continuous throttling of high-thrust liquid-oxygen–alcohol engines and made important contributions to missilry. These spectacular achievements demonstrate how airmen have traditionally operated at and beyond the very threshold of knowledge. Another example is the Rocket Engine Advancement Program. Initiated in 1951, it has provided the basis for all large oxygen-hydrocarbon engine work in the United States. Future refinements and new developments are sure to follow. Probably before the end of this year Captain Iven Kincheloe will have a look at our old planet from an altitude of some 100 miles, and it is no secret that the X-15 which will take him there and its follow-on aircraft will be striving for orbital speeds.

Airframes. Airmen have been wrestling with the knotty problems associated with obtaining required structural strengths at the lightest possible weights since the very inception of the airplane. They progressed through the wood, fabric, and wire of the earliest airplanes, through the all-metal monocoque construction of the 1920's, to the extremely efficient weight-strength ratios found in modern missiles. They have also long been in the forefront of adapting new materials —new metals and new bonding techniques—to the peculiar requirements of the airframe construction. Solving the strength and vibration requirements for transonic flight and progress made toward developing heat-resistant materials for operational speeds close to the heat barrier attest to the success of their endeavors. Indeed in this area it appears that we may have approached the practical ultimate in strength of materials. Experts state that no important advances have been made in developing new materials during the past ten years. Rather the advances have been in ingenious design and fabrication techniques, which of course have largely stemmed from the airframe industry. Work on the MX-774, initiated in 1946, and its successor the Atlas in 1951, provided the basis for all ultra-lightweight tank structures employed in modern missiles.

General Orval Cook, President of Aircraft Industries Association, disclosed recently that there are 43 Department of Defense missile projects now under development or in production; and in every missile the aircraft industry supplies the airframe, propulsion, guidance system, or a major component. To do this, it draws on the same hard-won and laboriously accumulated reservoir of scientific and technical knowledge that brought manned aircraft to their present advanced state, as well as on the one-hundred-million-dollar production facilities which the industry has built for the ballistic missile alone. All told, the aircraft industry has spent a billion dollars on research and test facilities since World War II and plans to spend another billion during the next five years. Airmen everywhere should keep these facts in mind as a partial but telling answer to the question of where the modern American missile came from.

Concepts of Employment. The foregoing has attempted to demonstrate how the development of missiles is a natural evolution from the airman's quest for greater speeds, ranges, and altitudes. The concept for the operational employment of these new weapons likewise finds the airman in a familiar enviroment, backed by years of experience with the subtle problems involved. The resources, skills, and techniques for the production of necessary target data have long been available in the Air Force. Calculations of required weights of effort to achieve acceptable probabilities of success, problems of reaction times, and the complex timing of world-wide operations to attain maximum tactical advantages are familiar exercises to the airman. Another prerequisite to successful missile application is reconnaissance—prestrike, poststrike, and follow-on surveillance. In this important field the airman has been active since the first utilization of the airplane as a military instrument. He has evolved techniques for prehostility reconnaissance, postattack damage assessment, and data processing which exist nowhere else. Of course the capabilities to employ long-range missiles have resulted in new requirements in this field, such as refinements in the geodetic datum plane and investigations of gravitational anomalies. The Air Force has long had an active interest in these studies.

Airmen pioneered and refined concepts of the third-dimensional and global nature of modern warfare. Strategic bombardment of vital elements of an enemy's heartland to end his capability to conduct effective military operations was conceived by forward-looking airmen. The possibility of a counter-nation—as distinguished from a counter-force—strategy was early recognized. These concepts are entirely compatible with the nature of missiles.

The Air Force concept for the operational employment of missiles is that they will be assigned specific tasks in emergency war plans just as soon as they have demonstrated a reliable capability to perform a given task better than the older weapon system which they replace or supplement. The first strategic missiles will be directed against relatively soft, heavily defended targets where extreme accuracies and yields are not stringent requirements and where fast reaction times and invulnerability to enemy defenses are important. The smaller, harder targets will still be left to the manned bombers, which can destroy them more efficiently.

As future developments in missiles improve their reliability, accuracy, and yield, they will be programed against targets that are consistent with their capabilities at any particular point in time. As for tactical missiles it appears that their inherent inflexibility must be complemented by the flexibility of manned airplanes for as far as we can see into the future. Defensive missiles will provide a powerful addition to the capabilitity to defend against air attacks, but for a considerable period into the future they will complement the manned interceptor. Surface-to-air missiles cannot operate beyond contiguous radar coverage. On the other hand manned interceptors with their own airborne radars can perform effectively against targets that have been spotted by early-warning techniques but that have not yet entered the zone where continuous radar tracking is possible.

Complementary nature of the missile

Missile applications fit quite naturally and logically into the framework of the traditional Air Force roles and missions. This is not to say that the airman fails to recognize the formidable problems involved in integrating operational missile systems into the active inventory. The Air Force is charged with the grave responsibility for maintaining an ever-ready combat capability that can be put into action literally on only moments of notice. Our offensive forces must be capable of instant retaliation in the event of attack. This is the deterrent to war which is the cornerstone of our national policy. Our defensive forces must be ready every minute of every day to inflict maximum attrition on enemy attacking forces. Any gaps in these capabilities caused by faulty phasing of new weapons into the active inventory could well be fatal. Likewise a failure to maintain continuously a force structure that embodies the proper balance between offensive and defensive capabilities and the required degree of flexibility could have disastrous consequences.

These considerations suggest two important conclusions: First, that for an indeterminate period the Air Force will have a mixed complement of more or less conventional manned vehicles and unmanned and manned missiles. The inherently limited flexibility of missiles must be offset by the more flexible manned airplanes, and programs must be implemented in such a way that missiles are integrated without creating even a temporary hiatus in our day-to-day combat capability.

The second conclusion stems directly from the first: The commander charged with the operational control of this mixed system has a tremendous responsibility as well as some tough problems. His judgment in determining how best to employ the most effective combination of manned airplanes and missiles in a given situation will be of crucial importance. He should be accorded an appropriate freedom of action in determining when an older weapon system becomes obsolete and when a new weapon system achieves all the necessary prerequisites for being phased into the active inventory. He must also have at his disposal the vast communications and control facilities to enable him to conduct operations on a global basis. And perhaps most important, he must be able to draw freely and almost automatically on a broad background of experience in three-dimensional global war.

Human factors

The adaptation of man to the new and still somewhat mysterious environment high above the surface of the earth has proceeded along with other aeronautical advances. As soon as it was discovered that it is cold up there and that keen eyesight and certain psychological attributes are necessary to the successful operation of airplanes there, the flight surgeon entered the picture and has been doing stalwart service ever since. The list of his contributions is quite as impressive as those of the propulsion and airframe engineers. They range from protective clothing in the very infancy of flight, through safety devices during World War I and oxygen equipment in the 1920's, to air conditioning and pressurized cabins in the 1930's. The jet age saw the evolution of anti-G suits, crash helmets, and continuous refinements in the earlier equipment.

The flight surgeon's exhaustive investigations into the physics of the upper atmosphere and man's physiological reactions to this hostile environment furnished a sound foundation for the development of the equipment required to enable man to probe the limits of the sensible atmosphere and to invade space itself. Air Corps Captains Orvil A. Anderson and A. W. Stevens set the world's altitude record of 72,395 feet in a hermetically sealed balloon on 11 November 1935. They were followed in 1957 by Major David G. Simons, who attained a height of 102,000 feet and stayed above 100,000 feet for almost 24 hours.

Current USAF Aeromedical Laboratory studies involve such problems as weightlessness and its nutritional, circulatory, and psychological implications. Their people are also investigating the effects on the human being of confinement in a small container for the extended periods which space flight will involve, as well as shielding against cosmic rays and nuclear radiation. Air-conditioning requirements to counter the blistering heat of the ionosphere have received intensive attention. Colonel John P. Stapp's widely publicized experiments on the tolerance of the human body to acceleration and deceleration constitute important contributions.

What should all this suggest to the airman? The answer seems quite clear: Man is headed for outer space, and the missile is just another step in the long process of evolutionary development which will allow him to get there. Just as the evolution of the airplane furnished the basic technology for the missile, so will the art of missilry make important contributions to the development of the space vehicle. This is not to imply that the airman will in any way disparage the military implications of the missile or fail to continue its vigorous development and improvement to achieve the benefits of its maximum capabilities. It is to suggest that while doing these things to the best of his ability, he should direct his aspirations toward the higher achievements and never lose sight of the farther horizons. This is part of the tradition and heritage of the airman.

There is indeed something symbolic about that dead dog hurtling overhead at the fringes of outer space which should be portentous for all airmen. Relatively soon it will be replaced by a live human being with a very conscious mission in mind, and the end is not yet in sight. Technology is rapidly reaching for the moon, Mars, and

Venus, and the mysteries of our universe are sure to unfold. This is a dazzling prospect for the airman and a magnificent duty for the Air Force, for which it is soundly prepared by virtue of the building blocks painstakingly and laboriously accumulated during fifty years of progress.

Air War College

CHAPTER 3

Command and Control of Ballistic Missiles

MAJOR GENERAL CHARLES M. McCORKLE, USAF

During the past year intensive effort has been devoted to planning for the command and control of guided missiles. I would like briefly to point out some of the problems involved with this planning and to give a few personal thoughts on the likely evolution of command and control of ballistic missiles. By no means do I have all the answers. My primary purpose is to stimulate thinking on the subject.

It is significant that for the first time we are engaged in detailed operational planning for a weapon system that has not yet emerged from the development stage. There is no time to wait for the information we usually have when we plan for the introduction of a weapon into the air inventory. With very preliminary data we must begin to integrate ballistic missiles into the existing Air Force command and control structure, taking into account those unusual requirements stemming from the nature of the weapon.

Since command and control can mean different things to different people, perhaps it is necessary to establish a meaning for the purpose of this discussion. At the very least it must include general considerations of command channels, organizational structure, and the problems of operational control and coordination. Effective control by the commander is absolutely necessary if the ballistic missile is to fulfill its dual function as a deterrent to war and as a devastating weapon if war comes.

In planning for effective control by a commander we can subdivide our task along several lines: defining objectives, preparing plans and programs, developing a suitable organization, establishing policies and procedures, placing into effect a system of reporting, allocating personnel, carefully training and orienting personnel, and adopting strict inspection procedures. It is especially important for ballistic missiles that we establish a means of reserving to the commander final decision in all major undertakings.

We are making good progress in these tasks, but we have by no stretch of the imagination solved all the problems or fully explored all the ramifications these weapons bring to any consideration of command and control. Because there are still many decisions to be made, we must continue the same level of effort that we are applying to the accelerated development programs. The necessity for this approach was implicitly recognized when the responsibility for attaining the initial operational capability was assigned to the Air Research and Development Command along with its development responsibilities.

Differences and similarities

Even without a great deal of study it becomes apparent that we cannot treat the command and control of ballistic missiles as though we were simply integrating additional bombers into our forces. The special characteristics of the missiles bring about a new operational environment and unique operational problems. The dispersed locations of the early units will pose problems of control that do not hamper the tightly knit operations of a compact air base. But I think that perhaps the most difficult problems we have to face are that the primary job of the ballistic missile organization is to *stay ready* year-in and year-out and that instead of flying most of the work will be "dry-running."

Not everything is new, however. Some of the problems of integrating the ballistic missile into our forces will be quite similar to those encountered in replacing the B-36 with the B-52. With the passing of any weapon system certain skills are no longer required and new ones must be developed. For years, in one way or another, we have been coping with this problem. Nor should we have too much trouble with many of the normal housekeeping functions. Men of the ballistic missile wings will certainly eat and sleep much the same as the men in other organizations.

It is in the operational control and logistics areas that we find the need for substantial departures from established practices. Such characteristics as quick reaction time, the ability to strike an enemy within minutes after launch, the capacity for a high rate of fire, and relative invulnerability once in the air lend a new significance to the ballistic missile.

First let us consider the operational control problem. The nature of the weapon and its potential as an instrument of national policy dictate that the command and control structure be immediately and entirely responsive to the highest national authorities. The initial use of ballistic missiles will likely be closely controlled by the President, both personally and by means of instructions governing actions under various conditions. This circumstance places certain restrictions and requirements on the command and control of ballistic missiles that do not generally apply to other weapon systems. We must be very sure that we are being attacked before launching the retaliatory ballistic missiles. The margin for errors in judgment or information is very narrow. It is with these ideas in mind that the general framework for command and control should be established.

Although ballistic missiles will bring new and powerful capabilities to the Air Force, I think it is necessary that we treat them as part of the family of long-range offensive weapons when considering their application to warfare. This is necessary because for a long time to come it appears that an optimum strategic force will have both manned aircraft and long-range missiles.

In order to gain maximum benefit from the several manned bombers and guided missiles the various elements must be employed with careful regard to coordination of attack. While each weapon has its peculiar characteristics, there are many factors which they have in common. They all have long range; they have heavy warheads for destroying large or hard targets; their design is such that they should be used in strikes at the heart of enemy strength rather than at his minor defenses; for best effect they must be employed in large numbers; they require central planning; and the target examination, evaluation, and assignment process is one that must be centrally and closely controlled.

These features indicate that, while ballistic missiles should have close attention by the highest national authorities, there is nothing which should preclude the use of the existing command and control structure of the Strategic Air Command. The principle of central control of all strategic systems remains valid. I think it is absolutely necessary that all uses of large nuclear weapons, except in the missions of air defense and close support of the surface battle, be coordinated by a central agency. Therefore I believe that the decisions which have been made assigning the ICBM and the land-based IRBM to SAC are wise.

Complications

It is then necessary to examine the structure of ballistic missile command and control in light of two very fundamental ideas: first, close control by the highest national authorities and, second, incorporation of the weapon into the existing strategic air power command and control structure. After consideration of such factors as the effect of specific employment aspects, physical aspects, and support characteristics, it should be possible to determine just how much the existing strategic command and control must be modified.

As opposed to the general considerations mentioned previously, it is necessary to consider certain aspects in some detail. For example, when would ballistic missiles be used—only after an actual attack, or at some other unmistakable sign of aggression? This is not a decision which the military can or should make. It is a decision which should be made only at the highest level of government. Even though the military is not directly responsible for the answer to this question, I offer it as food for thought because we are directly concerned with the answer. In our basic planning for command and control we must build in sufficient flexibility to be able to accept various orders. For example, even if our first warning is the observance of hypersonic blips on Dewline radarscopes, we must be able immediately to launch a counterattack if our orders so dictate.

Since a very obvious advantage of ballistic missiles is their quick reaction time, we must take every precaution to protect our missile sites from crippling damage or destruction. There are two obvious courses we can follow here. The first possibility is to harden the sites so that any nuclear burst other than a direct hit would do relatively little damage. The cost of such a program runs into very high figures. The other approach is to provide protection by dispersal of our sites over wide areas. Although this is a cheaper method, it complicates the problems of organization, communications, and logistics. Initially we may depend upon dispersion to afford us the assurance that we will have a force-in-being at an early date. But there is no doubt that we must also eventually harden our bases to some degree.

The target complexes assigned to the early ballistic missiles must be compatible with their capability. Industrial complexes or large military concentrations are representative of the type of targets that can be most profitably attacked by our early ballistic weapons.

Another complex problem with which we are confronted is that we are unable to divert the ballistic missile after a very short time in the air; and of course the missile, once launched, cannot be recalled. This means, then, that we must have a very tight command structure that does not allow any mistakes. We are dealing here with decisions to be made in minutes rather than hours or days. We must balance the need to react quickly with the equally important need for a system of checks and balances which will prevent premature or accidental firings. Our command and control structure must be devised so as to make it immune to unauthorized firings—such as might be accomplished by saboteurs.

Several other physical aspects of the missile are important to a consideration of command and control. The inability of the missile to tell us what it did after being launched presents a problem. Based upon launch reports, radar track reports, and any other information he can lay hands on, the ballistic missile commander must decide whether enough missiles have been sent against any particular target. This points to the need for concurrent work in reconnaissance systems that will help tell us what the enemy is up to and what our missiles and aircraft are doing to him. Information of this kind will permit us to make much better use of a mixed force. For example, we might want to send several ballistic missiles against a target, knowing that the chances were against a good hit. But we might do it anyway in an effort to avoid high risks to our bombers. Yet without some kind of intelligence as to what happened to the missiles we would not be in a very good position to make a decision as to whether to follow up with bombers against that particular target.

Closely related to this problem is the difficulty of shifting the missile aiming point to any of a large number of targets. This creates the need for more detailed planning than is required for the manned bomber. Sequencing arrangements must be worked out well in advance to cover numerous operational situations.

A matter of logistics

Earlier I mentioned that in the logistics area we should expect to find the need for substantial departure from established practices. Since only a very small part of the workload of ballistic missile organizations will be "flying" and the greatest share will be keeping ready, command and control must reflect this situation. I think it is apparent that logistics will be more important to ballistic missiles than to manned aircraft. The aircraft can usually absorb a large number of malfunctions and still complete its mission or return home. Not so with the missile. We must begin to exploit all the newest techniques and methods developed in the field of logistics. For example, the use of electronic data-processing equipments and methods seems to have great potential for coping with the complex problems of supplying and maintaining ballistic missiles. This system should give the commander a much firmer control over his logistics than he has had in the past.

Communications requirements will be of far greater importance and larger magnitude than any system we have today. The communications system must be capable of handling a vast flow of information in a very short time. It must react instantaneously and transmit orders from one side of the country to the other in a matter of seconds. In addition there must be a backup system depending upon another entirely different means of communication. We may even need a backup for the backup. All of these systems must be completely tamperproof to prevent unauthorized orders precipitating a nuclear war. Without assurance of an effective and rapid communications system, any talk of a quick-reaction weapon system loses a great deal of its meaning. And still we must be prepared to act under prearranged orders in the event communications are knocked out in spite of all our precautions. In effect, we must have a completely foolproof communications system.

The actual sites chosen for the ballistic missile launch areas will have a serious effect on the command and control structure. It is reasonable to assume that Strategic Air Command strike bases would be a prime target of Soviet attack. We cannot afford to site our ballistic missiles on or very near these particular bases. But because of tremendous logistics problems we cannot afford to place them in a wilderness. For this reason and for economy considerations we must compromise and site ballistic missiles near enough to existing military bases so that logistic support is comparatively easy, but still far enough away so that an attack aimed at the base will not destroy the missile launch area.

I have mentioned earlier the problem of maintaining an alert status month after month, year after year. It is worthy of special note that the ballistic missile commander will encounter some fairly difficult personnel problems as a result of this type of operation. Keeping skilled men and maintaining morale in the face of boredom will require exceptionally qualified commanders. Capturing and developing the elusive esprit de corps will be one of their most important jobs.

Command and control structure

Now that I have touched on some of the major factors that will affect the command and control of ballistic missiles, I think it appropriate to consider how our command and control structure could be formulated. To get a clearer picture of what the organization of our ballistic missile structure should be, I want to make a few necessary assumptions:

- That we can develop and produce the necessary communications net for the use of Strategic Air Command.
- That the President only will be authorized to direct an attack, either directly or by standing order.

- That the missile sites will be widely dispersed.
- That the personnel and logistics problems can be solved.
- That targets will be assigned.

So far nothing has developed which demands that we throw out the conventional organizational plan of air forces: air divisions, wings, groups, and squadrons. Perhaps it will be necessary to make some revisions in nomenclature, but in the main I think the organizational theory will still apply. Initially I visualize a ballistic missile air division consisting of wings, each with several squadrons. As additional missiles are phased into the inventory, additional wings could be activated. When the quantities of ballistic missiles are sufficient, the entire ballistic missile organization could be placed under the commander of a numbered air force whose sole mission would be the control of ballistic missiles. This concept differs somewhat from the concept that intercontinental air-breathing missiles should be integrated under the same commander who commands manned aircraft.

There are proponents of this latter concept who would extend it to include ballistic missiles. Under this proposal a certain number of ballistic missiles would be assigned to each numbered air force of the Strategic Air Command. Their belief is that integration of these missiles will bring familiarity throughout the Air Force with these new weapons and the transition period will be covered more easily. My own view is that the ballistic missile is so different from other strategic systems in its operational characteristics that it must have special treatment. This can be offered best by a separate controlling organization.

One important aspect is that operational control of actual directions for launching must be placed high in the chain of command. If we are to use effectively the short reaction times being developed into the system we cannot possibly depend upon a system of relaying commands to numerous points in the organizational structure. This becomes even more apparent when we consider the problem of coordinating attacks of other weapons.

In summary, these are the elements we must have in an effective command and control structure for ballistic missiles:

- A safe, dependable, and rapid communications system.

- A time-phased plan for the use of ballistic missiles in conjunction with other weapons.
- A tight, well-knit command structure running from the highest national authorities to the launch position.
- A well-trained, dedicated nucleus of personnel upon whom the effectiveness of the launch operation will depend.
- A logistics system which is entirely responsive to the stringent demands of the weapon system.
- An effective means of maintaining esprit de corps in the missile organization.

Our problems are difficult but not insurmountable. Many of the problems we faced a year ago have been solved. No matter how they are finally settled, it is clear that the ballistic missile is arriving fast, that it is a potent weapon, and that it is here to stay. In the command and control function it will demand of our leaders and planners imagination, objectivity, and a freedom from preconceived ideas that can only be compared with the demands made upon military men when they first became the possessors of our old friend the airplane.

Headquarters United States Air Force

CHAPTER 4

Organizing and Manning Ballistic Missile Units

LIEUTENANT COLONEL WILLIAM L. ANDERSON, USAF

All the Israelite judges were instructed by Moses to decide the small matters, saving only the hard cases for the prophet. In the law this great organizational principle survives to this day. Despite its durability this ancient precept may be of little use in ballistic missile organizations. Ballistic missile leadership is characterized by the demand for prompt decision-making at all levels. The commander of a missile complex with his mighty responsibilities or the antenna specialist in his narrow area must face this challenge, each in his own way. This conclusion caps all our ballistic missile organizational studies to date. It promises to be a reliable rule for the future.

When the Air Force Ballistic Missile Division began operational planning concurrently with ballistic research and development activities, all the usual weapon system building blocks were missing. There was neither manpower nor personnel information. Organizational data was nonexistent. Hence this project was at once a test of and a stimulus to existing weapon system procedures. As with many new weapons, there was a tendency to overemphasize the complexity of the system, to exaggerate the difficulty of training, and to suspect the adequacy of the personnel identification system. For the most part these difficulties have not materialized. In fact the adaptability of existing manpower and personnel staff procedures has been a real asset.

Developing operational criteria when a weapon is still in the rudimentary research and development stages involves the planner in a struggle to obtain basic information. In this search we have been greatly assisted by the Technical Training Air Force of the Air Training Command. The TTAF training-requirements specialists have shown admirable professionalism in supporting BMD planning. In future projects of this type it will serve the responsible agency well to consult with the Air Training Command at the outset.

Role of Air Force personnel and training research

As has been mentioned, operational building blocks have been the scarce article. The difficulty here cannot be overestimated. The contractors are of course the sources of such data as may be available. But conversion and evaluation of contractor information require time and experience. Hence early in the program we turned for assistance to the Air Force Personnel and Training Research Center (AFPTRC). This has proved profitable. By timely employment of qualitative personnel information (QPI) reporting procedures, we have enjoyed the use of excellent data reflecting job functions, and specifying training depth and equipment.

To provide qualitative personnel information for our schedules, AFPTRC has a direct working relationship with the weapon system contractors. This allows the freest flow of information via AFPTRC to the Ballistic Missile Division. Prior to our receipt of job function and ancillary data, conversion and editing are accomplished by AFPTRC. The QPI has become a principal operational building block, the source for much organizational and manpower planning.

An example of the QPI application is shown in the section following page 170. This is an early illustration of the Atlas (SM-65) crew requirements. Note the arrangement of crew members with respect to equipment and the resultant organizational logic. The use of this preliminary information, with occasional revisions, has facilitated operational planning of good quality. Our experience also teaches that operational planning is usually upward—the smaller questions tend to answer the larger. In short we have found AFPTRC our best source for the provision of specialized support in the personnel field.

During the several years of this project a characteristic pattern for crew manpower requirements has evolved from the QPI series. This pattern, shown in the following chart, should be of interest to future weapon system groups. The forecast crew requirement continues to grow during the first two years of the project. This is due to additional identification of system components. This growth period may be regarded as a time for matching men against machines. For

Forecast of Atlas Crew Requirements
Derived from QPR Information

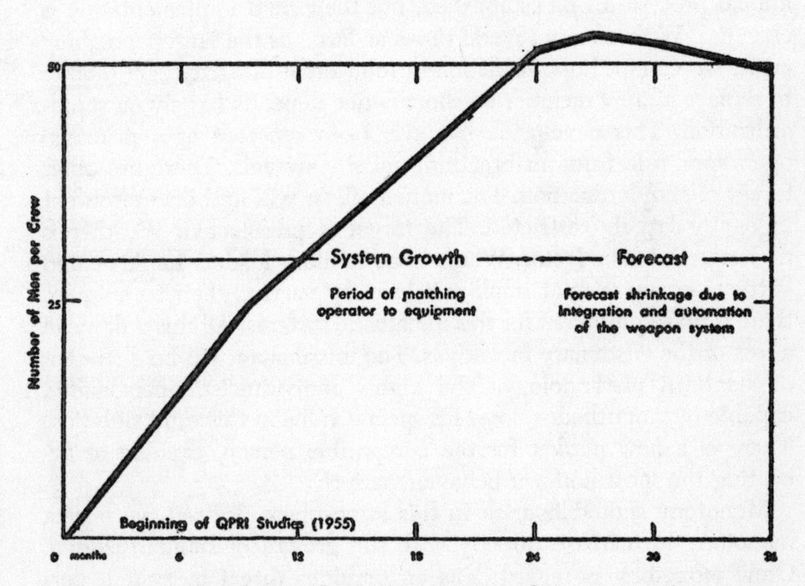

the future a shrinkage of requirements is forecast as the system engineers, having designed the basic parts, turn to integration and automation.

Human performance factors

The combination of requirements for short readiness time and high reliability emphasizes a dimension of human performance in ballistic systems. These two measures have of course always existed with other weapons. For ballistic missiles they will be indivisible. It has been said that reliability is the leading trait of the good airman. The ballistic environment presages an equality of time and reliability. The missile countdown is replete with timed-performance demands. Naturally the various crew members are interdependent. The knowledge of how to do the job, together with timely and reliable performance, marks the successful crewman. There may be little opportunity to check individual performance when the serious game is being played.

The timed-performance demand is abetted by a second major influence. This is standardization. Not only must standard crew operational procedures be established, but their rigid implementation is essential. With a crew several times as large as the largest bombing crew, we cannot hope to maintain total crew integrity. The ability to replace a crew member on short notice depends largely on standardization. This conclusion has also been reported as a principal operations rule from air-breathing missile systems. There are other forces of standardization. The launch officer will find his exercise of ingenuity largely restricted. The target is preselected. Weather is no longer a major factor. Where once military leaders implemented battle doctrine even at small-unit level by varying their techniques, there is no requirement for this in ballistic systems. All this will mean a loss of the customary incentives. The missileman will be a student of standard methodology. The highly individualistic personality, capable but unorthodox, loses his special value in this rigid situation. There is a new market for the compatible person, capable of accepting the most uniform behavior pattern.

Monotony should flourish in this atmosphere. Indeed we expect monotony to increase directly with the growth of standardization. Crew monotony is regarded as an ominous threat to system performance. To counter this, the commander will seek effective motivation. But how? First by crew exercises, using operational equipment together with simulation gear. The crew must be kept busy. Problems of every description must be fed into the system. Crews at random must be unexpectedly called to bring a missile from some lesser degree of readiness down to firing condition. In some exercises hold-down firings of short duration may be specified. These alerts must

Typical Officer and Airman Job Descriptions in Ballistic Missile Unit

Launch Operations and Control Officer—AFSC 3265

General Features:

Although the importance of the checkout operations required to hold the missiles at their states of readiness cannot be denied, the operations which must take place at the launch site during final countdown can be judged as more critical to mission success than those which take place at other times. The critical nature of the final countdown operations is associated with the following: (1) the pressure of time on all persons who have functions to perform during this period, (2) the lack of opportunity to correct malfunctions and the associated requirement for decisions as to whether to override or abort the mission, (3) the hazards generated by the fueling operations which take place at this time.

Duties and Tasks:

1. Prepares for a launching and operates Master Operations Console during an actual or simulated final countdown.
   - 1.1 Receives launching instructions from a higher headquarters.
   - 1.2 Instructs guidance station of launch requirement.
   - 1.3 Coordinates ongoing maintenance and servicing activities with launch requirement.
   - 1.4 Initiates a final countdown by instructing blockhouse personnel to perform the checks.
   - 1.5 Monitors and evaluates the status of subsystem checkout, fueling, and firing sequence.

Guidance System Specialist (IGS)—AFSC 31450

General Features:

The guidance system components are checked out at the launch site on a go no-go basis using the countdown controller equipment.

He receives technical assistance and direction from the Guidance System Analyst in performing his duties during checkout and countdown. When performing work at the missile he is assisted by the Launch Site Missile and Launcher Mechanic.

Duties and Tasks:

1. Performs operations necessary to bring a new missile to the readiness condition.
   - 1.1 Inspects the airborne components for signs of damage and checks installation of equipment in the missile.
   - 1.2 Operates countdown controller console to accomplish the necessary steps to bring the guidance system to the point of irreversibility.
2. Performs unscheduled and periodic maintenance of the ground equipment and airborne system.

Launch Site Propellant Handling and Storage Specialist—AFSC 64350

General Features:

The functions of this incumbent are principally those of operating and maintaining propellant transfer equipment.

Duties and Tasks:

1. Operates propellant transfer equipment during countdown or simulated countdown.
   - 1.1 Defuels missile at the direction of the operator of the Master Operations Console or the Launch Site Operations and Control Officer.
2. Performs maintenance and servicing functions of propellant transfer equipment.

be flashed at all hours, even during crew changes. Surprise is an essential characteristic of the motivation effort. Actual launch of obsolescent missiles in appropriate circumstances will be the occasional culmination of motivation exercises.

A second motivation is to create a spirit of crew excellence. The crew must be brought to realize that it is a foremost element of the defense structure, that the functioning of the crew is of supreme importance. Considering the probable conditions of crew service and the irregular duty hours, the creation of this spirit is a harsh challenge to leadership. No sterner test of commanders is foreseen.

The ballistic commander, unlike a conventional weapon commander, has several crews for each missile complex. This is occasioned by an earlier Air Staff decision to preserve in ballistic systems the normal number of work hours per day. This normalcy for crew work-schedules promises to forestall major motivation problems. It is regarded as a great improvement over the "30 days on—30 days off" schemes previously suggested in some quarters. Some hope is even held that this normal crew shift will improve the bleak prospect in personnel turnover. It is interesting to note that those officers most likely to receive crew assignments have been the leading proponents of an eight-hour crew shift.

An eight-hour day and a sense of importance do not answer all the commander's needs. He must have an adequate physical plant to do the full job of motivation. He needs good barracks and good quarters. The level of intelligence required for effective crew members is one that will instinctively expect adequate living conditions. Ballistic missiles are not to be located within easy commuting distance of a pleasant city. Saving defense money by ignoring the requirement for personal accommodations simply will not work in this case. If we do not spend the money for quarters and barracks, we will spend it again and again in personnel turnover—a cost that few private enterprises could long endure.

Organization and internal communications

When one looks at the planned ballistic missile organization, one can see a layering of integrated interests. True organizational unity of action is demanded by the interdependence between job site centers. To achieve this unity of effort, it has not been necessary to derive a new type of organization. The launch complex is a performance-functional element, and its compatibility with traditional Air Force organizational concepts is self-evident. Since the complex is functionally oriented, considerable effort has been devoted to the exclusion of nonoperational elements. The projected organization is designed to be a functional package, totally executive in character.

No matter how singular the organizational objective or how functional the unit design, certain practices may dilute and distort the intended pattern of group activities. Within conventional Air Force organizations, there is a marked tendency toward long span of control. Responsible operating officials are often prevented from making decisions on those matters about which they have the most direct knowledge. This is largely attributable to the growth and secularization of staff elements. There is no denying that integrated control of missiles requires that operational command levels be empowered with essential information. Missile status and targeting orders are foremost examples of the data required by successive levels of command. Conversely the launch complex, the lowest entity, must be freed from all unnecessary staff interference. An example of this is safety. Ballistic missiles are inherently so dangerous that safety is an integral element of the operation. The usual activity of a base safety officer, endlessly visiting and writing reports to some safety section in a distant staff, promises little but interference to the launch commander. Advisory safety services from a staff element may be helpful, but the relationship should be simplified and the tendency toward staff supervision of operations eliminated. In essence effective missile operation means organization in which self-reliant men may freely exercise competence. There is neither time nor circumstance for an appellate relationship to a remote staff. Delegation is the prime rule for success.

All the lines stretching from one operator to another in the first chart would perhaps seem quite a long span of control, but these lines are for the most part merely indicative of the communications pattern. In this communications growth we see a notable characteristic of missile organization. The fueling function may be virtually an independent operation with little or no supervision. Yet the volatile nature of fuels and the importance of rapid fueling make it necessary for the launch commander to know at any point in time the exact status of this function. Rapid communication answers such demands. This example is perfectly compatible with the principle of delegation of function and functionalization itself. Future organizational efficiency may be served by regrouping and thereby shortening communications within a complex. In any event communication is and will continue to be a servant of function.

The growth of communications in the local command of missiles is accompanied by a lessening of informal relationships. By contrast, successful corporate efforts, such as du Pont's, have long prospered on informal relationships and on de-emphasis of the functional chart. Although organized under functional charts, military units in fact operate with unpublished relationships to some extent. The method of operation is bound up in a web of informal relations based upon personalities and accessibility of people. In a ballistic organization the informality is doomed by the physical layout and the personal separations. The flow pattern and sources of information in the launch complex are born on the drawing board. Hardware design determines speaking parties. Missile organization promises to be of unparalleled formality and characterized by intensity of communication.

I HAVE attempted to forecast a few of the ballistic organizational considerations for the future. It may be argued that some of these observations are not organization matters at all. Indeed this may be true. It is exceedingly difficult to separate personnel policies and operational conditions from organization. In the interest of provoking the reader's thought, I am listing a few more preliminary conclusions for him to ponder. Only time and experience will test these conclusions:

- There will be no requirement for a traditional reserve system.
- Airmen to be assigned to missile units will have careers exclusively in such units.
- There will be unusually high personnel turnover in missile units.
- Individual responsibility will be greatly increased, but operating practices will be highly standardized.
- Contractor participation will be greatly enlarged in logistics and maintenance.

• Difficulty will be encountered in the integration of missile units into conventional weapon commands because of differences of hardware, logistical methods, and force deployment.

Air Force Ballistic Missile Division, Hq ARDC

CHAPTER 5

The Ballistic Missile and Operational Capability

MAJOR ROY L. FERGUSON, JR., USAF

Much has been said about the acceleration of our missile development. Little has been said about the monumental effort required to place the ballistic missile in the field in large numbers and to incorporate this weapon into a system that will be operationally effective. For no matter how well a system is developed and engineered, it cannot be aligned with other strategic forces until enough people are trained in its use, unique support systems established, and facilities constructed. To meet this operational urgency, the Air Force has called for speed-up in the development of an initial operational force, to be known as "initial operational capability." To ensure that a militarily useful system will emerge on the close schedules established, the responsibility for developing this IOC was assigned to the Air Force Ballistic Missile Division of the Air Research and Development Command and recently transferred to the Strategic Air Command.

From the outset it was evident that AFBMD could not undertake a task of this magnitude without assistance from other Air Force commands. Active participation of the Strategic Air Command, the Air Training Command, the Air Materiel Command, and ARDC

Centers was essential. These commands responded and located well-staffed project offices within the Ballistic Missile Division complex. As changes occur in the development program, this group can evaluate their implications for every facet of the IOC.

Normally weapon system planning begins some years after commencement of the research and development effort, and only after it has been demonstrated that the weapon will be usable in the intended period of time. In the case of the ballistic missile, technical advances already ensure its development success, even with the accelerated effort. The problem that remains is how to employ the forces using these weapons. Ways must be found of overcoming the many problems which arise during this shortening-up process. For example, acceleration plus the operational complexity of any new system makes training abnormally difficult. There are limits to personnel capacities for learning and retaining skills required to operate ballistic missiles, and these skills can be acquired only through adequate instruction and training aids. Accordingly operational planning for the IOC began concurrently with the accelerated development program.

Under existing Air Force regulations and policies, which govern complete operational weapon system planning, much time is consumed in coordination among the development agencies, the using command, and Headquarters USAF. Although this method has normally proved desirable for weapon developments, the establishing of the Ballistic Missile Division as the USAF single focal point for ballistic missile management has made possible the combining of all efforts of the Air Force and the missile contractors, with appreciable benefit to IOC planning. In fact this unprecedented arrangement in USAF weapon development is highly essential if development-to-user schedules are to be effectively compressed. The need for close relationship to facilitate interaction and mutual feedback between the operational and development teams is, of course, magnified by the fact that production engineering is being done almost simultaneously with research and development.

Weapon system planning

Because the ballistic missile is a new weapon, its concept of use, its support, its manning, and its facilities necessarily are also new. Each element must be devised to exploit the full capability of the weapon itself. The task of developing the initial operational capability is therefore exacting, and to provide a unit capable of fulfilling its mission it is first necessary to examine in the smallest detail all phases of operations, logistics, personnel, and installations.

To ensure the most workable and optimum weapon system, compromises must be made in both developmental and operational programs. The operator wants standard equipment that is small, movable, yet easy to maintain. He wants rugged equipment that can operate in any temperature or climate, yet be reliable. He wants equipment that can react to any given situation, yet be foolproof. He wants precise instruments that can be operated without environmental conditioning. He wants simplicity, yet delicacy of operation. He expects long shelf-life. To provide a weapon system that meets these exacting requirements is the responsibility of both developmental and operational agencies.

For the past three years the Air Force Ballistic Missile Division has been engaged in establishing optimum operational, logistic, personnel, and installation needs and in translating these needs into detailed plans. These plans contain specific and exacting definition of every facet of the system. A brief description of each of these areas may provide a better appreciation of the task to be performed and of its status today.

Operations. The ballistic missile is designed to destroy an enemy target thousands of miles away in a few minutes. The supporting elements, i.e., equipment and facilities, must also be capable of fast reaction. They cannot, because of their design or construction, dictate to an operational commander how he must launch his missiles, but rather must be responsive to any tactical situation that might arise. The ballistic missile unit must be in readiness twenty-four hours a day, seven days a week. There can be no weak link. All portions of the system must be equally protected from either covert or overt aggression. Its communications likewise must be responsive and secure. Since there are many ways in which these operational objectives can be attained, each method has been explored and tied to the equipment and facility design. The operational objective plans for the ballistic missiles, now completed, state the desired system use, force requirements, reaction times, and communication ties to major command elements.

Personnel and Training. Sometimes in our admiration for mechanical miracles we lose sight of the man who must operate and maintain them. We forget that these marvels are not a replacement, except in a very limited sense, for the human brain. Despite the talk of pushbutton warfare, it is the man who counts, not the button.

The single element of a weapon system that defies force acceleration and operational readiness more than any other is the personnel and training area. As the weapon system becomes increasingly complicated and more efficient, we find ourselves facing the paradox that with every increase in the synthetic skills we build in these systems a corresponding increase is required in human skill in making decisions and in the human ability to coordinate men and machines. This very coordination of manpower and machines is our most compelling concern as we advance into a new age of automation.

Yet a solution to this problem must be found before the operational units can be deployed. Toward this end, equipment to be used by the operational units is being designed to be operated by the "average airman." Airman training courses are being job-oriented. Identification of special skills and preparation of training handbooks are in progress. Each in its own way is attempting to ease the problem.

But what about personnel turnover, a problem not likely to be solved by human engineering or by tailoring training courses to the average airman? The personnel turnover rate in the Air Force is high and is not expected to decrease appreciably in ballistic missile units. It takes three years to give an aircraft airman the technical education and on-the-job experience required to bring him to the requisite level of professional skill, and we expect the same to be true of a missile airman. But after three years of this training we can call upon his services for only one more year. According to statistics he is likely to leave the service at the end of his fourth year of enlistment. This problem is of special seriousness in view of the fact that early ballistic missile units must have thoroughly qualified personnel trained in all phases and that our military resources in this type are limited.

Plans now envision standard work hours, good housing and messing accommodations, recreational facilities, and personnel incentive programs for the ballistic missile crews. All measures possible must be taken to relieve this critical factor.

Logistics. As much as any other area, logistics must be responsive to the operational plan of employment. The ballistic missile, with its fast-reacting system, requires an immediately responsive support system. It would be a serious waste if a missile were to remain out of commission for a prolonged period of time because some part was not available. To meet this need the Air Materiel Command has instituted a new system of logistic control for ballistic missile units. This system, using electronic means, will ensure proper control and availability of high-dollar-value and critical short-supply items. Accessibility of missile components, methods of repair, and equipment required at the missile site are all being tabulated and evaluated as to their impact on the other weapon system areas.

Unit maintenance is now introducing changes into the basic missile design. Within the ballistic missile programs no special missiles are being designed purely for the purpose of research and development. The entire development effort is based around the missile configuration which will eventually be used in the operational program. Since this is the case, changes resulting from operating requirements are now being integrated into the development program, even at this early date. Even now, maintenance technicians can study each component of the system to be sure that each can be maintained in unit facilities with unit equipments.

The reverse is also true. Maintenance plans are now being drawn which will reflect types of people required and procedures to be used. Transportation needs, environmental conditioning, monitoring devices, and handling equipment are all a part of this.

Installations. Ballistic missile units, perhaps even more than other weapon systems, will be only as effective as their facilities will allow them to be. It is of little consequence how many missiles are produced or how fast, unless launchers, blockhouses, and associated ground facilities are in place to launch them. Strangely, the launcher then becomes the unit of force structure, the missile the bomb.

Facility design is well under way. The facilities now being designed will meet all operational objectives. They will also be capable of accepting expected growth potential of the missile and its associated equipments. The operational and technical requirements have already been placed in the hands of site selection teams who must select and recommend tracts of land most suited to this type of operation.

Even during the operational studies which precede site selection, the ballistic missile installation groups have been designing the operational facilities from equipment mockups. These facilities include storage, the technical facilities themselves, and the quarters and messing facilities for the personnel to be assigned to these units.

Allied areas which affect all phases of the operational units are also well into the formulation stage, areas such as security safety and support system maintainability.

The matrix, then, begins to form. All these items affect each other; all must be weighed and their over-all implications determined before this force can be ready. This planning and equipment design, which is the first step in attaining an operational force, is well under way.

Implementation

The second step is the marriage of the man to the machine in an operational environment. Our survival may well depend on how well he does his job. For missiles, using as they do automatic devices of bewildering complexity and capability, will make heavier demands than any other weapon system in history on the human element, requiring human ability to act resourcefully, responsibly, and speedily with the equipment. Although the necessity to man a large number of missile bases is some time removed, the problem of implementation is of such immediate importance that the nation's first ballistic missile training center has already been activated at Cooke Air Force Base, California.

Cooke AFB uniquely lends itself to the over-all ballistic program. It is situated in close proximity to the Ballistic Missile Division and many major contractor establishments. It is of sufficient size to accommodate even the most ambitious training programs of the ICBM and IRBM, and it has existing buildings that can be readily converted into billets and classrooms. Cooke is a base of many functions but its most important is the training and evaluation of crews and equipment to ensure that both are welded into a true fighting potential.

Personnel will enter Cooke as a group who have completed basic Air Force training. Then, depending on individual aptitudes and preferences, these personnel will complete extensive training in industrial plants in fields specific to missile operation—fields such as electronic computers, guidance systems, rocket engines, automatic flight control systems, and thermonuclear warhead handling.

These individuals must learn to work with their unit. Before their arrival at this base they have seen only their own part of the job. At Cooke they will learn where they fit into the over-all scheme, the precise functions they must perform, and the time allotted for performance.

Their training will be rigid and exact. Upon completion they must be professional men in every sense of the word. One slip or hesitation in the launch sequence, during which many actions are taking place almost simultaneously, could result in disaster. Mental demands will be exacting. Crews must perform their assignments with the knowledge that a single mistake may cause the failure of the entire mission. If the order to launch were given, there would be no time for deliberation and no margin for error. Once the need for launching a missile arises, our very hope of survival will depend upon each man's ability to react in a prescribed manner.

The achievement of an effective operational force is well begun. The 1st Missile Division is now far into the task of implementing the plans outlined in this discussion. Although many problems remain to be studied and new decisions are yet to be made, the framework of an effective initial operational capability has already been fashioned. We may have every confidence that our fateful lightning of retaliation will be swift and terrible in the face of aggression by the enemy.

Air Force Ballistic Missile Division, Hq ARDC

CHAPTER 6

Missilemen—Present and Future

COLONEL ALLEN W. STEPHENS, USAF

When General Nathan Twining was Air Force Chief of Staff, he once laid before the Congress and the taxpayers a new military fact of life that cannot be circumvented:

> In the past, we have kept modern by replacing obsolete and obsolescent aircraft and associated equipment with newer models of the same general type. In other words, we have gone down one road. Today as we develop and prepare to introduce guided missiles into our primary combat units, we have no choice but to go down two at the same time.
>
> The introduction of missiles causes this kind of difficulty with all three services, but it is a particularly acute problem for the Air Force. Development and introduction of guided missiles into each of our major force areas must be done in order to gain the tremendous advances in strategic, air defense and tactical weapon capabilities that missiles provide.

General Twining's testimony before the members of the Senate Appropriations Committee was in the nature of a plea for funds to sustain the entire Air Force program, including research, weapons, equipment, facilities, and people. His proposition promised to be inescapably expensive, but there is obviously no alternative to the "dual road" responsibility of the Air Force. With international tensions continuing as they are, the Air Force cannot afford to drop its guard by weakening the Strategic Air Command. Yet the potential threats posed by Soviet scientific breakthroughs in missile development make it mandatory that more missile power go into our deterrent punch. The deterrent capability of SAC must be kept and improved while the Air Force goes full blast ahead toward development of a "Sunday punch" with operational ballistic missiles.

It is not my intention here to explore the political or economic impact of this circumstance, as fascinating and tempting as such a venture would be. It is necessary, however, that any discussion of men and missiles, as we know them both today, take its departure from the "two road" fact of Air Force life as stated by General Twining.

His premise has the most vital significance when applied to the people that make up our Air Force—aircraftmen or missilemen. The laws of nature are such that it still takes nine months to produce a new-model human being. It takes a little longer to produce an original ballistic missile prototype. But the original production time for human or missile is much less than the time involved in teaching a new airman recruit all he must know to become a full-fledged missileman.

The same has been true for a long time in training the people who make SAC the war-deterrent force it is today. It has been a giant struggle to find and train enough technicians to maintain and operate the complex equipment and weaponry of our B-47 and B-52 manned-aircraft force. It has been an even greater struggle to keep these technicians in uniform after they are fully trained.

Ralph J. Cordiner, President of General Electric Company and Chairman of the Defense Advisory Committee on Professional and Technical Compensation, had this to say about the problems of technology and the demand for technically skilled people in his report to the Secretary of Defense last May:

> Research, development and innovation on an expanding scale have become a way of life, not only in industry but in the military field as well. The dramatic technological changes symbolized by

> nuclear energy, electronics, supersonic aircraft and missiles systems are causing an explosion of change and growth in almost every social, political and economic institution, including the military establishment. . . . The Armed Forces are competing with the civilian economy for a relatively scarce resource. Technically skilled personnel are in great demand in this expanding, technically-powered economy . . .

This competitive demand for expert technicians is the point of departure for any analysis of the human element and its impact on operational performance of unmanned ballistic missiles. And it prompts some perplexing questions about the missileman resource:

- Where do we stand today in development of the missileman?
- What qualifications must the missileman have?
- From what source do we get the missilemen of tomorrow?
- How many must we have and how soon must we have them?
- How long can we keep them after we get them trained?
- What will be the conditions of service for the missileman, compared to Air Force life as we know it today?

The Air Force literally has been running a carrousel, with thousands of trainees going round and round after one another and with all too many skilled and experienced technicians dropping off at the first opportunity into the more lucrative jobs offered by industry. Thus the second road promises to be at least as rocky as the older, well-traveled one. And there is the added complication that, at least in the beginning, the people for manning of both systems must come from the same existing resources.

Lead time for training has always been a limiting factor in developing and employing new weapon systems, particularly in recent years with the rapid advance of technology and the resulting complexity of modern military hardware. The problems of complexity and training lead time are compounded in the ballistic missile program because organization and training of operational units must proceed simultaneously with research, development, and testing of the missiles. Most of the missile know-how is now concentrated in the laboratories, production plants, and test facilities. Research, development, and testing must go on, however—even after the first and subsequent operational "birds" are pointed upward and cocked for potential firing in anger.

To establish the earliest operational capability with ballistic missiles, therefore, the Air Force must breed its missilemen and its missiles at the same time, so to speak. Officers and men of the Air Force are now sprinkled throughout all contractor plants to learn what can be learned only by "over-the-shoulder" training. Many more will be entered into training at these facilities in the next few months. They will work in the laboratories, on the production lines, and at the test sites alongside engineers who themselves are still studying and experimenting with techniques of rocketry, guidance, fuel systems, and the like. There is no other way to produce the missilemen for our initial operational units. There is not time to wait until the full cycle of research, development, and testing has been completed, as we would do normally with a new aircraft model.

The most significant human limitation on operational performance of ballistic missiles, then, is the incubation time from no missile knowledge to perfected technical competence for the many missilemen we need. The Air Force is well along, after months of preparation, toward General Twining's second road—the creation of an operational ballistic missile force.

The 1st Missile Division was organized at Cooke Air Force Base, California, in July 1957 by the Ballistic Missile Division of Air Research and Development Command. This first-of-its-kind organization was given the dual mission of training Air Force missilemen and developing an initial operational capability with intermediate-range and intercontinental ballistic missiles. In July 1957 the 704th Strategic Missile Wing was organized, also at Cooke, as the "incubator" unit for the first ballistic missile squadrons. The plan was that ARDC would create operational units concurrently with development and testing of the hardware and turn the fully trained units over to SAC coincident with delivery of fully tested, ready-to-fire operational missiles.

Events overtook this plan, and on 1 January 1958 the 1st Missile Division and its fledgling units were transferred to Strategic Air Command, under the command of Major General David Wade, formerly Chief of Staff at SAC Headquarters. With assistance from ARDC's Ballistic Missile Division at Inglewood, California, Strategic Air Command is pulling all stops to expedite the training of missilemen and to accelerate creation of the first operationally ready ballistic missile units.

An IRBM training squadron has been activated at Cooke Air Force Base. It is the task of this squadron to supervise training of all IRBM units. The first two operational Air Force IRBM squadrons also have been activated, the 672nd Strategic Missile Squadron (Thor) at Cooke AFB and the 864th Strategic Missile Squadron (Jupiter) at Huntsville, Alabama. Personnel for all these squadrons have been selected and are now in various stages of training. The ICBM training program has not progressed quite as far, but it will follow along in similar manner in phase with delivery of the first ICBM weapons to launch sites.

In a combined effort with the missile contractors and the Ballistic Missile Division of ARDC, the 1st Missile Division will supervise the training of all IRBM units and will train and command all ICBM units. The IRBM units will be deployed overseas by Strategic Air Command upon completion of training. Most of the training in the early stages will be done by the contractors in their plants. This is the training of individuals in the variety of special skills required. As soon as facilities are completed and missiles and associated equipment are delivered to Cooke AFB, unit training for Thor, Atlas, and Titan missiles will be accomplished there. Individual training on the Jupiter missile will be conducted in part at the Army Ballistic Missile Arsenal at Huntsville, Alabama. Ultimately it is expected that a substantial portion of the Jupiter training will be done at Cooke AFB.

The individual-training program has been developed to a large degree by the contractors concurrently with development of the missiles. This is standing procedure, for the design of the missiles and their component parts is predominantly influenced by the ability of ordinary people to maintain and operate them.

During a recent visit to the Convair plant at San Diego, 1st Missile Division officers asked Jim Dempsey, Chief Atlas Project Engineer, this question: "The general idea seems to prevail that all missilemen must be in the genius category—what is your view as to the kind of people we will have to have in our operational units?" Mr. Dempsey's answer was that missilemen could and would be of the same ilk as

Ballistic Missile Training Organization

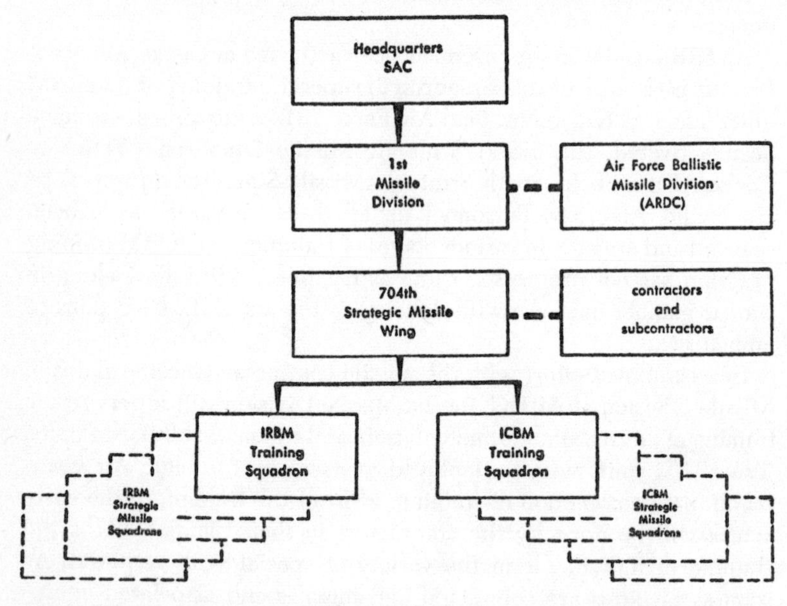

those we have trained by the thousands in the maintenance and operation of B-47's, B-52's, and other modern aircraft. He reiterated that design criteria on the Atlas and other missiles are oriented to personnel qualifications and limitations and that qualitative personnel requirements are being developed jointly by the contractors and the Air Force concurrently with development of the hardware. In effect the missiles are being tailored to the man.

It is feasible, then, that the combination of individual training and specialized unit training as presently conceived will qualify missilemen in all the skills required for operational ballistic missile units. Many of these missile skills are new, while many are variations of other occupational specialties already existing in SAC and other Air Force commands.

It is quite logical to expect that a technical sergeant Electronic Navigation Equipment Technician (Air Force Specialty Code 30171) now maintaining B-47 or B-52 equipment in SAC can transition fairly rapidly to effective performance as a Missile Guidance Systems

Technician (AFSC 31170B). He will require specialized training, of course, but his existing skill and experience are readily transferable to missile maintenance.

At the outset our military missilemen of today, except for those associated with research and development and the few trained on Matadors, Snarks, and other air-breathing "birds," are the electronics officers and technicians, the fire-control experts, the mechanics, and other technicians now in our inventory, most of whom are in SAC keeping the manned aircraft flying. They are the best we have been able to get and keep, and they have already proved themselves. These trained and experienced aircraftmen, both in SAC and elsewhere in the Air Force, are the only *immediate* resource of people to be retrained into ballistic missile skills.

Here, of course, we run head-on into the crucial aspect of the "two roads" dilemma: How can we avoid weakening our existing manned-aircraft deterrent force in the process of manning ballistic missile units? Our only recourse is to nurse along our existing manned bomber and fighter force, weaning some of its offspring gradually to make up a nucleus for fledgling ballistic missile units. But for every man we take out of SAC bomber units, we must train a replacement—at least until ballistic missiles actually begin to supplement manned bombers in the SAC emergency war plan.

Where do we find the many other missileman candidates we must have to build up the ballistic missile operational force? The answer is the same place we found the SAC men—on the streets, on the farms, or wherever Air Force–motivated youngsters come from. The missilemen of the future are the ordinary, but alert and trainable, young men who stop and read the recruiters' signs. There is no other resource. But if they can master the intricacies of the thousands of gadgets that make a B-52 capable of delivering an H-bomb to Soviet targets, they can learn what they need to know to boost ballistic missiles off the ground and onto target track.

So now we come back to the laws of nature and science. We can raise the manpower and we can produce the missiles. We can teach the men to do all the things that have to be done to countdown and fire the missiles. But we must have them in vast numbers, and we must allow for the training lead time required to make them reliable and competent.

The trick comes in keeping them once we have trained them. It has been difficult to hold them in uniform up to now, even with the traditional challenge, excitement, and satisfaction that has always been inherent in preparing for and taking off with a flight of bristling B-47's or B-52's. In missile units the atmosphere is certain to be one of even greater challenge. But the training launches will be much less frequent than aircraft flights, and each firing will be preceded by long periods of tension and strain. Crews will find themselves sitting at consoles and working in isolated underground facilities where everything is done by remote control. Boredom and monotony will be a constant companion except for the times when missiles are actually being fired. Multiple-shift operations will be required to maintain a state of constant readiness. In many cases the men will be separated from their families.

All these things will have to be overcome by an enlightened, new approach to the problem of individual motivations. We cannot afford to stand by and hope that trained missilemen will stay with us. We must be able to attract thousands of officers and men into a missile career and keep them there for at least an eight-year tour. To do so we must make their life as missilemen the best the country can offer.

How do we do this? We do not know the complete answer yet. We do know that we cannot expect intelligent, technically qualified experts to submit to the privations and restrictions of a missileman's life for pay that is less than they can get right on the same launch pad in civilian status from any one of the contractors. We know also that the man of missile caliber will not tolerate shabby, overpriced quarters for his family when he can provide decently for them by shucking his uniform. Nor will he submit to prolonged separation from his family without suitable compensating reward. We know these things from recent and vivid experience.

We believe, on the other hand, there are plenty of men who can be motivated to follow the career of a missileman if they are offered conditions of service and life that measure up to alternative civilian standards. This has been the guiding philosophy behind all that has been done to develop the first ballistic missile operational and training facility at Cooke Air Force Base. Army mobilization-type barracks for airmen that once housed 74 men have been converted into modern, highly attractive dormitories, with separate two- and three-man rooms. Bachelor officer quarters have been converted into comfortable, spacious apartment units that will assure young bachelor officers of value received for their forfeited quarters allowance. Some 880 new three- and four-bedroom Capehart family quarters are under construction on the base, with 525 more to follow. Cooke will have the Air Force's first three- and four-bedroom quarters for airmen—more than six hundred of them. In short, everything possible is being done to make the standard of living at Cooke AFB second to none and thus enhance the life of our first operational missilemen.

But will these physical innovations be enough without realistic attention to the primary motivating influence on missilemen and their families—their economic standing? I believe they will not.

The case for an improved military compensation system and other military career enhancements has been well documented by the Defense Advisory Committee on Professional and Technical Compensation (Cordiner Committee). It appears likely that the Congress will enact some kind of legislation to steepen the military pay curve. But there appears much less probability of legislation to make quarters allowances more realistic, to establish some form of isolation or remote duty pay, or to bring into reality the other improvements recommended by the Cordiner Committee.

If the Air Force is to build and maintain ballistic missile units up to the required level of operational readiness, the missileman's career must be brought up to standards more competitive with those available in the civilian economy.

That is for the future units. At this early stage there is great enthusiasm and pride among the officers and men of the 1st Missile Division. We are charging ahead in preparation for the day when the first operational "bird" will stand upright and be counted in SAC's emergency war plan capability. "Hangar flying" sessions produce all sorts of strange but fascinating new lingo. Altitude to the missileman becomes "apogee," peak of the missile's flight path arc. Fuel is "propellant," a combination of kerosene and LOX (liquid oxygen). The hangar has been replaced by a "RIM" building, the building where the missiles will be received, inspected, and maintained.

Every man at Cooke AFB is a missileman, from the general commanding to the cook in the mess. It is an exciting experience to be traveling down General Twining's "second road" with the country's first operational ballistic missile command.

The atmosphere is loaded with challenge for the missileman of the future. As Author Albro Gaul says in his introduction to *The Complete Book of Space Travel:* "The first space pilot has already been born. He is probably between ten and 16 years old at this moment . . ."

The line forms to the right.

Headquarters 1st Missile Division (*SAC*)

CHAPTER 7

The Ballistic Missile Test Program

LT. COL. EDWARD A. SWANKE, USAF AND
LT. COL. RICHARD K. JACOBSON, USAF

At Cape Canaveral Auxiliary Air Force Base, Florida, weird gantries push steel fingers toward the sky, wisps of vapor from LOX tanks drift away, and exhaust trails crisscross the sky. More and more frequently, the exhaust trails are created by and are symbols of the ballistic missile program. Cape Canaveral is the site of all ballistic missile flight test activities and is a part of the Air Force Missile Test Center. It constitutes the start of the long-range proving ground which stretches out 5000 miles over the South Atlantic.

In addition to the activities at the Cape and at Patrick Air Force Base, 14 miles away, there are many other mainland sites for instrumentation and a string of instrumented islands extending to tiny Ascension Island some 500 miles south of the equator. The ballistic missile program has changed the face of Cape Canaveral as new facilities have been identified and programed to support this effort. These will further change the Cape until it has the highest concentration of missile activity in the country.

Guided missiles are the daily business of the Air Force Missile Test Center. There missile testing is a concrete reality, and more than ten thousand Air Force, Civil Service, and contractor personnel are engaged in it daily. Approximately one third of these people are directly supporting the Air Force ballistic missile program and the number will increase.

This activity at the Air Force Missile Test Center represents only a part, and a small part, of the ballistic missile test program. It is the visual evidence of progress in the program and certainly the culmination of any test effort. Flight testing in this program has been compared to the visible portion of an iceberg. The major portion of the test effort is conducted at numerous sites throughout the country.

To understand the magnitude of the ballistic missile test program, it is necessary to understand the test philosophy of the program. At the outset several factors were recognized as having an important relationship to any philosophies specifically oriented toward rocket ballistic weapons. These factors included consideration of the following:

• The test philosophy for manned aircraft, which was well established and has been demonstrated to be effective, seemed applicable to ballistic missile testing. This philosophy includes comprehensive testing of individual components up to and including complete weapon systems.

• The Unsatisfactory Report System which has contributed so heavily to the successful development and improvement of manned aircraft is not directly applicable to the missile program, since the constant scrutiny of equipment by pilots, crew members, and maintenance personnel is unavailable.

• The vast complex of test facilities uniquely adapted to manned aircraft had not been duplicated in the guided missile field and was virtually nonexistent for the rocket-powered ballistic weapon systems.

• Guided missiles were to be highly complex systems comprising many complex subsystems. More so than in manned aircraft, the failure of any part could mean the failure of the entire missile. All these systems are in series as regards over-all reliability.

• The aircraft-testing practice of relying primarily on flight testing could not provide the data on which to base needed improvements in missile design. Simulation of potential difficulties and the development of reliability would have to be done on the ground before flight testing.

The testing philosophy

These factors were summarized in a letter written by the Commander, Air Research and Development Command, to the Chief of Staff, Headquarters USAF, in which he recommended a philosophy of testing rocket ballistic weapons. This philosophy as established and operating in this program establishes three general principles:

Avoid Dead-end Testing. Within the ballistic missile program no components are designed and tested unless they are ultimately to be a part of the system. Accordingly the first missiles are in the final configuration, minus certain components. As the program progresses and as our knowledge increases, the complexity of the test program increases. While the first series encompasses test of an airframe, autopilot, and propulsion system only, the minimum capability for flight, these components are designed as portions of the ultimate operational missiles. As the test program progresses, guidance, auxiliary power, nose cone, warhead, and other subsystems are successively added.

Rely on Ground Tests. Primary dependence on flight testing for rocket-powered ballistic weapon development is inadequate and extremely expensive. Consequently a comprehensive ground test program is a prerequisite to flight testing. It has been proved that captive vehicle testing can be effective and economical. Thus in the ICBM program the first missile of any series is assigned to a captive test stand. Facilities similar to the launch complexes at Patrick can be found at Edwards Rocket Base, California, and in the "backyard" of various contractors. The number of these systems test facilities exceeds the number of the launch complexes at AFMTC. In this type of testing the missiles may be run many times, providing masses of statistical information to aid in the development of a reliable system. Because of the hazards involved in such testing, each program has in it a so-called "battleship facility." This stand has heavy tanks of battleship steel built in the exact configuration of the actual missile tanks for use in repeated testings. In addition to the battleship facilities the ground test program includes hydrostatic test stands to check the reaction of the missile to pressurization. To measure the reaction of the missile to fast servicing and to determine the potential hazard of any given missile, a complete facility for check-out of fast-servicing procedures and hazards has been developed at the Air

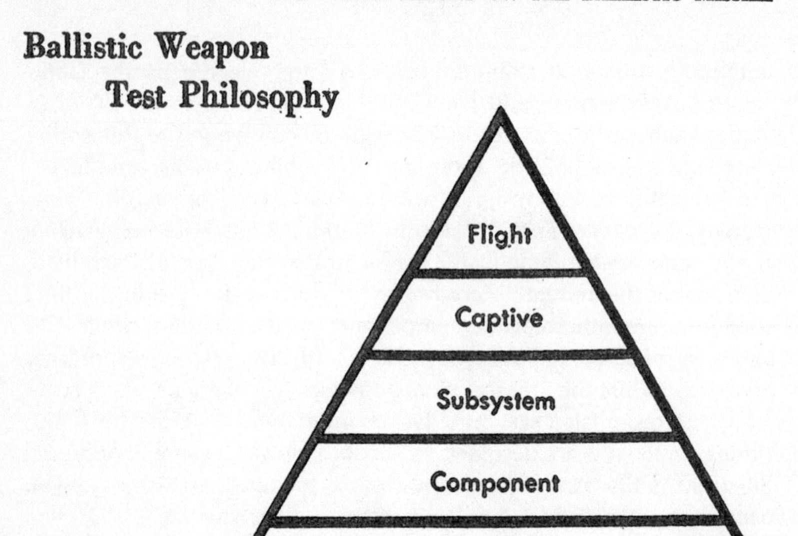

"Testing will be accomplished at the lowest possible level"

Force Flight Test Center, Edwards Air Force Base, California, adjacent to the Rocket Base.

Test the Systems Early. No testing is done at any level if it could be carried out at a lower level. Systems testing is never designed merely to check the operation of a given subsystem but to determine the relationship between subsystems. For example, early flight tests demonstrate the compatibility of airframe, engine, and autopilot subsystems. The operation of each subsystem has been tested in advance on its own test facilities. Likewise testing of engines is not programed to test components of the system. Turbopumps, valves, and other components of the propulsion system are checked out independently. Schematically the test program looks like a pyramid. Relating the efforts to the flight test program, we find that numerically flight testing represents only a small part of the total test effort. Captive tests will number an order of magnitude greater than the programed flight tests. Tests of the rocket engine will number to an order of magnitude greater than the captive tests and several orders of magnitude greater than the flight tests. Component tests will exceed by several orders of magnitude the programed subsystem testing. Thus any flight test represents tens of thousands of tests on captive facilities, subsystems test facilities, and components testing facilities.

This philosophy determines the requirement for facilities to support the test program. In recognizing this philosophy and its translation into specific test plans and programs, one must examine the installations and facilities requirements that it dictates. The Air Force Missile Test Center, where missiles are actually flight tested, rests on a broad base of support facilities throughout the United States required for the success of its flight-test mission. The test plans have established the scope, number, character, and location of our test facilities.

Since the ballistic missile program was accelerated in 1954, approximately $500,000,000 has been made available for new test installations and contractor plant expansions. A substantial percentage of this total, over $100,000,000, is privately financed by both prime contractors and subcontractors. The impact of a test program of this magnitude at installations like Patrick and Edwards Air Force Bases has called for a considerable expansion of the technical, administrative, and support facilities to handle the significant increase in contractor and Air Force equipment and personnel. Such a buildup of testing effort can obviously only be supported by substantial expansion in the industrial facilities to support the fabrication of test hardware and to provide a development and engineering capability at contractors' plants. Laboratory test equipment, such as environmental test chambers, random-noise vibration equipment, and data-reduction equipment, has been installed at contractors' plants for the extensive developmental and reliability testing required to support this major effort.

Flight test

The size of the installation required to support a successful flight-test program is readily appreciated in the Cape Canaveral launch area of the Air Force Missile Test Center. Here one can see numerous ballistic missile launch stands flanked by guidance complexes, assembly and checkout areas, and the related technical support facilities. An Atlas ICBM launch complex includes blockhouse, instrumentation ducts, elevated ramp, launch stand, LOX, fuel, and gas systems, and gantry service tower. The stand is elevated to provide a water-cooled flame deflector to permit preflight static testing prior to the actual launch. Representative of another type launch stand is a Thor IRBM launcher. It too encompasses the major features of a blockhouse, elevated launch stand, and supporting LOX, fuel, and high-pressure gas systems. Design criteria and site layout for these unique facilities are based on the safety conditions required at the launch area and the range safety criteria of the Air Force Missile Test Center.

The ground-based radio-inertial guidance system being used on tests of the Atlas weapon system is complex. It encompasses the major elements of central guidance operations, Doppler radars, and the rate transmitters—with the rate receivers accurately positioned at the ends of four 5000-foot legs of a cross. No operations could succeed without a vast supporting area where the assembly hangars, LOX plants, shops, storage, data reduction, and engineering space are located. This entire complex is tied together by a network of roads, communications, and water and power distribution, and dotted with a myriad of range instrumentation devices to ensure maximum effectiveness of the test program.

Range. Included in this huge installations and equipment buildup for testing of the complete weapon systems are thousands of miles of instrumented range whose scope and complexities dwarf any previous missile effort. There is not space here to cover this vast project in detail.

A typical range station is on San Salvador. It is manned and operated by the range contractor (Pan American Airways and RCA) for the Air Force.

Captive test

Of significant importance is the static testing of the complete weapon system, which the test philosophy requires in support of a successful flight-test schedule. For example, at the Edwards Rocket

Base both the Atlas and Thor weapons are undergoing captive testing. Representative of this test effort is Test Stand 1-A, which was designed as a one-million-pound-thrust test stand. It has been modified for use by Convair in testing the Atlas missile. To ensure reliability of propulsion system plumbing, a tank made of battleship steel and having the same configuration as the missile tankage was put on Test Stand 1-A. This type of battleship tank testing will permit a determination of those factors that relate to the marriage of the propulsion system and the airframe without having to use an actual missile for this testing. The stand also permits an early location at which some test-crew training can be accomplished. Also at the Edwards Rocket Base other facilities are in place to support testing of ground-support equipment and other tests which in themselves have a high risk and cannot be done at other locations.

Since additional captive testing is done in the contractor's backyard, one will see static test stands at the airframe contractor's plant for the Thor, Titan, and Atlas weapon systems. The proximity of this type of test stand to the engineering and fabrication facilities of the contractor makes for rapid fixes during development and the efficient use of highly trained personnel responsible for the conduct of these activities.

Subsystem testing

Weapon system testing cannot be successful within the terms of the test philosophy without a broad capability for subsystem testing and individual component testing.

Airframe. The Air Force ballistic missile program involves the development, fabrication, and testing of three airframes: namely, Atlas by Convair, Titan by Martin, and Thor by Douglas. Support of this development effort has called for a considerable expansion of engineering laboratories, fabrication facilities, and environmental test facilities. Representative of this type of activity is the Convair Point Loma test area, where components and elements are tested prior to assembly of the missile airframe.

As in the case of other contractors a large area adjacent to the engineering and fabrication facilities is required in the interest of safety, security, noise suppression, and other problems arising in ballistic missile testing. Martin, for example, has moved to the Denver region and established a new plant with associated facilities.

Propulsion. In all probability, the most impressive facility buildup to support a development and test program was accomplished in the propulsion area. The Rocketdyne Division of North American Aviation, with Air Force assistance, has established a Field Propulsion Laboratory in the hills above San Fernando Valley. At North American are an engineering development facility, a cold-flow calibration laboratory, environmental testing fixtures, and a battery of eighteen rocket-engine test stands. Similarly, at Aerojet-General in Sacramento, a sizable facility buildup can be noted. These two contractors are obviously large users of liquid oxygen. The Air Force considered it economical to provide on-site LOX plants and such facilities have been constructed.

Guidance. Perhaps the best example of subsystem and component testing can be seen in the guidance-system testing. There are approximately eight prime contractors working in guidance, and their test capability buildup has been tremendous. A tour through their facilities would reveal environmental test equipment, data-processing equipment, reliability test facilities, and backyard field test setups.

Nose Cone. The remaining subsystem of the ballistic missile weapon system is the nose cone and its warhead. Here also a substantial buildup of laboratory, fabrication, and test equipment and facilities can be observed. This subsystem requires a considerable amount of systems analysis equipment to ensure, insofar as possible before flight test, the nose cone's ability to operate satisfactorily under actual flight environment.

In the small space of two years this half-billion-dollar facility expansion program has been more than 75 per cent completed and represents to the Air Force, and to the nation, a significant milestone in the progress made toward the development of effective ballistic missile weapon systems. This effort also forms the basic building block for further and future Air Force investigation into the problems associated with man's attempt to conquer space. One can readily appreciate that the ballistic missile flight-test program is in fact like the visible portion of an iceberg, when the total test and facilities support of test objectives is backed by so vast a base of facilities and testing effort, the architecture of which was shaped by the test philosophy established.

Air Force Ballistic Missile Division, Hq ARDC

CHAPTER 8

Logistics for the Ballistic Missile

MAJOR GENERAL BEN I. FUNK, USAF

It has long been conceded that combat units must be provided with immediately responsive logistics support if they are to continually maintain a state of peak operational readiness. The advent of missiles in the operational inventory further intensifies the need to streamline logistics actions. The ballistic missile, with its requirement for launching in a very short time after the signal is given, is a case in point.

When the over-all Air Force logistics picture is examined in terms of the requirements of the ICBM/IRBM weapon systems, an incompatibility is evident. The Air Force has embarked upon a program calculated to achieve a fast-reacting, reflex logistics system within the next ten years. There are many manifestations of this. Logair, in the transportation field, is a major step toward attaining a proper logistics airlift posture. Air Materiel Command conducts service tests in many aspects of logistics, particularly in electronic data processing. Base supply is undergoing a mechanization program. But these long-range logistics goals, called "jet-age logistics," cannot be attained in the near future for the entire Air Force. The size and inertia of the present complex logistics system simply will not permit it. A streamlined logistics system of this size must be achieved by evolution, by a gradual injection of new and advanced techniques and procedures.

A closer analysis of the problem reveals that if we do not attempt to cure all the Air Force logistics ailments with one dose, the same objectives can be realized in a relatively short time. We can do this by focusing attention on segments of the operational force, thus confining the problem to a manageable size. The ballistic missiles represent such a manageable segment. It may well be that in streamlining logistics support for the ballistic missiles we will find that we have crossed the threshold into a new era of "rocket-age logistics."

The attainment of an early operational ballistic missile capability is obviously a matter of pre-eminent national importance. An extreme concentration of technical and management attention has been invested in this program, resulting in a marked compression of the normal cycle for bringing a new weapon into the operational inventory. Since the Air Force is denied the opportunity of preparing for the logistics-support task at its leisure, many of the present methods of doing things must be critically examined. Further we cannot afford the luxury of errors in preplanning. It is unnecessary to go into a lengthy discourse on planning deficiencies of past programs. One example is that Air Force packaging techniques in the past have not been fully in consonance with weapon design. And how many times have operational units been deployed when they were not fully equipped, thus degrading their capability?

It appears at first glance that there are insurmountable constraints to a proper approach to the ballistic missile logistics problems. Upon closer examination, however, these apparently burdensome conditions change character. It may be that a critical examination of some of the current procedures and ways of doing things, caused in this case by necessity, is a blessing in disguise. The realization that there is not enough time to do the things that must be done will cause attention to be concentrated on quicker and more efficient methods. The realization that a planning error of the order of some committed in the past would be disastrous in a program of this nature is another big step. The very establishment of the Ballistic Missile Division (ARDC), Ballistic Missiles Office (AMC), and Space Technology Laboratories of Ramo-Wooldridge Corporation as a management team signifies the awareness of the need to vest the authority and responsibility for prosecuting a high-priority weapon system development program in an organization of unusual competence. This same philosophy must be applied in all of the complementing support areas such as logistics and training.

The problem of having to support operational weapons of quick reaction capability has been briefly touched upon. Ballistic missiles are weapons which can wreak devastation on their assigned targets thousands of miles away within a very short time after they are launched. Most assuredly they cannot be allowed to remain in a state of disrepair for any appreciable length of time. Lack of proper supporting spares and maintenance capability would be sheer waste of the inherent capability which the weapons possess. The tremendous cost of these weapons makes completely unacceptable overprograming of additional weapons, supporting equipment, or spares to compensate for those out of commission.

In our manned aircraft, components may be found to be defective after take-off and still not cause a mission abort. Skilled crew members can often take up the slack. In some guided missiles, such as pilotless aircraft, we cannot rely on the human factor but we still have in the guidance system a means for retaining control of the missile for a considerable period of time after launch. Such is not the case, of course, with the ballistic missile. Little time is allowed for correction of errors. The missile is soon beyond a point where we can exert any control over it. Reliability then becomes paramount. This applies not only to reliability of the weapon and its ground support equipment but equally to all contributing elements of the weapon system.

The logistics control

If attention is narrowed specifically to ballistic missile logistics it will be noted that many contractors are involved in the development of these missiles. Under the present Air Materiel Area (AMA) depot system many AMC field agencies would automatically, by virtue of the contractor alignment, be involved in the direct support of ballistic missile operational units. With such dispersion a logistics reaction capability satisfying the requirements of the ICBM/IRBM would have to invoke the utmost in cooperation, coordinated planning, and concentrated effort. To preserve the operational effectiveness of the ballistic missiles, the Air Force would have to expect a degree of fully coordinated efficiency that could not possibly be attained in any organization this large and compartmentalized without some form of central control.

The direction to be taken is clear. It has been necessary to delegate to one individual within the AMC structure full responsibility to develop a logistics system fully tuned to the requirements of these new weapon systems. At the same time we would be seriously remiss if we did not, in designing such a system, fully exploit those logistics procedures and techniques of an advanced nature which have been service-tested piece by piece during the past several years. We have an opportunity to give birth to some long-conceived tenets and to shake down in an isolated, yet not insulated, environment a logistics package based upon the weapon system management concept.

In recognition of the need to develop an advanced logistics system in close harmony with the research and development effort and to ensure readiness to operate on the date the first operational unit must be deployed, AMC published logistics plans early in the life of the ballistic missile program. Distributed in November 1956, these documents have the approval of the Air Force Ballistic Missile Division, the Strategic Air Command, the Air Training Command, and Headquarters USAF. They provide for the appointment of a ballistic missiles manager for ballistic missile logistics, charged with the responsibility of establishing and maintaining a streamlined ICBM/IRBM logistics system. The ballistic missiles manager has been established as a separate organizational element of Headquarters AMC, responsible directly to the Commander. He has been assigned prime and executive AMC responsibilities for ballistic missiles.

The plans prescribe a logistics system that makes maximum use of electronic data-processing devices to aid the ballistic missiles manager in performing the logistics functions connected with mission support of the ballistic missiles. They are based upon minimum stock levels, minimum pipeline time, direct support from source to user, minimum administration at the operational unit level, and optimum use of contractor maintenance.

The logistics system

Let us examine more in detail the features of this plan. All components required in support of the ICBM/IRBM units and not currently stocked within the Air Force depot system as standard Air Force items will be initially supported for both supply and maintenance by the contractor who is developing the particular subsystem. As soon as such support can be rendered more effectively by an AMC agency, responsibility will shift to the AMA/depot structure. To provide the ballistic missiles manager with a full measure of control, those items stocked within the current Air Force system required for direct mission support of ICBM/IRBM strategic missile squadrons are also under his jurisdiction. This is not, it should be emphasized, a huge amount of materiel, but rather a small working stock of fast-moving items.

Ballistic missile operating squadrons will be satellited on host bases for housekeeping support. Those items required in the essential day-to-day operations of the squadrons to maintain them in a constant state of readiness will be provided by the ballistic missiles manager, on a direct basis. There will be no requirement for these items to be accounted for by a base-level, numbered, stock-record account as we now know it. Accountability will be held centrally by the ballistic missiles manager. Naturally operational squadrons will be provided with the small stock of items they require to perform their mission. Their record-keeping requirements will be held to an absolute minimum. They will not be required to submit formal requisitions through the long-familiar procedures to obtain supplies. On the basis of periodic reports, both emergency and routine, they will be automatically supplied with their needs. They will be authorized to perform such maintenance as can logically be effected with available skills, facilities, and space, and considering system complexity and reliability requirements. Any item requiring maintenance beyond the capability of the strategic missile squadron will be evacuated directly to the appropriate contractor or AMA/depot for repair and return to stock.

Maximum utilization will be made of mobile teams as backup maintenance support. A streamlined unsatisfactory-reporting system is being devised to ensure quick reaction to the demands of the situation. Within the United States, Logair will be used to transport components to and from ICBM squadrons and the depot-level support agencies. Arrangements have been made to extend similar service to IRBM units overseas. Air Force airlift capability will be used to transport the weapons themselves.

A fully integrated electronic data-processing system, along with a communications system, will link the ballistic missiles manager, the operating squadrons, a storage site for common items of supply, and the applicable contractor. All activities in this system will be provided with the latest communications terminal equipment to ease the problem of communicating between elements. The heart of the system will be an electronic data-processing center which will streamline logistics action by predetermining and placing into a computer as many management actions as possible. All transaction information for the entire system will funnel into this location for proper recording and necessary action.

Considerations of vulnerability have not been overlooked. Backup provisions have been made in the event of any equipment failure. Provisions have also been made for the using command to participate in all levels of the development of this logistics system and in its operation. This will make for immediate responsiveness to the programing and operational requirements of the using agency.

THE system just described has not been planned on an "it would be nice if" basis. The system is attainable in the time period in question, if it is restricted initially to the ballistic missile organization. The ability to react instantaneously to a requirement, coupled with the close inventory control this system will permit, will save countless millions of dollars usually expended to stock larger quantities of spares. This is not to say that the establishment of this system will not be difficult. Highly trained personnel have been assigned to the effort because there is little time for the training of semiskilled personnel in the fields of electronic data processing, supply, maintenance, and transportation. Those personnel chosen for the effort have had to undergo a highly selective qualification review. Full use will be made of heretofore separate and unintegrated electronic data-processing research programs recently completed, currently in process, and now being planned within the Air Force and industry. The best talent in the business has been marshaled to the task. There is little doubt that the service-testing of this support concept and of the fully integrated electronic data-processing system it uses will provide a wealth of data useful to all echelons of management within the Air Force. It will doubtless become a signpost to the future of the entire Air Force logistics structure. It should point the way for other weapon systems on the drawing board and in early stages of development.

Ballistic Missiles Office, Hq AMC

CHAPTER 9

Impact of the Ballistic Missile on Warfare

COLONEL ALEXANDER SHERIDAN, USAF

There have been immense changes in the art of warfare within the past century. The use of mass, the substitution of artillery, rifle, and machine gun for massed troops, the entrenchments of the Civil War and World War I, the swing back to movement with the panzer thrust of early World War II have each had profound effects. The advent of the air-delivered nuclear weapon is so big and so different that many planners, still bound by the traditional thinking of the last war, have yet to fully appreciate this weapon system.

Now we are on the threshold of the ballistic missile. This event has given rise to a host of writers and publicists, and some military planners, who might be called "futurists." These people often evaluate future expected capabilities of a new weapon system within the present-day framework, with everything except their new weapon system remaining at today's state of development. These futurists are so bemused and enchanted by the ultimate possibilities of the ballistic missile with the nuclear warhead that they are prone to lull the United States into a false sense of military prowess. The futurist is just as dangerous to the security of the United States as the traditionalist. The latter is rooted firmly in the rut of the past; the former has his feet well off the ground, floating off ten years into tomorrow.

Sound planning for this future master-weapon system is imperative, and some good work is being done. For the most part, however, it has been done only by a small group intimately associated with missile development. Proper evaluation and full utilization of the ballistic missile, within the perspective of the political climate anticipated, are tasks of the greatest importance for United States leaders today.

Initial impact

The initial capability of the first ballistic missiles will set neatly into the U.S. philosophy of modern warfare. The philosophy of modern warfare evolved in the United States since World War II is based upon the ability to mount an immediate and decisive attack against enemy forces and heartland. This philosophy embraces the proposition that the sheer potential destructiveness of such an attack will deter enemy aggression. Since the avowed policy of the United States leaves the initiative in the hands of the enemy, our ability to launch quickly and decisively a counterstrike against the enemy requires a force-in-being. This ready force must be secure from enemy attack and capable of winning the decisive phase of the war, should its deterrent effect fail. Such a force will be an effective deterrent to an enemy only if the enemy has knowledge of the force's capability and invulnerability and, at the same time, knows of the intention to exercise this force.

The primary deterrent to enemy aggression since World War II has been the U.S. strategic air forces equipped with manned bombers. The deterrent effect of this force is being slowly diminished by improved counter-bomber defenses. The early ballistic missiles, if handled properly, will have the characteristics to assist in the deterrent task. The manned bomber will be an important part of the total deterrent force for a long time to come, and the first ballistic missiles will supplement the bomber and help restore the effectiveness of the deterrent force.

The relationship of the ballistic missile newcomer to the family of strategic weapons will be determined by capabilities and limitations. The tremendous speed of the weapon is possibly the characteristic most important to its strategic role. The quick reaction to enemy threat and the improved ability to penetrate enemy defenses are two attributes of the missile's hypersonic speed which make the missile far superior to aircraft. The possibility of hardening and camouflaging the launching site of the missile will make it less vulnerable to surprise attack than the large runway complex of the aircraft's ground environment.

Certain conditions must be met to capitalize on the advantages of fast reaction and improved ability to penetrate defenses. Some changes in operations or tactics will be mandatory, and as capabilities of the missiles increase with the advance of technology, more profound operational changes will be indicated. Advance planning and detailed targeting information, including postshot reconnaissance, will be a necessity. Intelligence information, always a prerequisite for a successful aircraft strike, will be most important since the missile's entire mission will be predicated on this information. Extensive logistic support will be required. The unusual nature of fuels used, the intricate instrumentation and electronic gear will all demand unique facilities and highly skilled personnel. This materiel and manpower will have to be prepositioned and made secure to ensure prelaunch survivability.

Aside from imposed operational requirements the early ballistic missiles have inherent limitations that must be considered for a full appreciation of the missile's initial employment. One such limitation will be an inability to attack fleeting targets and targets on which detailed information is lacking. Initially even its fixed targets will be large-area ones, because of expected inaccuracies in the guidance systems. Selectivity of warhead size to fit the tactical situation will be restricted. It would not be profitable to deliver small-yield warheads, because the use of the totally expendable missile can only be economically justified if the damage effected is in favorable ratio to the cost involved. Too, there are those who feel the first missiles will be limited in effectiveness by the restricted size of the warhead that can be carried. Considering the accuracy allowance for guidance error in the first missiles, the yield may not be great enough to destroy the target. With its one-shot performance the weapon will be limited to priority targets commensurate with its delivery yield and guidance accuracy. Also reliability must not be ignored. Estimates on the reliability of the first ballistic missile force vary, and it will probably take considerable testing and practice firing to establish a dependability that could be termed "combat ready."

Even the ballistic missile's extreme speed, the characteristic that has the greatest potential, is somewhat modified by limitations imposed. The first missiles will be so limited in terms of accuracy and yield that it will be impossible to take advantage of speed to hit enemy forces and thus eliminate the enemy's capability to retaliate. The restriction of the early missiles to large-area targets, control centers, or industrial areas compromises the advantages of speed. These large-area targets are impossible to hide and are completely immobile. Warning time or preparation for expected attack will have little effect. Certain precautionary means can be taken to save life through passive defense, shelters, and evacuation; any enemy government initiating hostilities presumably would take these steps before attacking. Destruction to the target area itself cannot be evaded, but speed of attack in this instance would be of little consequence.

Even with its known limitations the ballistic missile lends itself ideally to some of the missions now performed by the long-range manned bomber. Within the next two decades it appears that the ballistic missile will become the primary means of conducting offensive strategic operations against an enemy, superseding the conventional manned bomber aircraft. In the interim, substitution of the missiles for the more conventional systems will be made as rapidly as technical progress permits. The transition period will see a gradual change, with the ballistic missile and the long-range manned bomber being used concurrently.

Initially the ballistic missile could best supplement the strategic aircraft force by providing a very fast reaction to any enemy war action. The psychological effect of even the relatively inaccurate early missiles falling on the enemy heartland within a matter of minutes of the first outbreak of general war would be considerable. The shock generated by such an attack would facilitate the application of other forces. Fast missile strikes in advance of the aircraft could aid the more accurate manned bomber attack by causing general confusion, disruption of communications, and possible damage to enemy defenses, particularly point defenses adjacent to the large-area missile targets. Enemy defenses against aircraft attack are improving considerably. It is conceivable that there might be some important, heavily defended targets that would be almost impossible to destroy with manned bombers without unacceptable losses. In such a situation the ballistic missile may be the only practicable method of destroying these vital targets. Salvos of the early ballistic missiles could be used to compensate for inaccuracies and limited yields. Immediate missile retaliatory strikes, assistance to manned-bomber penetration, and attacks on heavily guarded, large-area targets will be the contributions of the early missiles to the bombardment force in the execution of the strategic mission.

Future impact

The eventual long-range impact of the ballistic missile on warfare is difficult, if not impossible, to ascertain. No armament of warfare is ever static in its development or application. The eternal swing of the pendulum from offensive weapon to counter defensive measure alone could conceivably render this seemingly master weapon of the future obsolete before it is ever used in warfare. In the present stage of development any defense against the ballistic missile in flight, with its extremely high altitudes and speeds, appears to be a task of gigantic proportions. Yet the very nature of the ballistic trajectory, a path that is unvariable and easily and quickly computed, may be its undoing. The political ramifications of the use of nuclear-armed ballistic missiles may decide whether this weapon will have any impact at all on active warfare or any influence in peacetime. There is evidence of growing concern with the coming of "atomic parity" and the possibility of acts that some have termed bordering on "mutual suicide." World political conditions change and so does the U.S. national policy of which the military is an instrument. Any projection of warfare embracing the use of new weapon systems must also take into account the probable political-military grand strategy.

In endeavoring to understand the future impact of missiles it would probably be better not to try to probe too far into the future. The changes wrought by their introduction will be great, and the changes in warfare after the next twenty years, when the missiles will have reached their advanced capability, will be revolutionary.

For the purpose of discussion and to establish some terms of reference, the advanced capability of the ballistic missile may be described as extreme accuracy, unlimited range, and the carrying of a variable warhead. Other assumptions about the perfected ballistic missile must include a high degree of dependability, an adequate stockpile, and a continuing reconnaissance sufficient to supply accurate and detailed target information. The future ballistic missile described here may never be realized; but if the advanced weapon approximates the capabilities assumed on the basis of today's technological promise, it will be a formidable weapon indeed.

The paramount characteristic of this future weapon system will be its compression of firepower in time and space. This compression effect on the long-revered principles of war and on the more recent doctrinal decrees of the present-day services will be great. Adjustments will be difficult. The old, tested principles and much of the modern-day doctrine will still be valid from the purist viewpoint, but the time compression by the weapon will give them new significance and altered emphasis.

For instance, economy of force and concentration of force will have new meaning. The inevitable completion of the ballistic missile mission coupled with the large destructive power of the nuclear warhead will make possible an orderly neutralization of complete target systems performed with the utmost economy to friendly forces. The free disposal or placement of forces, a principle of war which can include mobility, flexibility, and surprise, will not change, though the concept of operations will be greatly modified. The new weapon, prepositioned as it must be, gives new meaning to mobility and flexibility. Because of the weapon's speed, range, and accuracy any target system selected could be hit with any degree of intensity desired. With movement of forces at the rate of 16,000 miles per hour, the surprise to be effected will be achieved in a matter of minutes. Disposition of forces and security are principles that will govern even national survival in the compressed time phasing of the new atomic-ballistic age. Force deployment and force-in-being will have to be on immediate, battle-ready vigilance at all times. The security of the force will determine its potential destructive power and in turn its deterrent effect, for this will also be the age of counter-force operation. With each combatant holding quick life or death over the other by virtue of superarmament, the superarmament itself becomes the prime target. The destruction of an enemy national capital is small gain when traded against the annihilation of the friendly nation's own capital. The new era will demand disposition of forces in instant-ready position, relatively secure against enemy action, and aimed at countering the enemy offensive power.

The grand strategy of the United States—the maintenance of ineluctable force with destructive power unacceptable to an enemy—will not change with the coming of age of the missile. The compression of time, the ability to react very quickly to any act of aggression, will become increasingly important as universal improvements are made in the ballistic missile weapons. Until an enemy is assured that the United States' nuclear-armed ballistic missile capability can be destroyed, or until an enemy creates an impregnable defense against the missile, there seems little danger that all-out war will be deliberately initiated except as an act of irrationality. Immediate ballistic missile retaliation reduces the initiation of unlimited war to sheer adventurism. Calculation of risks becomes unreal; the cost of miscalculation becomes unacceptable in logic. The strategy will strengthen to such an extent that general all-out war, always abhorrent in the eyes of reasonable men, may become a thing of the past.

Tactics will change. Conventionally the term "tactics" applies to actions taken after the start of the battle in support of the over-all campaign plan or strategy. Here again, old concepts must be bent to meet new conditions. The compression of time by the new weapon will mean prehostility planning and operational readiness to an extent heretofore unknown. Under such conditions of complete wartime readiness, the force must be ready to strike vital enemy heartland targets literally at a moment's notice. Proper deployment, both in the continental United States and in strategically located and secure sites overseas, will have to be made. Vast logistical arrangements and networks, the lifeblood of the force, will have to be established. Complete and undisruptive communication nets, the nerve system of the force, will have to be maintained. Training, placement, and management of skilled personnel will be required; and all these things must be functioning on a full wartime basis in any period of uneasy peace.

Future control

Control of the force will have to be unequivocal and absolute. In this field of control, perhaps more than in any other, changes will be most difficult. New technology produces new hardware, and new hardware requires new operational concepts. These, in turn, require new supporting logistics and new skills and training of personnel. These things, for the most part, are readily recognized and accepted within the military.

Unfortunately this is not always true with anything approaching organizational or command and control arrangements designed to fit new modes of warfare. These subjects, fraught as they are with interservice prejudices and with service traditions, rarely receive objective military study. A purely military solution to command arrangement is impossible, and, in the last analysis, perhaps this is a good thing. Any arrangement affecting the very survival of the nation should be the concern of all. The trouble is that too many people have honorable interests and individual loyalites that sometimes conflict with the hard, clear-cut decision that would give the United States military the kind of control it needs if it is not to vitiate the time-compression characteristic that makes the new weapon so potent. The changes to our military control structure will have to be of large magnitude, stemming from the commander-in-chief and on down. The luxury of several agencies performing the same tasks, the gentlemanly agreements of cooperation and noninfringement on traditional prerogatives—real or fancied, the leisurely talk-talk ending in the innocuous compromise, will all be inadequate to cope with a weapon system that can kill a nation in half an hour. Military command structure should be arranged to fight the next war, not the last one. Perhaps no other problem is more deserving of our best study and early resolution than the one of organization and command control necessary to fight the advanced ballistic missile in tomorrow's battle.

The controlling element transcends the military. Any weapon that has the potential of starting and ending a conflict in one action will be the concern of the highest authority. Because the political aspects involved will be great and lasting, any decision to unleash the future ballistic missile force can be made by no less than the President with the consent of the Congress. Since our national policy is firmly dedicated to preventing war and our military capability geared to reacting against aggression, there appears little likelihood that Congress will be confronted with the decision to declare war. Thus, any decision will undoubtedly come from the President as Commander-in-Chief, in a situation clearly requiring and receiving public endorsement and Congressional approval.

The use of offensive weapons of the caliber of the nuclear-armed ballistic missile against enemy territory, regardless of the provocation, is an unmistakable invitation to unlimited war. Authority to launch such weapons, even when we are confronted with imminent attack, is not very likely to be delegated by the President. Decision to launch an attack will probably have to depend upon strategic warning that an enemy attack is imminent and inevitable. Warning of this nature is difficult to obtain. When obtainable it could easily be misinterpreted. A country no longer will have the advantage of observing the conventional intelligence signs: stockpiling, troop buildup, maneuvers—all the paraphernalia of former preparation for war. Rather preparations will be made months and years in advance, with the final preparation nothing more than topping off fuel containers and final choice from among preselected targets. Long-range or advance intelligence, by its very paucity, will not be reliable enough for decision. Short-range intelligence reports of a positive nature, e.g., missiles in flight, will be available for only a few minutes and be practically worthless as a means of buying time for decision.

Although administrative and technical procedures have been established to keep the President fully informed, there is always the danger that an enemy surprise attack could destroy communication facilities. Since this will be a counterforce attack, even the means of retaliation may be destroyed before a decision could be rendered. Thus national survival under the conditions of complete surprise attack will depend upon prearranged rules of engagement as well as upon military readiness. There is a distinct requirement for the formulation of automatic rules of engagement approved by the President and the Congress and made known to the world.

The initial capability of the ballistic missile will assist the United States strategic air forces in performing the deterrent mission. The advanced nuclear-armed ballistic missile, with its extreme accuracy and range, will not change U.S. basic philosophy of war but it will revolutionize operations as the missile becomes the principal instrument of offensive force. The key to the weapon's impact, in either its initial or ultimate role, upon warfare and thus upon the nations of the world is its terrific compression of time and space. This capability in the hands of an enemy nation bent on domination may be the very incentive for aggression. Its possession by an enemy becomes even more dangerous if it happens to be in the hands of those who would not mind the destruction of a million lives or a dozen cities to obtain their objectives. In any evaluation of the future of the ballistic missile, one fact is clear: the United States should keep as far in advance as possible in the development of both the ballistic missile and the defensive measures against it. An enemy is not likely to launch an attack that has small chance of a quick success. Means of missile defense bear directly on the problem of deterrence.

The era of the missile will make war more unattractive than ever. The very great and immediate destruction envisaged on both vanquished and victor—if indeed one side could be called a victor—may be so great as to spark some system of international control and settlement of differences short of all-out war. American morality has been reaching for such a goal for some time. The benevolent if quixotic disarmament attempts of the past are proof of good intention. It is further a fact that the United States has not used its preponderance of force in the recent past to gain any kind of dominance over other nations, even in the face of extreme provocation. This too was at a time when American power was supreme and could be applied without thought or danger of retaliation to the United States. Although not indicated in the foreseeable future, public opinion in support of a world authority may bring about an eventual understanding and acceptance of the implications of the ballistic missile era. The United States, by all means, should encourage any overtures in this direction.

It is probably agreed by all that any sort of firm universal limitations on the use of weapons could be achieved only under a supranational government that, in turn, would have to be armed with the latest, most powerful weapon—the nuclear-warhead ballistic missile. There is no indication that sovereign states will relinquish such power to a supranational government in the present or foreseeable future. It seems that the best the world can expect from the ballistic missile's impact on warfare will be a period of uneasy, mutual deterrence.

Evaluation Staff, Air War College

CHAPTER 10

Impact of the Ballistic Missile on Defense

COLONEL HARVEY W. C. SHELTON, USAF

Few areas of military and scientific thought are more beset with conjecture, as opposed to fact-based logic, than is that concerning defense against the ballistic missile. One hears the cliché that no offensive armament in the history of warfare has long existed without effective counters to it being devised. But it is also true that no competent scientific or military authority will today confidently predict that any particular defensive scheme against the ICBM is really practicable. Be that as it may, there is an abiding urgency about the threat which demands that we not simply ignore it and hope that it will go away.

Before we examine some of the possibilities in defense against ballistic missiles it might be well to review some of the principles of defense against any military threat, if only to fix a few terms that will be used from time to time in this writing.

A defense against military threat must be rooted in a recognition of the threat, including a knowledge of the enemy's strategic intent. Logically the attacker's strategic intent is consistent with the capabilities of his weapon system, so the defender—armed with knowledge of that intent—is equipped to make appropriate strategic preparations. That is, the defender can now devise the best possible defensive system and formulate concepts and, to a degree, plans for its employment. Traditionally the defense function to this point proceeds at a comparatively leisurely pace and draws more on technical and political skills than on classical military skills. It has been common, as well, for the resultant defensive capability to lag behind the offensive capability, sometimes by a pretty frightening margin. This is the case with the ballistic missile.

Once the attack is launched the relative pace of the defensive effort increases greatly, and it is at this time that the classical military skills—notably tactical judgment—come into play. Again speaking historically, superior tactical judgment has often succeeded in spite of poor strategic preparation; faulty tactical judgment has often dissipated an apparent strategic advantage. Tactical judgment on the part of the defender involves such actions as gathering necessary information, waiting until the essential bits can be had and not wasting further time once they are available, divining the attacker's tactical intent while there is still time to frustrate it, and vigorously proceeding with the indicated counterstroke. Defense has always placed a high premium on sure knowledge or shrewd guess, and has imposed a severe penalty on uncertainty.

Application to the missile

We shall see that all these classical functions and principles must play their part in the defense against the ballistic missile. Our problem can be stated as one of determining how to alter and adapt them. This current consideration will examine some of the characteristics of the ballistic missile system itself that must shape the defense against it. This effort may limit the area of our ignorance of how to fashion an effective defensive effort. It may then be possible to point with some confidence toward the avenues that more explicit scientific and military exploration must follow.

Looking first at pertinent characteristics of the ballistic missile system itself, I realize that all these are covered rather extensively elsewhere in this book. It seems useful, though, to note them here and now so that they may be borne in mind in our further considerations.

Flight Time. One of the most frightening aspects of the ballistic missile is its extremely short flight time. Even people who routinely deal in the art of air battle at a thousand miles per hour or so tend to blanch when they think of doing battle with a vehicle whose entire tactical life span is of the order of a half hour or less. Certainly the opportunities for bringing human judgment and tactical skill to bear in such a duel are to be fantastically more limited than we have ever encountered before, even in the fast-evolving air age. Somewhat on the other side of the coin, however, is the relative inflexibility of the ballistic missile system. For instance, it may be that a prepared missile cannot be shifted from one target to another or among a large variety of targets without some rather time-consuming preparations. More to the point—once committed, a missile is destined for only one target, and its trajectory, while short-lived and far-flung, is also rigidly constrained by laws of nature.

Trajectory. An unaccelerated body, such as the ballistic missile be-

Ballistic Missile Trajectory

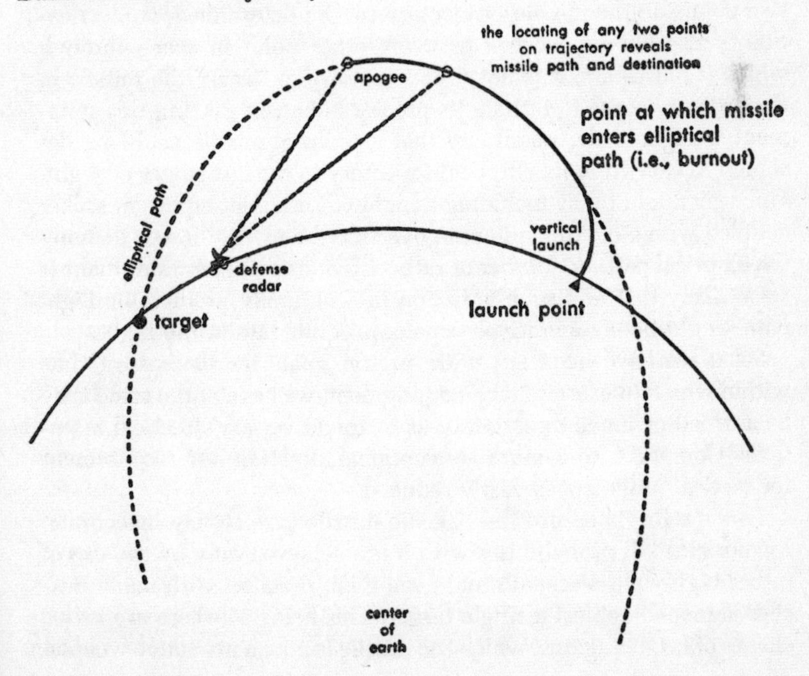

comes after fuel burnout, must travel in an elliptical path which intersects the earth's surface at two points. If we neglect atmospheric friction, the ellipse containing the flight path to a particular target is determined by two factors: the velocity of the body and the fact that the nether focus of the ellipse is at the center of the earth's gravitational field, i.e., at the center of the earth. The greater the velocity, the more elongated will be the ellipse, which is to say the higher above the surface of the earth will be the apogee of the trajectory. For any given range between two points on the earth's surface there is a minimum apogee corresponding to the minimum velocity which will propel a missile that far. This minimum velocity may be said to define the optimum flight trajectory, since even small increases in velocity exact relatively enormous penalties in the interrelated factors of thrust and weight. Actually, of course, a ballistic missile's flight does not take place in a true and constant vacuum, but the deformation of the elliptical trajectory from atmospheric effects is both minor and predictable. It can be seen, then, that if any two points on the missile's trajectory can be determined, its destination is also known, as well as every other point in space through which it must pass; it is not even necessary to "track" the missile in the ordinary sense to fathom its precise intent. In making this statement we ignore the possibility that a ballistic missile could be designed to vary from its elliptical trajectory in the last stages of flight. One way might be by including a highly discriminating target seeker coupled with a control system to override the natural forces defining the elliptical path. A number of rather obvious considerations make it seem likely that any such variation in a naturally predictable flight path would be comparatively small and quite late in the flight.

So, if we have been left with pretty small increments of time within which to exercise tactical judgment, we have at the same time been freed of much uncertainty as to the adversary's tactical intentions. Compared to a more conventional situation our requirement for tactical judgment is vastly reduced.

Targets. By its nature the ballistic missile is relatively inaccurate. Meaningful kill probabilities with it are achieved only by the use of rather high-yield warheads and even then, perhaps, with many missiles launched against a single target. This being so, there are broad classes of targets against which the missile is not an attractive weapon system. We, as defenders, are provided with some insight of the strategic intent of the attacking system. We may be able to recognize target areas that we can be reasonably certain will not be attacked

Ballistic Missile Angle of Attack

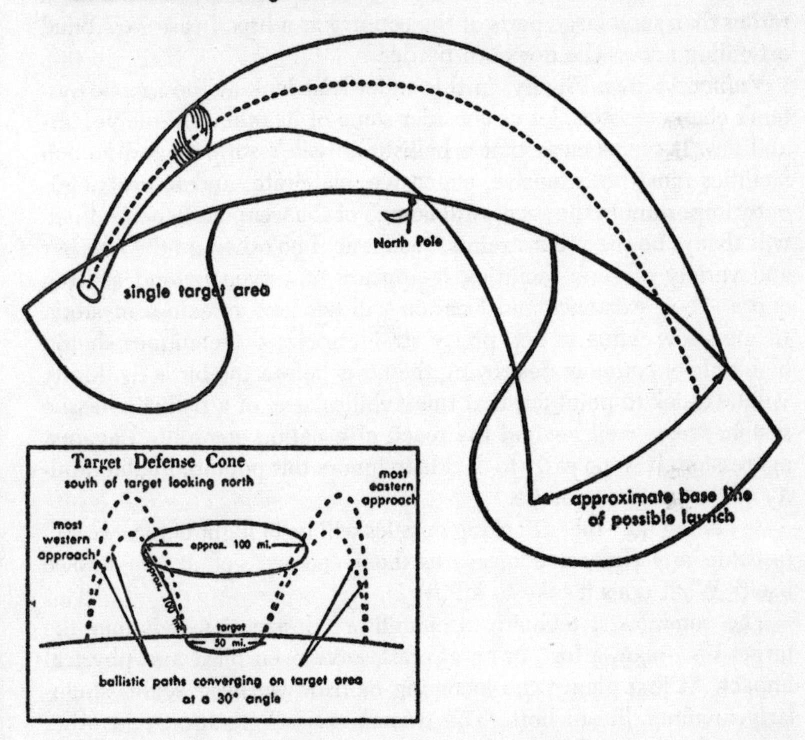

A salient difference in defense against the ballistic missile from against the manned bomber is the relatively small approach corridor to be defended for each target. The bomber can attack from any direction. All the missile trajectories that could hit any particular area-target in the U.S. from any point in the U.S.S.R. would describe an envelope looking rather like a "wilted funnel," of roughly elliptical cross section and inclined toward Soviet Russia at an angle of about 30° from the target surface. Any defense system that could bring the "funnel" under surveillance and intercept the missile coming down through it would suffice.

by ballistic missiles because of the prohibitively large number of missiles required to provide the enemy with acceptable expectation of success. Just how much this foreknowledge can be turned to our advantage is not altogether clear, but we could conceivably decide to defend only a number of "islands" of comparatively modest area rather than such large parts of the country as a broad east-west band extending across the northern border.

Vulnerabilities. Finally, in this superficial look at the missile system's characteristics, let us consider some of its other unique vulnerabilities. It seems clear that a ballistic missile's support and launch facilities must be extensive, expensive, elaborate, and interdependently important to the successful launch of the weapon. Because there will always be sharp constraints, economic if no other, on the number and variety of such facilities, it appears that even behind an iron curtain their existence and location will not long remain a mystery. If one knew when to act, pretty straightforward techniques should be highly effective in destroying the nests before the birds fly. Many will be quick to point out that this Achilles' heel of a ballistic missile system seems well beyond the reach of a nation committed against aggression. It is too early to decide to ignore this potential vulnerability of the ballistic missile.

Assuming now that attacking missiles will be in flight before we can institute any defensive measures, how can we get at the missile itself? What does it take to kill it?

The commonest techniques of military destruction, whether the target be a man, a fort, or an aircraft, have been blast and physical impact. At first glance the incoming ballistic warhead seems singularly invulnerable to both. The tremendous acceleration and other forces of its normal regime would require a design that should be highly impervious to blast overpressures—not to mention the warhead's vast kinetic energy and the fact that during most of its flight it is in a region where blast has little or no medium in which to operate. It is hard to imagine a body more difficult to strike with another body than this warhead hurtling toward us at twenty-odd thousand feet per second.

The very speed of the warhead that makes its interception such a problem may contain the seeds of solution. Recent investigations have suggested that at very high impact velocities very small "projectiles" have a rather explosive effect completely out of proportion to the impact effect normally to be expected from their kinetic energy. Perhaps it would be possible to use billions of sandlike particles that could be laid in comparatively dense clouds over hundreds of cubic miles in the path of the approaching warhead.

A nuclear explosion releases large amounts of energy in the form of nuclear and thermal radiation. A ballistic missile warhead may be peculiarly vulnerable to either or both of these phenomena. It is a well-known physical fact, for instance, that one of the trickiest technical problems in the design of a ballistic missile is enabling it to survive the intense heat generated by friction as it re-enters the atmosphere at tremendous speed. Granted that this problem can be solved, other design criteria may dictate that the missile re-entry body operate very near its thermal tolerance. If so, any measure that would materially increase the ambient temperature through which the missile had to pass would be just what it would take to make the missile consume itself in a meteorlike blaze. Suitable proximity of a nuclear fireball would turn the trick. It is even conceivable that a radiation field from some other source could be devised with equal effect. Or it might be possible to create nuclear radiation fields of sufficient intensity to effectively disarm the nuclear warhead of the attacking missile or to cause the missile to destroy itself.

Parameters of defense

The foregoing suggests some rather formidable technical pursuits. Just as large, however, looms a number of problems not necessarily or exclusively technical. Most of these spring from parameters of a ballistic missile force and consequent parameters of a ballistic missile counterforce. Let us now consider some of these.

Reaction. A signal characteristic of a ballistic missile force is its inherent capacity to launch a truly massive attack with a very high degree of simultaneity. It seems completely feasible to cause a large fraction of a very large attacking force to cross a defense net or strike a wide variety of targets in concert within one or two minutes. The defensive system obviously must have high resistance to saturation and, since its reaction time is one of the important parameters of any defense force, it is apparent that a missile defense force requires a very rapid reaction capability indeed.

It may be useful to coin two definitions at this point: "*force* reaction time," the period from the time competent military authority orders commitment of the force until active defense measures are brought to bear; and "*national* reaction time," the longer period from the time when a threat is first recognized or suspected, including all necessary gathering of information, making of decisions, and passage of orders and ending again when active defense measures are brought to bear. Up to now there has been little occasion to make the distinction drawn by the above definitions. If the *force* reaction time is and can afford to be several hours, the fact that *national* reaction time is an hour or so longer is not particularly alarming. But if the *total reaction time available* is in the order of a half hour, the distinction becomes vastly more important for this reason: it probably is comparatively easy to reduce *force* reaction time; but even if this is pared to near-zero we are still in deep trouble if the other factors that make up *national* reaction time have not been drastically reduced.

Today *force* and *national* reaction times can be concurrent to a considerable extent. That may not be the case in the ballistic missile era. Today, for example, if the President received information on an apparently imminent attack, he could immediately order all neces-

Reaction Time in the Ballistic Missile Age

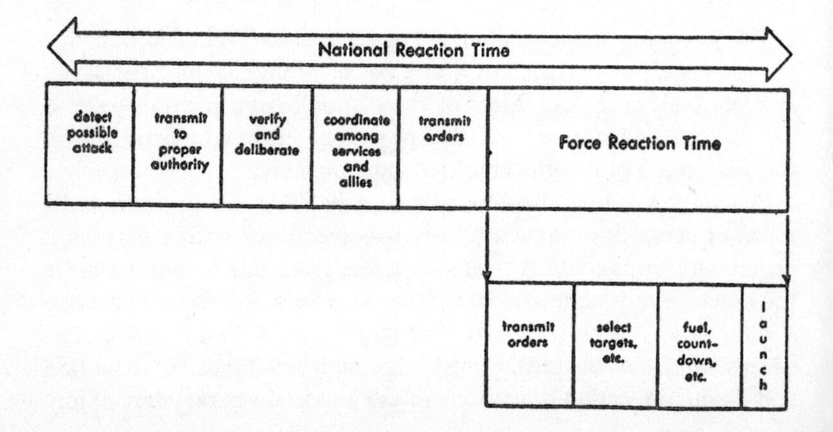

sary preparations, knowing that at any time in the next several hours he could abort or recall the retaliatory strike if further developments proved his initial information to be misleading. On the other hand a retaliatory ballistic missile system ideally would be designed so that its force reaction time would be in the order of a quarter hour. Once that quarter hour had begun to run its course, quite likely very little could be done to recall the commitment, at least without jettisoning a large part of the force. The implication is that the supreme authority could not start the force reaction time until the other elements of the national reaction time had proceeded to an irrevocable conclusion of commitment.

Warning. Compounding the reaction-time difficulties of a ballistic missile attack is the glum outlook for strategic warning. It probably is true that we will have strategic warning in the sense that we will know of the existence of a threatening missile force before it is prepared to attack, but the likelihood that we will know much more than that until missiles are actually fired is rather remote. A manned-bomber force of significant size represents a far-flung operation. Its launching involves many elaborate preparations such as assembly of people and fuel in conspicuous quantities, intricately timed deployments, and a number of other such activities that differ observably from the routine activities of a bomber force *not* on the eve of a strike. The result is that, even with the low-order intelligence we suffer on doings behind the iron curtain, it is hard to believe that a really significant bomber strike could be launched against us without some days' foreknowledge, at least to the extent of learning that such a thing *could* happen. By contrast, in a ballistic missile force all the materiel and people that must be deployed for it to attack must be deployed continuously. Thus the pattern of activity around and about a ballistic missile facility on "H-hour minus 2" is apt to be completely indistinguishable from that on "D-day minus 200" or any other time. This underlines the requirement that whatever our defensive measures are, they be capable of moving from long-term alert status to fully effective operation within minutes. Naturally there is an extremely high premium on learning of an attack as early in its life as possible.

Automation. There now emerges a parameter of the defensive force design: it must incorporate a high degree of automation. The requirement for human judgment must be brought to an irreducible minimum. Means must be provided to assemble the problems which human judgments must solve and present them with negligible delay to those centers where the necessary judgment can be exercised. At the same time the old adage that "haste makes waste" never had more dreadful import. The defense force designed for near-instantaneous reaction cannot be so designed at the risk of implementing false decisions, particularly if retaliation in kind must be part of the defensive measures. Imagine a two-way, intercontinental exchange of ballistic missile forces that was triggered off by one radar which could not tell the difference between a meteorite and an ICBM!

Cost. Yet another parameter of the required defense force is suggested. It is a foregone conclusion that our current air defense force is of little value against ballistic missiles. For just the reasons that this is true, the converse is probably true: a countermissile defense force will have limited value against other threats. Since for at least several years to come a ballistic missile force will confront us as part of a *spectrum* of threats, it follows that any ballistic missile defense force we fashion must be in addition to, rather than instead of, such air defense forces as we now have. Indeed ballistic missile defense measures will tend to compete economically with other necessary defensive measures in an era when the missile is by no means the most fearsome threat. This could serve to make countermissile measures that are technically feasible practically infeasible from a cost standpoint.

What we must do

What can we now recognize as the net impact of the ballistic missile on air defense? What can we say of the defense force that must be fashioned for the era ahead?

We must take steps to reduce national reaction time while designing force reaction time to a minimum. There must be foolproof and delay-free organizational machinery to inform the highest levels of government of an imminent or possible attack and to transmit top-level decisions to the force or forces concerned. There may be a requirement in this connection for reviewing the laws, traditions, and policies governing who can act under varying circumstances "for and in the absence of" the President and other high officials. There also is a requirement, whether or not it is apt to be met, for extensions of international law. Clearly, for example, moves falling far short of what is now internationally recognized as aggression could in fact foretell the virtual annihilation of a major nation within an hour or so.

It almost goes without saying that the more we know about a ballistic missile attack, including the intent to launch it, the better off we will be in countering it. Any improvement we can make, then, in our intelligence gathering or preattack reconnaissance is certainly to be sought. Perhaps we shall have to devise entirely new types of "indicators," such as the widespread evacuation of the enemy's urban populations—a predictable course for him to take if he were about to launch a strike and thus expected a retaliatory strike. A reconnaissance satellite or other technique that could detect the launching of a ballistic missile or fix its trajectory at an early stage of the flight would be invaluable, if we could learn of these things almost as soon as the satellite did. This communication problem might dictate a whole system of satellites capable of almost instantaneous relay of information. A next, obvious line of defense would be suitable radar or other detection devices that could be home based yet able to detect the existence and path of an incoming trajectory, presumably not much before apogee but hopefully not much after.

Rather involved computing and informing systems would have to be married to the detection systems and somewhere between them positive identification, with appropriate human judgment exercised, would have to be effected. That accomplished, the force reaction could be preplanned and made nearly automatic, quite possibly aided by a tentative alert status dating from initial detection.

It is less clear what active defensive measures, if any, should be provided to take advantage of the knowledge gained and the decisions made. There are a number of technical investigations in the realm of nuclear weapon effects, for example, to be pursued. For other suggestions the frontiers of scientific knowledge must be examined as they move forward.

It is entirely possible that for a long time to come the only really practical defense against the ballistic missile threat will be the passive one represented by our deterrent retaliatory force, including our own ballistic missiles. Even if that proves true, there is much to be done to fit ourselves for defense in the missile age.

Air War College

CHAPTER 11

Impact of the Ballistic Missile on Industry

PART I: FROM THE AIR FORCE'S VIEWPOINT

MAJOR GENERAL BEN I. FUNK, USAF

The real impact of the development-production of ICBM/IRBM is found in our current position. We are producing in quantity a weapon system that is still in development. Except for this time compression, the problems in converting a development to a production program in ballistic missile systems are similar to those encountered in the development-production of any major Air Force weapon system.

This weapon system, however, is the largest project in point of dollars and ultimate yield in the Air Force program. The reasoning that dictated the time compression of development-production gave the basis for according the ballistic missile the highest Air Force priority and ultimately the highest national priority. The decision by the President that this program was "second to none" has been well publicized.

The original action to make this program "second to none" was to give it top listing among a small number of the nation's vital projects. While this served to establish the program as a vital project, the practical effect was to make it "second to none" but equal to several. All projects in this group had equal priority and the effect of top listing was largely psychological. In many instances the ballistic missile was competing with conventional programs for critical goods and services. Even though red tape was cut, valuable time was lost in justifying diversion of material or effort to the ballistic missile. The conventional industrial priority rating of "DO" was simply not getting the job done.

As the first step in obtaining more emphasis for the ballistic missile effort, particularly in the lower tiers of subcontractors and suppliers, a distinctive ballistic missile stamp indicating "urgency" was devised and its use was authorized by the Department of Defense. Although carrying no priority in itself, its psychological effect was highly beneficial. Contractors and subcontractors promptly applied it to their subcontracts and purchase orders. It had the very practical effect of indicating to a manufacturer that his particular product was destined for a ballistic missile. But despite the benefit obtained from conventional priority ratings and distinctive identification of contractors' orders, something more finite was needed.

This came early in 1957 when the Office of Defense Mobilization decided to award the highest industrial priority rating, the "DX" rating, to the ballistic missile program. Used heretofore as an identification of directive action by the Business and Defense Services Administration (the agency charged with administrating industrial priorities), this rating was now to be applied to all ballistic missile contracts, subcontracts, and purchase orders. The ballistic missile program is now in truth "second to none."

This action has in itself brought an impact on the over-all aircraft and missile industry. When competition for application of effort or time of delivery exists, the manufacturer must now give precedence to the ballistic missile orders over lower priority orders. This may mean that the supplier must devote his effort to smaller or even less profitable orders to honor the high priority of the program. At the same time his other customers must wait in line. The supplier of critical materials may experience delivery conflicts even within the ballistic missile program. These are resolved within the BMD-BMO complex on the basis of in-program urgency.

Principal contractors

Who, then, makes up the industry that is taking the impact of the ballistic missile development-production time compression, the great costs involved, and the pressures of its primary urgency? There are fifteen carefully selected prime contractors within the ballistic missile complex, three in airframes, three in propulsion, six in guidance, two in nose cones (or warheads), and one contractor with over-all technical guidance. Stemming from these primes are approximately two hundred principal subcontractors in all parts of the country.

The anchor man on the Atlas missile team is the Convair Division of the General Dynamics Corporation as producer of the airframe. Convair, builder of many planes from B-24's to B-58's, certainly needs no introduction. Atlas propulsion is the responsibility of North American Aviation's Rocketdyne Division. North American is best known as the home of World War II's T-6, B-25, and P-51 aircraft and the postwar Sabre series. American Machine & Foundry, a manufacturer of tools and intricate equipment for industry, is furnishing the accessory power supply. The guidance system is the responsibility of the Missile Section of General Electric's Heavy Military Electronic Equipment Department. The accompanying computer is being manufactured by the Burroughs Corporation, a well-known name in business machines. As builder of the nose cone or warhead, the "payload" of the ballistic missile, General Electric's Missile and Ordnance Systems Department was selected.

On the Titan The Martin Company, an aviation industry pioneer, is producing the airframe. The engine as well as the accessory power supply comes from the new liquid-rocket plant of Aerojet-General, a division of General Tire and Rubber Company, well known as producers of solid-propellant assist take-off units for the armed services. Alternate radio-inertial and all-inertial guidance systems are being provided by the Western Electric Company, the communication experts, in conjunction with the Bell Telephone Laboratories and American Bosch Arma. The latter firm has had long experience in building highly precise diesel injection systems and more recently in supplying gun fire-control systems to the Air Force. The computer on this weapon system is the responsibility of Remington Rand Univac, a leader in the computer field. The warhead on the Titan is being produced by the Research and Advanced Development Division of Avco. Avco, a diversified manufacturer, pioneered the shock tube experiments in connection with the problem of re-entry of the nose cone into the atmosphere.

The Thor, as may be seen, has benefited from experience in other ballistic missiles. The Douglas Aircraft Company was selected as the airframe producer, with North American's Rocketdyne Division manufacturing the engine. Western Electric is providing the guidance system, and the accompanying computer is by Remington Rand Univac. An alternate guidance system is being developed by the A C Spark Plug Division of General Motors, best known to the Air Force as makers of fire-control and bomb-navigation system components. The nose cone is being produced by General Electric in conjunction with its Atlas effort.

In addition, of course, are many research and study contractors, including such well-known organizations as Lockheed, Massachusetts Institute of Technology, and Union Carbide & Carbon.

Finally, to provide technical direction for the entire program, the Ramo-Wooldridge Corporation is on contract as a nonhardware-producing partner of the Air Force. Ramo-Wooldridge is a relatively new but extremely well-qualified engineering and scientific contractor, whose Space Technology Laboratories provide the integration and coordination of the activities of all separate contractors contributing to the program.

Subcontracting ranges from bearing manufacturers to electric instrument companies, from valve producers to foundries, from universities to machine shops. The resources of experts in every necessary skill have been tapped for the exacting requirements in point of time and accuracy. Beyond these two hundred first-tier subcontractors, and down the subcontract chain, are the myriad suppliers and vendors, producing to tight schedules and in many instances endeavoring to meet simultaneous demands of several ballistic missile contractors for critical material or equipment from highly specialized but limited production.

Industrial facilities

The advent of the ballistic missile has placed a new impact on industrial facilities, both contractor-owned and Government-owned. The requirements for the highest possible degree of reliability are paramount and inherent to the eventual success of the ballistic missile as an operational weapon system. This demands more exacting manufacturing and prooftesting of a type and scale not encountered in the production of manned aircraft. Additional quantities of precision machine tools had to be manufactured, a huge amount of new laboratory and test equipment had to be created, and an entirely new family of contractor and Government test complexes had to be utilized in testing entire systems and individual components. Most of the major corporations participating in the ballistic missile program have chosen to segregate their ballistic missile activities by establishing separate, essentially autonomous divisions, and have been or are in the process of building new plants to house them.

The magnitude of the impact of the ballistic missile program on industry and on industrial facilities can be best expressed statistically. From late 1954 into 1957 the Air Force has provided contractors participating in the program with industrial facilities amounting to $154,000,000. This figure excludes investments at test sites. By July 1957 the industrial facility investment approached $200,000,000. Contractors have also made substantial investments and have spent about $100,000,000 of their own funds for industrial facilities during these three years. Most of the funds provided by the Air Force have been spent for machine tools and related production equipment, for laboratory and test equipment, and for test stands located in the vicinity of contractors' plants. Included in the contractors' investment are seven new plants built to support the ballistic missile program.

In that program, more than in other defense programs, there has been a demand for highly specialized facilities that would be of no value to a contractor for other work. Defense contractors normally are unwilling to invest large amounts of their own capital under such high-risk circumstances. Many of them expect the Government to provide all or a major portion of the required facilities. Yet the Government has provided to the total of all contractors in the ballistic missile program a smaller dollar amount of industrial facilities than was previously provided a single Air Force contractor for facilities in support of an aircraft engine program. Contractor investment, as previously shown, has been substantial, in spite of the fact that the work to date has been principally developmental and that no contractor has complete assurance he will be given a contract for quantity production. Program priority reduced administrative lead time in the processing of contractor facilities requests. It has not reduced the requirement to justify Government-facilities assistance. On the contrary, the Ballistic Missile Division—Ballistic Missiles Office—Ramo-Wooldridge complex, as the result of program priority, reviews very carefully each request for Government assistance and requires detailed justification prior to granting such assistance.

Comparison with conventional aircraft

We have established a substantial industrial capability which can produce the best engineered weapons that our technicians and industrial complex can provide. Of course the requirement to secure the earliest possible tactical capability has dictated this approach. We have a time-compression situation not duplicated in our previous experience with manned aircraft. With the manned vehicle we have the opportunity of amassing a large number of test hours and data. With the ballistic missile only a few minutes are available to secure test data since the missile is destroyed. Thus we must commit to production substantial quantities of material before conclusive test results are available.

As speeds increase, man's natural limitations force us to increasing dependence on electronic controls. The commander of a manned aircraft is becoming more of a "Chairman of the Board," the Board being a control board full of electronic devices. With the guided missile the man has been pulled out of the plane and his cockpit is on the ground. A new zenith of the trend appears in the ballistic missile. Here man and his control board aim the missile at its intended target. Virtually from that point on, a hit on the distant target depends on electronic resources within the weapon. Man, although handicapped by a narrow environmental tolerance, has a high reliability factor and the power to reason. Duplicating this reliability and reasoning, in terms of reaction, in materials and electronics is an awesome assignment. Quality and systems reliability must be stressed.

Obviously with such high goals of reliability and quality accompanied by the peculiar strains and stresses placed on this type of missile, advanced manufacturing techniques must be devised. This impact, not common with conventional aircraft, is being met by industry in design, application, metallurgy, metal working, circuitry, and tooling.

A program of this magnitude and complexity will generate competition for materials, parts, and equipment. The great impact is on lower priority programs competing for the material left after the higher priority needs have been satisfied. This could lead to shortages in other Air Force projects, both in production and field support. To prevent this, contractors on lower priority programs must submit requests for priorities assistance to the government to provide the needed material delivery. Ballistic missile contractors are also being limited in acquiring materials to a minimum rate consistent with their delivery schedule.

Another national resource subject to impact is manpower. In July 1957 approximately 40,000 people were employed in the prime contractors' plants for this program. This is an area less sensitive to priority ratings and directives but more reactive to company policy and skill availability. Considering the complexity of a weapon of this kind, it is understandable that a proportionately large part of the manpower must be devoted to engineering. The competition for engineering and scientific skills is further compounded by the speed necessary in manning the program. As development breakthroughs occur, they must be quickly engineered into the design. At the same time production people must incorporate the changes into the product with the least possible delay. Again time is the crucial element.

PART II: FROM AN AIRFRAME MANUFACTURER'S VIEWPOINT

THE MARTIN COMPANY

On first examination it appears that the impact of the ballistic missile on the airframe industry would necessitate little change in manpower or facilities. However the efficient production of the ballistic missile requires methods, techniques, and engineering concepts not previously encountered by the airframe manufacturer. This impact becomes evident only when the entire concept of the ballistic missile is compared to that of the manned aircraft.

The military aircraft has evolved from engineering knowledge and new concepts of manufacturing into a highly complex weapon system composed of mechanical, electronic, structural, and electromechanical subsystems and components. Its weight empty can be as much as fifty per cent of its take-off weight. Most of the elements that make up the system are designed to be directly operated or controlled by men—at least the crew of the aircraft can monitor the performance of the subsystems. The military aircraft is designed for repeated use, with provisions for maintenance and repair between missions. It is also designed for operation with other aircraft—thus the failure of one aircraft in a flight usually does not completely abort a given mission.

A ballistic missile is also a highly complex weapon system composed of the same basic elements as a manned aircraft. In fact, without the engineering knowledge and manufacturing skills developed for the production of manned aircraft, the evolution to missiles would not be possible. But the ballistic missile is significantly different in some respects. Its weight empty should not exceed ten per cent of its take-off weight (ninety per cent must be devoted to fuel). The subsystems of a ballistic missile cannot be directly controlled or monitored by man. The ballistic missile is a one-shot weapon—it either functions properly or the mission is aborted and an expensive vehicle is a total loss. Therefore the need for extreme reliability becomes the key to the success of any ballistic missile.

Reliability a must

The demand for extremely reliable components and subsystems in the ballistic missile has its most obvious effect on the personnel requirements of the airframe manufacturer. These requirements show a change in three respects. The general level of technical knowledge throughout the organization must be of the highest; the distribution of technically trained people between engineering, manufacturing, and testing functions shows a marked change; and the total number of people required to produce a ballistic missile is slightly less than that required to produce a manned aircraft.

The reliability requirements of the ballistic missile affect every item that goes into the final product from the smallest bolt to the most complex guidance system. The implications of any variation from quality standards must be recognized by every individual in the organization—designer, machinist, inspector, assembler, and test engineer—and require greater technical skill and knowledge in each individual. This demand for greater technical qualifications has been gradually increasing as the complexity of airborne vehicles has increased. The transition from manned aircraft to ballistic missiles increases the demand almost as much as the transition from wood-and-fabric to metal airplanes.

The greater technical skill and knowledge of each individual in the organization naturally tend to reduce the total number of people required to do the job. Here again reliability plays a part. By reducing the number of people concerned with a particular item, the chances of maintaining its reliability are increased throughout the production process.

The third point of impact of missile production on the airframe organization's personnel is in the distribution of people between engineering and testing functions and manufacturing operations. The higher speeds, new environments, and greater reliability of the ballistic missile will require a higher percentage of engineering effort, at least until the art of missile production becomes as familiar to us as the production of manned aircraft.

The impact of the ballistic missile on airframe manufacturing facilities can be illustrated many ways. The machine tools used to produce manned aircraft are also used for missiles. However, since ninety per cent of the ballistic missile's take-off weight is devoted to fuel tankage, there is an increase in facilities for welded sheet-metal construction. The reliability of the tankage is a function of the design, the quality of the material, the number of joints, and the finish of the metal. Thus the facilities for heat-treating, plating, and cleaning large sheet-metal units have increased. The need for automatic welding and nondestructive testing equipment is also greater in a missile production plant. But basically the ballistic missile only requires closer tolerances and more attention to reliability factors throughout the manufacturing process.

Testing

In the field of testing, the ballistic missile demands facilities not required by the production of manned aircraft. For convenience let us consider three basic types of testing—laboratory, captive, and flight testing.

The laboratory test facilities for ballistic missiles must be equipped to simulate environments whose characteristics are still conjectural. Materials, components, and subsystems must be subjected to extremes of temperature, pressure, acceleration, radiation, and shock. These conditions and the reliability requirements create a formidable quality control problem for the laboratories. Completely new facilities must be constructed.

The captive, or field, test facilities for ballistic missiles are of course vastly different from those required for manned aircraft. No airstrips are needed for taxi tests, but captive test stands capable of simulating all launch conditions and limited flight conditions must be available. The instrumentation required to test a ballistic missile is far greater than that for a manned aircraft. The nature of the missile and its behavior defy the direct human observation which is so valuable in the testing of conventional aircraft. In fact test personnel must be protected in concrete structures at some distance from the test firing. Yet the reliability requirements of the missile demand closer control of test conditions and more data recording than the ground testing of manned aircraft. The ballistic missile also multiplies the noise-suppression problem a hundredfold. The development of effective noise suppressors for jet engines is progressing rapidly but it will be years before a suppressor will be developed for the tremendous blast of a ballistic missile's rocket engine.

There are new problems in the handling of fuels in the test areas. We have been handling gasoline for years, and the safety precautions have become routine. The hazards in handling missile fuels and oxygen supplies are new and quite different in many respects. New facilities for the safe storage and handling of large volumes of these materials must be constructed.

The production of a ballistic missile obviates the need for any manufacturer's flight-test facilities. The Air Force Missile Test Center, with its range over the Atlantic, is the only available flight-test facility for long-range missiles. This is in contrast to the desirability of having a flight-test facility adjacent to the manufacturing operation for manned aircraft.

In general, then, it can be said that the impact of the ballistic missile on the airframe industry expresses itself in the need for more highly skilled and technically trained personnel, more exacting control of manufacturing processes, and more complex testing facilities. This effect is certainly consistent with the effects of all technical advances. As we gain the knowledge to conceive (and increased ability to construct) more technically complex products, our need for such skill, knowledge, and products increases by geometric progression.

PART III: FROM A ROCKET ENGINE PRODUCER'S VIEWPOINT

ROCKETDYNE DIVISION, NORTH AMERICAN AVIATION COMPANY

The development and production of high-thrust propulsion systems for ballistic missiles have created an industry at once similar and dissimilar to those producing conventional reciprocating and turbojet engines. Producers of rocket engines have built their industry with engineering and manufacturing skills essentially the same as those used in the production of other engines. But the engine itself—the high-thrust, liquid-propellant rocket—has created unique developmental and testing problems and has demanded concentrated effort to advance the state of the art.

With rocket engines the development engineer faced a propulsion system employing a liquid rather than a gaseous oxidizer for combustion. More important, his engine was required to produce 100 to 1000 times the thrust of conventional engines of comparable size and weight. At the same time his engine was required to operate through errorless, automatic sequences for brief durations. These factors created testing requirements that demanded new concepts in facilities and methods.

Engine reliability

The development engineer early encountered reliability problems that varied substantially from those encountered with conventional engines. Ballistic missiles demanded that the engine start without error and operate automatically, rather than that it run for thousands of hours after it started. Also it was apparent that this reliability had to be achieved largely through testing at the manufacturer's plant rather than through service use of the engine in operational vehicles.

With conventional reciprocating engines, for example, crews can run up an engine on the ground as often as necessary to gain proper operation. Failure of the engine to start the first, second, or third time the starter button is pushed usually produces no more of a trouble report than a swear word by the mechanic. Early coughs and sputters also go unreported if the engine clears and develops full power within a few minutes. Minor adjustments, such as plug changes, also fall in the category of unreported incidents unless they develop a pattern of frequency. Should the engine fail during runup prior to take-off, the pilot can taxi back to the flight line for service. While this could abort a military mission, such a failure in transport or liaison flying results in nothing more serious than a delayed take-off.

For the ballistic missile the rocket engine must start and operate smoothly and develop full thrust within less than a second after the start button is pushed. Any malfunction during the start or buildup of thrust could destroy both the engine and the missile. Furthermore the only preflight checks that probably can be made by the ground crew will be electrical, hydromatic, and pneumatic checkouts made with simulated test equipment. It may well be impractical to run the engine without flying the missile.

In a ballistic missile any malfunction of the power plant, which must be completely automatic, since there is no pilot, will cause an abort and loss of the missile. In a multiengine missile the malfunction of any one of the engines will cause the loss of the complete missile. Where a conventional engine must run many hours on a single flight and is expected to operate over and over again for thousands of hours before the engine is overhauled, the engine for the ballistic missile must operate only in durations measured in seconds and must fly only once.

These comparisons point out the differences in the nature of the reliability problem for the rocket engine compared to the conventional aircraft engine. Similar differences exist in testing.

Conventional engines normally are run for a large number of hours in test cells to develop sufficient endurance capability for safe operation in an airplane. Additional reliability is developed during flight tests. At a reasonably early date in their development, engines are installed in substantial numbers of aircraft to develop many hours of service operation within a relatively short period of time. This safely serves as an excellent means of uncovering design and manufacturing "bugs." As the service hours build up, a steady stream of reports flows back to the engine manufacturer. In the vast majority of malfunctions the engine is available for analysis by the user and the manufacturer. This information is invaluable to the engine developer in evolving the reliability desired in his product.

With rocket engines, feedback from service use is extremely limited. While they may be subjected to numerous simulated ground checks, rocket engines fly only once. And the engine is almost never available for analysis after flight whether it malfunctioned or not.

In view of these considerations it was evident that the reliability of liquid-propellant engines had to be developed by the manufacturer through extensive testing on static stands. With the pressure imposed upon the ballistic missile program to achieve operational dates as early as possible, it also became apparent that this testing had to be carried out with a minimum of elapsed time.

As a result new statistical techniques were developed to minimize the number of tests required to achieve a given reliability with a given confidence level. By varying many parameters of the test simultaneously to off-design-condition operating points, failures were induced more rapidly. These methods appreciably reduced the number of tests that were necessary.

Test facilities

One of the first problems faced by industry in the development of propulsion units for ballistic missiles was the design and construction of suitable test facilities. The requirements for operating and testing these engines have resulted in the construction of completely new test facilities differing radically in design concept and scope from those for aircraft engines. The first characteristic of the engine affecting the test facilities is its size. Developing thrust in the order of 100 to 1000 times that developed by conventional engines, rocket engines require test structures of massive proportions and create major civil and structural engineering design problems.

One of the most severe problems in the design of these test stands has been the handling of the flame after it leaves the engine nozzle. Missile engines are started and tested in a vertical position. Exhaust flames are 75 to 100 feet long. Early test stands were designed to hang engines over the side of a cliff, providing about 100 feet of free drop for the hot gases. Even at these distances, however, the flame cut out ground and concrete at the rate of an inch or more per run.

To remedy this, the flame deflector was developed to turn the flame approximately 90° almost immediately after it left the nozzle of the rocket engine. The flame deflector consists of a large steel elbow cooled by large quantities of water. Thanks to it, test stands are now built much smaller, simpler, and much less expensively than before, making it practical to build sufficient numbers for extensive and rapid reliability testing.

In the testing of conventional, air-breathing engines—both piston and turbojet—a major portion of the facilities is involved in the apparatus to provide the quantities of air required to run the engines. This equipment becomes quite large and complex as the size of the engines increases and as it becomes necessary to simulate the temperatures and densities encountered at high altitudes.

None of that type of equipment is required in rocket-engine testing, but test stands must provide tankage and associated feed systems for both liquid oxidizer and fuel. The flow rates of both propellants are so large—measured in thousands of gallons per minute—that the sudden starting and stopping of these tremendous flows create fluid dynamic transients that can materially affect the operation of the engine. The test apparatus must approximate the configuration of the missile in the size and the location of the propellant run tanks and of the propellant feed-system piping.

Even though the engine operates for only a few seconds at a time, large quantities of propellants are consumed. Each test entails the supply and handling of extensive quantities of propellants. The quantity of liquid oxygen required, for instance, soon exceeds that available from commercial sources. For this reason plants to produce considerable quantities of liquid oxygen have been built in the immediate vicinity of rocket-engine testing facilities.

Similarities and differences

Although some unique production problems have been encountered with the rocket engine, most have been conventional. Many of the parts for the rocket engine are quite different from conventional engines, but production methods and machinery have been developed through conventional industrial engineering and tool engineering practices. In some cases these have involved the use of new materials and the development of new welding, forming, and processing techniques. Generally the work has been within the scope of existing technology and manufacturing skills. Tolerances and quality requirements on certain parts have been severe but within the scope of good aircraft and engine practices.

Primarily affecting production operations has been the unique requirement that performance parameters of the rocket engine be held within very narrow maximum and minimum tolerances. Conventional engines must meet only a minimum performance requirement. With a conventional engine the user is only interested in assuring himself that the engine will develop a given power with a fuel consumption less than a specified amount while certain other minimum requirements are met. Performance exceeding these requirements, even by a large margin, is a bonus and users seldom complain.

In a ballistic missile, however, excess power can cause the missile to follow a different ballistic trajectory or otherwise produce missile performance for which the guidance and control system cannot correct.

Another very severe problem for the production organization in the rocket-engine field has been that of producing the large amounts of experimental hardware for the fast-moving development programs. Such hardware, designed for short duration in order to minimize weight and maximize performance, is subject to high attrition. In developmental testing it is not at all unusual to wear out components that would never wear out in service use. Secondly, much of the developmental and reliability testing on the engine is done under operating conditions purposely intended to induce malfunction. With the tremendous levels of power being developed in such lightweight components, there is a high probability of considerable damage when failure does occur. Thirdly, there is a high level of obsolescence of parts during the development phase, where the very purpose of the test-evaluate-redesign-fabricate-test cycle is to evolve quickly the necessary design changes. Large quantities of experimental hardware must be produced in a minimum of time to support the developmental and reliability testing program.

The problem of production is further complicated by the accelerated schedule of the ballistic missile program. Production must be carried on concurrently with development. This means that extraordinary techniques must be adopted by the manufacturing organization to handle the large numbers of production changes that result from concurrent development and product improvement.

PART IV: FROM THE ELECTRONIC INDUSTRY'S VIEWPOINT

AN ELECTRONIC INDUSTRY SYMPOSIUM

The ballistic missile program, superimposed on an already rapidly expanding electronic industry, has created an added impetus to expansion in specific fields. The urgency of the program dictated the need for compressing normal research and development time cycles to the barest minimum. Development time has been reduced from years to months in all areas of engineering effort. Great strides were required almost immediately in the state of the art as it applies to adaptation and improvement of existing equipment and the development of new equipment and materials to meet the environmental conditions, high reliability standards, and accuracy requirements. The need for highly complex ground and missile-borne equipment to ensure the accuracy of the ballistic trajectory of the missile has created a challenge which is presently being met by the electronic industry.

Possibly the greatest challenge to the industry is the need for developing and manufacturing electronic equipment capable of continuous, accurate performance under the extremely harsh environmental conditions in ballistic missile operations. Acceleration, altitude, speed, vibration, heat, and other environmental requirements are radically different than those we have had to cope with in other military programs.

These difficult operational requirements and the high accuracy and reliability requirements under which the missile must operate mean that an extensive test program must be established. This has been done and testing of electronic equipment is presently going on. The test program has had a significant impact on the manufacturers of test equipment. Many small companies producing telemetering equipment, vibration equipment, and other standard and special components of environmental test equipment have suddenly found the demand far beyond their ability to produce. They have rallied valiantly, and principally through their own efforts these problems are being met and the program has continued without delay.

The accelerated research and development required by the ballistic missile program have to a limited degree necessitated new manufacturing processes and created demands for new materials. They have greatly increased the need for items such as transistors and diodes. This is particularly true in computer design and production. Because of the extremely critical accuracy requirements the rejection rates for certain types have been very high, so that production rates have had to be increased to ensure an adequate yield. At the same time work has continued to improve the product and also lower the cost.

To meet the development schedules for electronics, it has been necessary to provide certain facilities. These facilities generally fall in the category of long-lead-time tools and test equipment that are immediately required to support the environmental test program. It is conceivable that the program might have suffered serious delay had not a great number of facilities items been readily available from Government inventories early in the program.

No great effect

The ballistic missile program has not as yet had any great effect on the over-all production capacity of the electronic industry. In terms of the national average, requirements are small. The additional productive effort attributable to this program is easily absorbed by existing industry. As indicated earlier, there has been a temporary effect on the portion of the industry that manufactures test equipment. This was caused by the need for significant quantities of equipment during a relatively short period of complete developmental testing and does not represent a continuing requirement, except in a very few specific areas.

In terms of utilization of available materials and existing resources, there is no significant impact in the electronic industry similar to that attributable to the requirement for huge quantities of liquid oxygen. There is a minor impact with respect to requirements for materials or components such as tantalum and diodes.

In short the ballistic missile program has had no significant impact on the electronic industry as a whole, in terms of greatly increased requirements. It has had a significant effect on certain specific portions of the industry, notably the manufacturers of electronic test equipment.

The greatest impact has been in the area of engineering as a whole. The great urgency of the program has resulted in rapid strides in the application of engineering theory to existing problems and their early solution. In guidance equipment this application has seen the development of two types of systems, pure-inertial and radio-inertial, both of which are undergoing testing and both of which show every evidence of meeting the almost impossible requirements for accuracy and reliability established for their use.

The development of equipment such as this in such a short period of time requires a tremendous engineering effort. The expenditure of this effort in support of the ballistic missile program represents the most significant impact of the program on the electronic industry.

The U. S. Air Force has largely created the industrial capability to produce ballistic missiles. The materials have been isolated, the machine tools are in place or on order, the manpower has been hired. We know that we will experience some failures, but we will learn from these failures. We know that we will have difficulties—strikes, material shortages, or possibly temporary shortages of the best kind of tooling. These are the problems that the Air Force has met and solved before. The Air Materiel Command is ready for these difficulties.

Recognizing the urgency of the requirement and the impact of time compression, AMC assigned highly experienced personnel in the materiel field to the Ballistic Missiles Office so that our maximum experience in procurement, production, and logistics would be brought to bear on the program and its problems. AMC has participated with BMD and R-W in the selection of production sources to ensure the highest order of selectivity and capability. In fact our policy is that we in BMO, in a supporting role, will be most sensitive and responsive to development and jointly with BMD will provide the nation with the most efficient industrial capability possible to secure an early USAF operational ballistic missile capability.

Ballistic Missiles Office, Hq AMC

Thor stands ready to fire, plumed with vapor from a liquid-oxygen vent

Nation-wide Facilities Support the USAF Missile Program

ICBM and IRBM Facilities

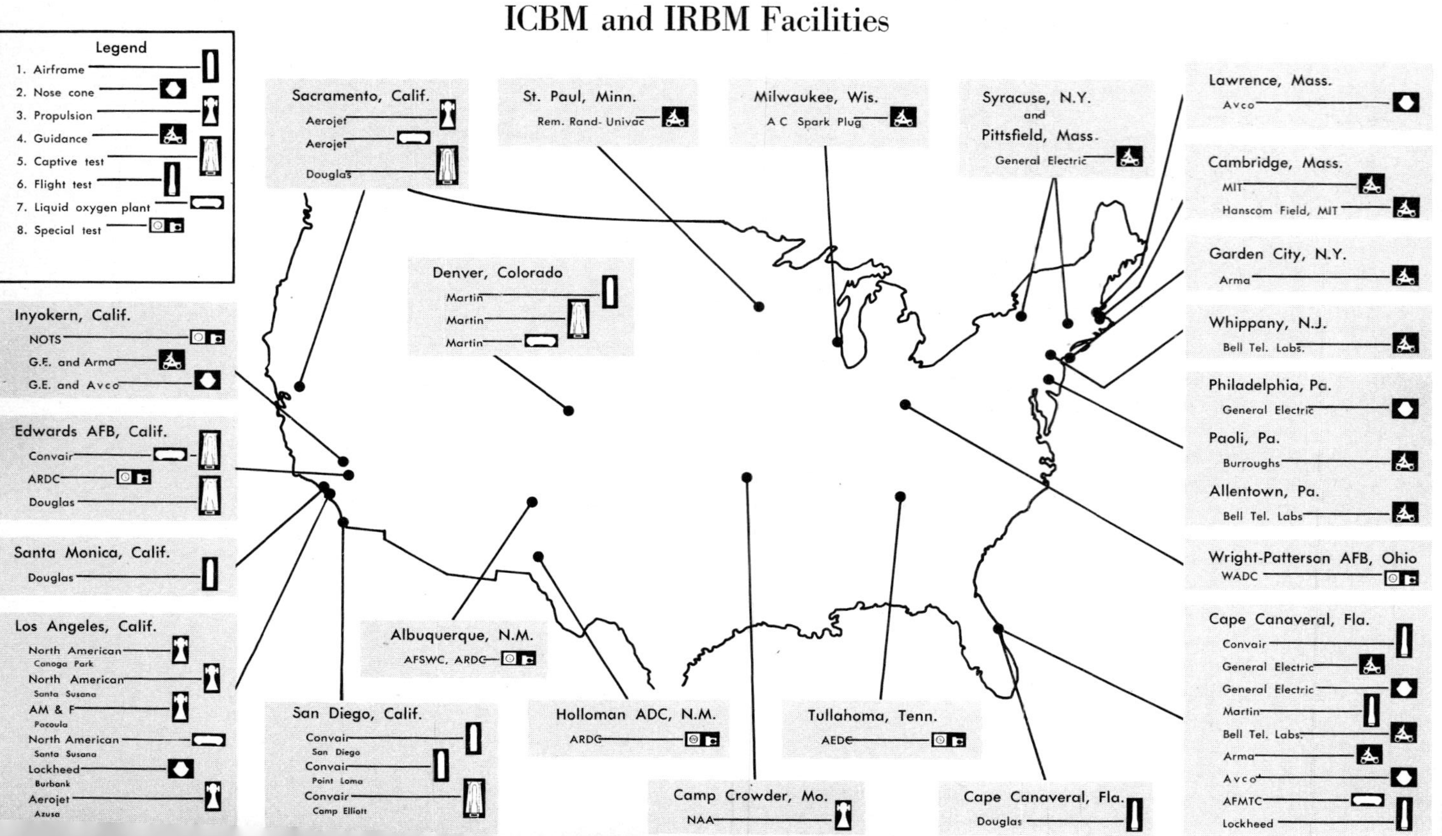

One-hundred-million-dollar Titan plant built by The Martin Company near Denver. Test stand in foreground

Astronautics plant under construction by Convair near San Diego

Weighing the Thor nose cone f
missile number 101

Thor and its field launching equ
ment for movability on display
the Culver City plant of the Doug
Aircraft Company

Control room for test stand at The Martin Company's Titan plant

Rocket propulsion engine test stand, Aerojet-General Corporation, at Azusa, California

Rocket engine blasts through test in Santa Susana Mountains for Rocketdyne Division of North American Aviation

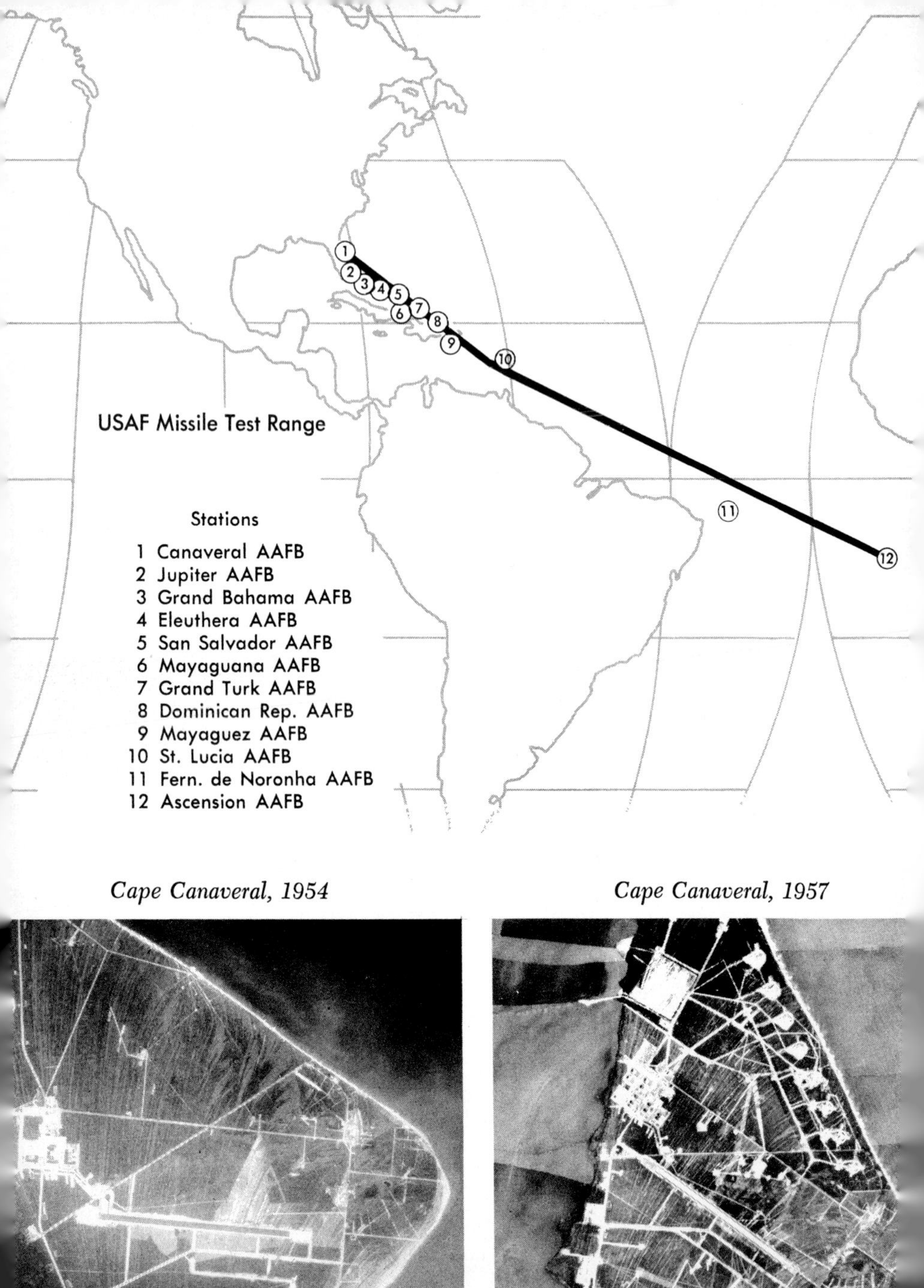

Cape Canaveral, 1954

Cape Canaveral, 1957

Air Force Missile Flight Test Center

Atlas ICBM Launch Complex

San Salvador AAFB

Thor IRBM Launcher

Ground Guidance Unit

Typical Support Area

Flight Testing at Canaveral Is Backed Up by Static Test Facilities Throughout the Air Force—U. S. Industry Complex

Support-Equipment Test Facilities

Captive Test Stand

North American Test Stands

Convair Airframe Component Testing, Point Loma

Aerojet's Engine
st Area, Sacramento

General Electric's
Hancock Field
Guidance System
Test Site

The Avco Shock Tube Used in Nose Cone Tests

A Missile Weapon System Demands Diverse Training

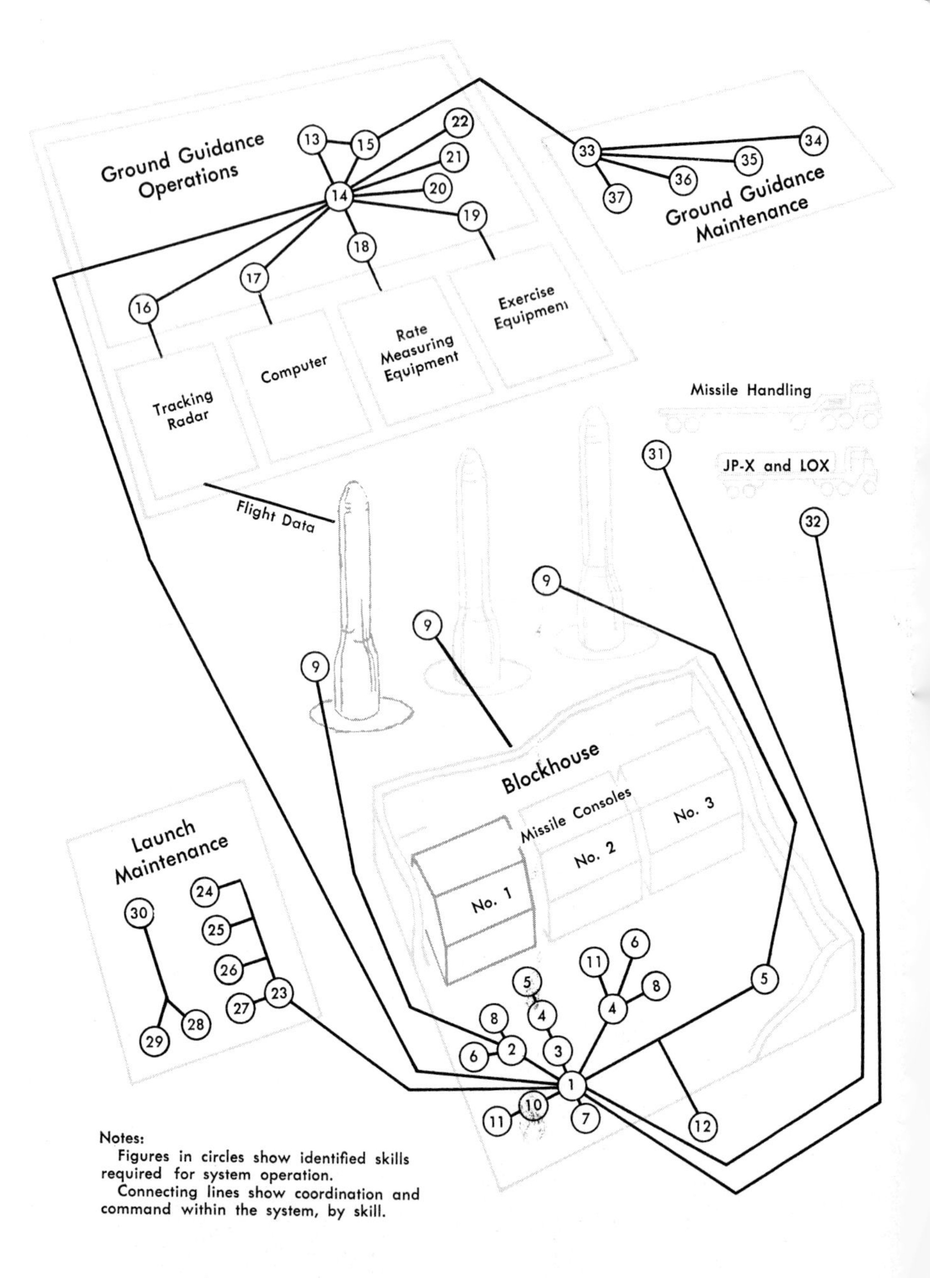

Notes:
Figures in circles show identified skills required for system operation.
Connecting lines show coordination and command within the system, by skill.

Initial Forecast of Job Functions for Atlas System

And Sophisticated Logistics To Mount Squadrons to the Line

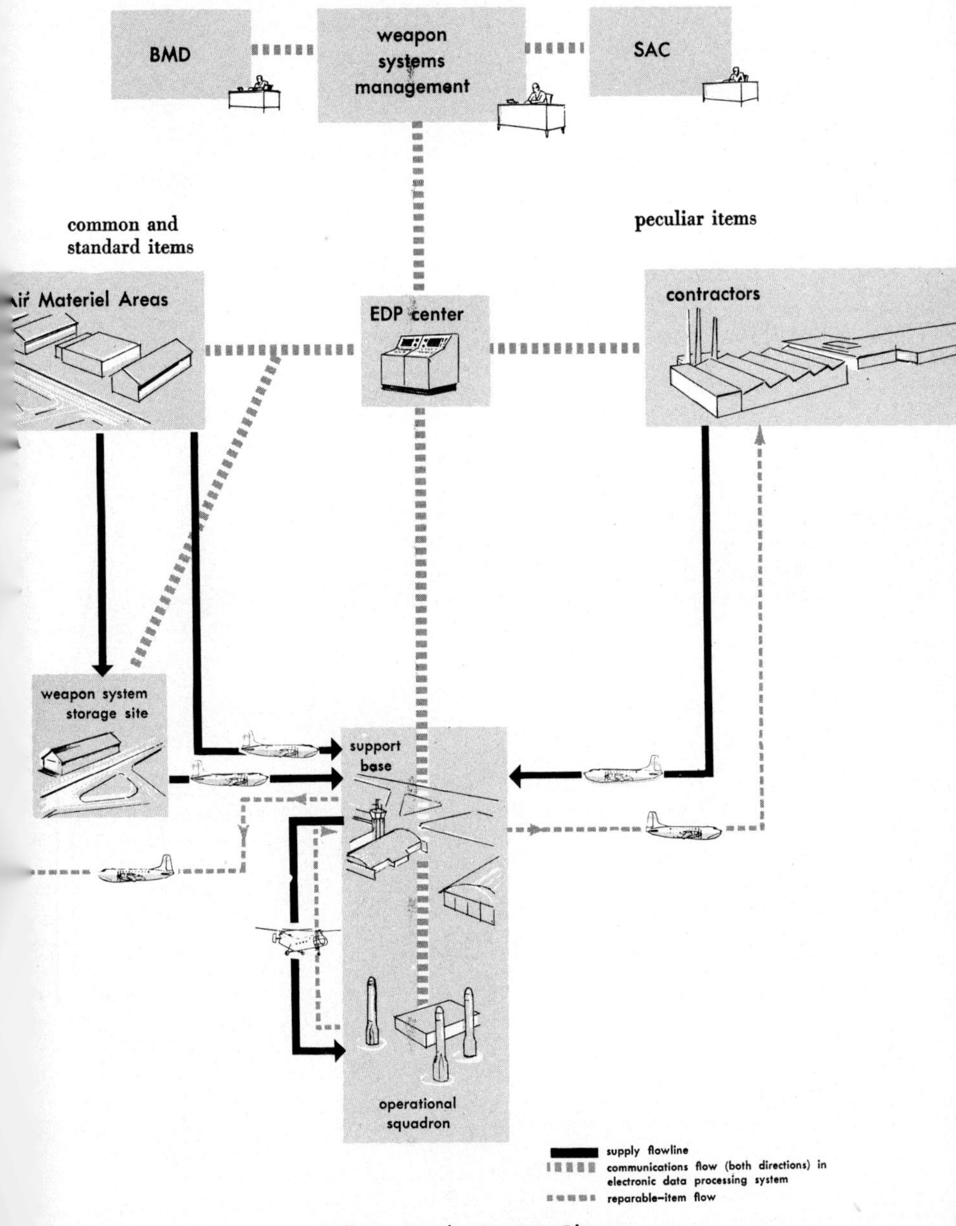

Ballistic Missiles Logistic Plan

Growth of Ballistic

Initial Capability

supplement to manned bombers

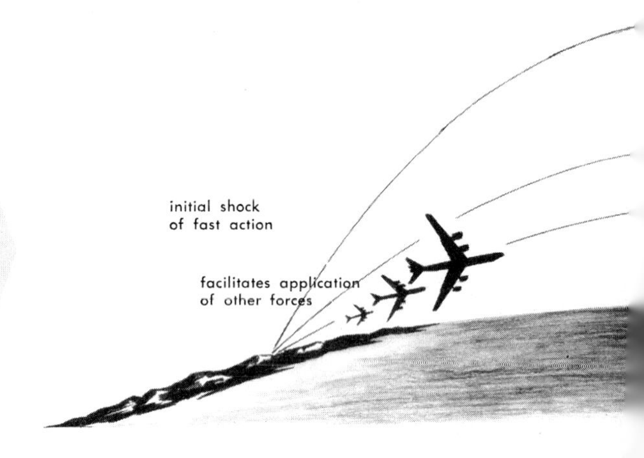

Mature Capability

missile force spearheads offense

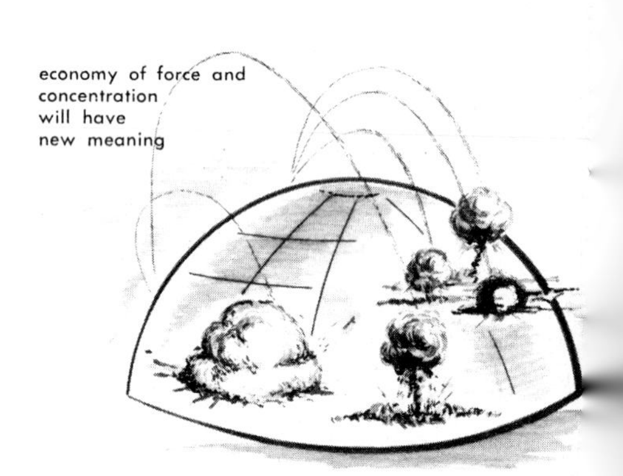

Mature Capability Requirements

effects of compression of time and space

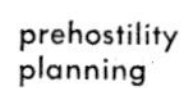

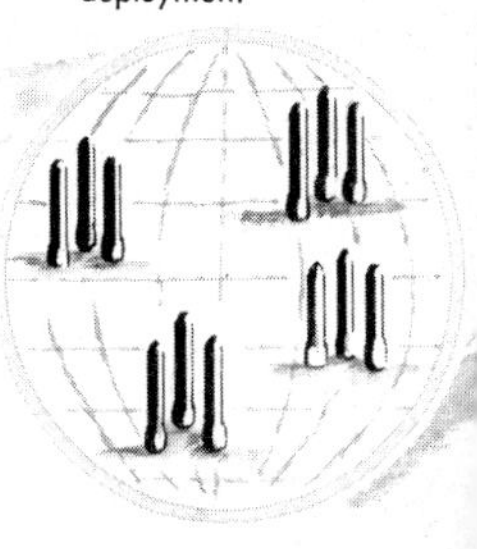

Missile Effectiveness

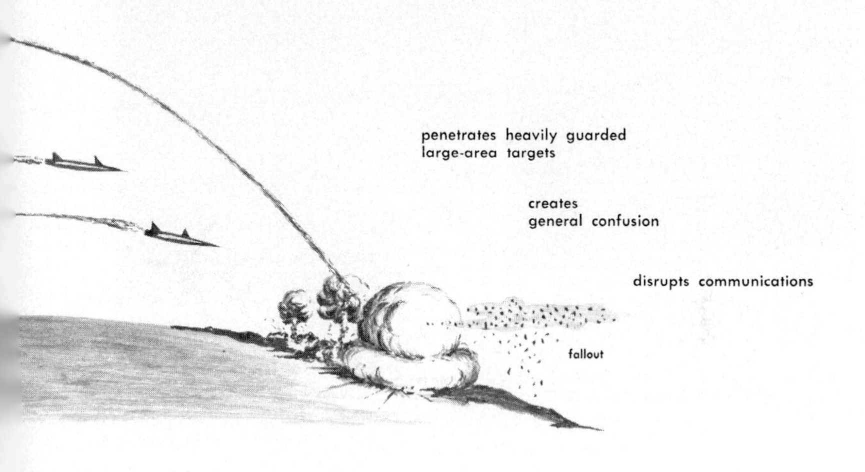

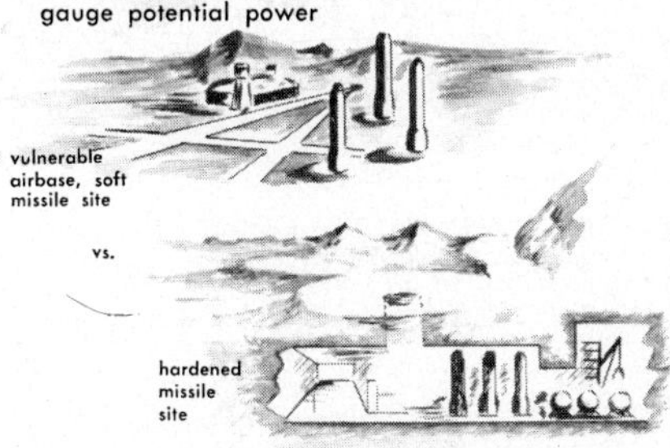

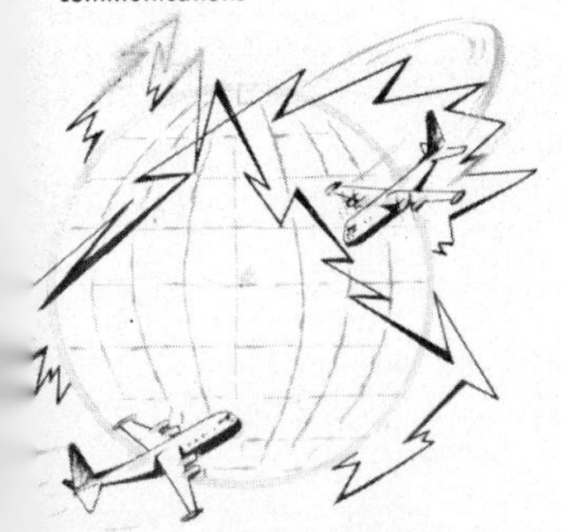

High as a four-story building, the Lockheed X-17 test missile points skyward ready for flight at Patrick AFB, Florida. The six-ton, three-stage rocket is saving millions of dollars. Its flights have helped solve problems connected with ballistic-missile nose-cone re-entry that otherwise must be answered only after many firings of the much more expensive full-scale missiles themselves. The X-17 has achieved speeds in excess of mach 14, thus making it the fastest instrumented test vehicle ever flown.

An Air Force Thor fumes during launching preparation at the Air Force Missile Test Range, Cape Canaveral, Florida

Thrust toward the sky by its driving gases, the big missile leaves its launching pad

Countdown at midnight. Another Thor is made ready to go

Mighty Atlas flames toward trajectory

CHAPTER 12

SAC and the Ballistic Missile

GENERAL THOMAS S. POWER, USAF

The capability of the Strategic Air Command to accomplish its assigned mission both in the current cold war and a potential hot war is, essentially, the product of three factors—organization, men, and weapon systems. The quality of the over-all product is contingent upon not only the individual quality of each of these factors but also the degree and congruity of their interrelationship.

While these considerations apply to a greater or lesser extent to any organized effort, they are of particular importance to SAC because of the unique nature of its mission and the manner in which it must accomplish that mission. SAC is the principal deterrent to aggression in the free world today and undoubtedly the most potent deterrent force ever created in military history. Its peacetime objective is actually a "negative" one: to establish and maintain a global offensive capability of such superior striking power that it minimizes the need for using it. At the same time SAC must be continually prepared to successfully achieve the "positive" objective of its mission: to retaliate decisively in case deterrence fails.

These seemingly contradictory objectives are in fact entirely compatible, although they entail unprecedented requirements with respect to the scope and character of SAC's operations. To meet these requirements SAC must maintain a centrally controlled, global organization possessing all the many diversified human and material resources needed in strategic air operations, yet flexible enough to be readily adaptable to any new weapon system or technique, no matter how revolutionary.

The interrelationship of SAC's three principal constituents—organization, men, and weapon systems—assumes particular significance with the introduction of ballistic missiles into the SAC inventory. The reason therefor is not merely the revolutionary character of the weapon systems involved. Even more significant is the fact that for the first time an operational element of the U.S. armed forces is integrating a new family of major weapons while these weapons are still in a research and development stage which, moreover, barely paces the current state of the art.

This radical departure from standard policy is designed to attain an initial operational capability at the earliest possible date. It was feasible only because the disadvantage inherent in the operational commitment of an untried weapon could be offset by the advantage of having in being a long-established and well-tried organization responsive to the effective employment of such a weapon, even in its early stages of evolution.

For these reasons, the following discussion will deal primarily with two specific aspects of the ballistic missile: its qualifications as a strategic weapon system, and its mutual relationship with those other factors which, in combination with the weapon system, represent strategic capability.

MISSILES AS STRATEGIC WEAPONS

SAC's mission, briefly stated, is ". . . to be prepared to conduct strategic air operations on a global basis so that, in the event of sudden aggression, SAC could immediately mount simultaneous nuclear attacks designed to destroy the vital elements of the aggressor's war-making capacity to the extent that he would no longer have the will nor ability to wage war."

With the emphasis on "global," "immediately," and "simultaneous," the ballistic missile represents a singularly attractive strategic weapon because of its three principal features: great range, very high speed, and quick-reaction capability. As continued advances in missile technology alleviate, if not eliminate, initial deficiencies and further improve existing capabilites, the ballistic missile will assume rapidly increasing importance as an air offensive weapon system. It will then be capable of performing an ever-growing number of strategic missions which at present must be assigned to manned bombers.

Characteristics and requirements

The most striking of the ballistic missile's characteristics is undoubtedly its high velocity, which, in itself, offers several major advantages in strategic operations. It reduces warning time to a maximum of a few minutes, permitting little if any preparation for defensive action. This poses an added problem for the defense which is already aggravated by the hypersonic speed of the vehicle and by the small size and toughness of the warhead once it has separated from the vehicle. Thus the short time of flight to the target enhances the possibility of destroying enemy bombers and missiles before they can be launched. In coordinated bomber-missile attacks, ballistic missiles can precede the bomber strikes and "degrade" the enemy's defenses.

The practically unlimited range of the ballistic missile is another characteristic of importance to strategic air operations, which by their very nature must cover great distances. Also ballistic ranges may vary from a few hundred miles to thousands of miles and eventually will extend to any desired point-to-point distance on earth. This provides considerable flexibility in locating launching sites and in the selection of the range best suited to meet specific demands for optimum yield, accuracy, and warning time.

Indeed it is technically feasible to develop a single ballistic missile configuration that could be used for any desired distance within the entire spectrum of strategic mission ranges. However, such a missile would be exceedingly uneconomical and create many operational problems. SAC's present approach entails the employment of two distinct families of ballistic missiles—the Intermediate-Range Ballistic

Missile (IRBM) and the Intercontinental Ballistic Missile (ICBM). These missiles were designed for optimum performance at the two ranges currently considered to be the strategically most desirable—1500 and 5500 nautical miles (NM), respectively.

The 1500-NM design range of the IRBM can be reduced considerably if, for instance, it is desired to trade distance for payload. Conversely, technological and operational improvements should make it possible to extend the IRBM's design range appreciably without reduction in payload. Similar reductions and extensions of the 5500-NM design range of the ICBM could ultimately provide such a wide choice of ballistic ranges as to meet almost any strategic requirement.

Any future operational requirements for ballistic ranges beyond those of even the improved ICBM would necessitate the development of a third ballistic missile family—the Global-Range Ballistic Missile (GRBM) with a range of over 10,000 NM—that is, sufficient to reach any target from any launch point on earth.

Added operational advantages of ballistic missiles include their quick reaction capability, which will be an invaluable asset to SAC's alert posture. Also they can be kept in continuous readiness with a minimum of maintenance. Passive defense is facilitated because missile launch sites are far more amenable to hardening than bomber bases and very suitable for extensive deployment. And, being unmanned, missiles reduce crew attrition suffered in combat.

Deterrent aspects

The unique characteristics of the ballistic missile may appear to be of greater benefit to the Soviets—or any other potential aggressor—in mounting a surprise attack against this country than they would be to us in deterring aggression. It is argued that the military advantages of the initiative coupled with those of a mass attack with advanced ballistic missiles could achieve a decisive victory within hours after initiation of the attack. But while such an attack would undoubtedly cause grave losses in lives and property, it could be decisive only if it succeeded in wiping out or seriously crippling our retaliatory strike capability.

As will be discussed later, various measures can and are being taken to ensure the survival of a sufficient percentage of SAC's strike forces—even in the face of a devastating surprise attack with bombers and missiles—to permit effective retaliation. In the retaliatory attack we would of course make optimum use of the most advanced strategic weapon systems available at the time aggression took place, including ballistic missiles. For this reason missiles will contribute increasingly to the maintenance of our deterrent margin—the difference between the Soviets' capability to wage aggression and our capability of countering it with decisive results. For the Soviets' decision to initiate an attack would be based on an estimate of the cost to them, which is measured in terms of our retaliation.

However, deterrence is a relative concept. What may appear to us as an unacceptable penalty may well be considered by the Communist dictators to be an entirely acceptable price for what they expect to gain. And once they have managed to build up a sizable stockpile of ballistic missiles, they may even be convinced that they can attack us with relative impunity. Therefore it is essential that we maintain the deterrent margin at the same convincing level which thus far has made aggression against this country appear too costly, even by Soviet standards. But as the Soviets' offensive capability grows, so must SAC's deterrent posture. Availability of a growing number of advanced and reliable ballistic missiles, widely deployed in hardened sites, will greatly enhance that posture.

Employment

There has been too little experience with strategic ballistic missiles to establish hard and fast rules for their employment. During the present stage of initial evolution, their operational employment would depend on the status of missile technology at the time a war started, the quality and quantity of operational missiles available to either side, and similar factors. These factors will change rapidly and radically in the years ahead, requiring frequent reassessment of the prevailing conditions affecting both employment of and defense against ballistic missiles.

As with every other new weapon system, SAC must make optimum use of current missile capabilities by exploiting their favorable characteristics and minimizing their deficiencies. This means that the first operational ballistic missiles would be assigned to soft or large targets and as penetration aids to manned bombers. Additional targets and missions can be assigned as the number and quality of operational missiles increase. Eventually the ballistic missile will probably become the principal weapon for destroying quickly those targets that pose a direct and immediate threat against the United States, as well as many other targets that contribute to an aggressor's ability to wage war.

OPERATIONAL ASPECTS OF MISSILE TECHNOLOGY

Discussions of ballistic missiles frequently point out that the first ballistic missile was launched when some prehistoric genius picked up a rock and heaved it at an adversary. The implication is that the art of ballistic missiles is a very old one. A somewhat similar cliché is used occasionally to emphasize the long history of rockets. Actually there can be no valid comparision between a projectile thrown or blasted in the general direction of a nearby target and the ballistic missile as we know it today, streaking at near-escape velocities out of and back into the atmosphere to hit a target thousands of miles away with fantastic accuracy and the destructive power of millions of tons of TNT.

The point is that the science of strategic ballistic missiles is very new. As in all new and revolutionary sciences it is subject to both many growing pains and rapid advances, especially in the very early stages. Operational employment of ballistic missiles during this period presents many problems, not only because of the lack of precedents in many phases of operation but also because of the constant changes resulting from day-to-day advances in missile technology. To exploit these advances to the utmost, there must be commensurate advances in the system created for the employment of the missile. A superior engineering product could well be militarily inferior unless it is properly applied and utilized.

Technological supremacy is established not by advances in some particular field or area but by correlated advances in all the many disciplines that contribute, directly or indirectly, to the state of the art. Similarly, strategic supremacy is established not merely by superior weapons but also by a superior system available for the operation, maintenance, and protection of these weapons. Indications are that, in such a comparison, SAC is still considerably superior to its Soviet counterpart. If the Soviets had in being a global and all-encompassing support organization equal or similar to that of SAC, it would be difficult—and illogical—to keep it secret.

To grow with the threat, SAC must make effective and immediate use of technological advances in strategic weapon systems, both manned and unmanned. This requires great flexibility in all areas of organization and operations so as to permit rapid and effective reorientation in planning, changes in procedures, and modification of support equipment.

The need for such flexibility is particularly apparent in dealing with advances in missile technology because there will probably be unpredictable technological breakthroughs which may result in dramatic improvements in performance. Even if no spectacular breakthroughs should occur, there are bound to be quantum advances in performance, greatly accelerated by the impetus and urgency given to the missile program which must be reflected without delay in the operational support systems.

These advances will result in continuous improvements with respect to accuracy, range, reliability, maintainability, mobility, and other operational features which will have considerable bearing on the manner and scope of missile employment. Anticipating these far-reaching changes SAC has established, as an integral part of its over-all organization, the nucleus of a missile capability which is responsive to all present as well as foreseeable future operational aspects of missile technology.

OPERATIONAL CONSIDERATIONS

Fascinated by the spectacular nature of the ballistic missile, a space-conscious public tends to consider it as "the ultimate weapon." Three reasons, in particular, make it highly unlikely that there will ever be such a thing as an "ultimate" strategic weapon. The first reason is that as a weapon becomes more complex and sophisticated it takes increasingly longer to develop and thus allows more time for the development of defensive measures against it. Also it is no longer probable that any one country will be able to monopolize the use of a highly advanced weapon for any appreciable length of time, as we were once able to do with the atomic bomb. Therefore introduction of a revolutionary weapon or weapon technique should henceforth have little bearing on relative technological strengths but only raise them to a higher plateau. This means that use of a potent new weapon by an aggressor will invite retaliatory use of the same weapon by the defender, spurring a race for a still more potent weapon.

The possibility of an "ultimate weapon" is further minimized by the fact that strategic operations entail a number of highly specialized missions that can best, or perhaps exclusively, be accomplished by a variety of specialized weapons or combinations of weapons.

Finally, any tool fashioned by the mind and hand of man has weaknesses and limitations. Some limitations may be inherent and best dealt with by avoiding those uses of the tool that would exaggerate the deficiencies.

The ballistic missile too has weaknesses and limitations. Most of these lend themselves to improvement, while some are inherent. Of immediate interest, however, are those deficiencies which have a profound effect on the establishment of SAC's Initial Operational Capability (IOC) in the ballistic missile field.

Problem areas affecting IOC

Operational limitations and problems affecting the employment of ballistic missiles in their present stage of development pertain primarily to accuracy, reliability, limited payload, maintainability, and lack of operational experience. Improvements in missile technology and increasing experience in the operation and maintenance of ballistic missiles will gradually alleviate these deficiencies. Others may continue to impose operational limitations for some time to come.

For one, the ballistic missile will eventually be more vulnerable to active defense measures—such as an antimissile missile—than a manned bomber as long as its trajectory is fixed and therefore predictable. Of course this deficiency becomes an advantage in our own defense against hostile missiles. A similar two-way consideration applies to the fact that ballistic missiles, in contrast to manned bombers, cannot be used for flexible tactics designed to aggravate detection.

Another and possibly even more serious problem stems from the inability to recall a ballistic missile once it is launched. To cancel a launching, it would be necessary to destroy the missiles in some manner before they impacted, which, indeed, would be a very high, if not fatal, price to pay for an error.

Nor is it possible to divert a ballistic missile from one target to another while in flight or to compensate for insufficient knowledge concerning the exact location and nature of a target. No matter how ingenious, the missile's "brain" has no reasoning power to deal with unexpected situations but can only follow the instructions given it prior to launch. Furthermore there is at present no positive and direct method of ascertaining whether and to what extent it followed these instructions.

All these elements inject a certain degree of inflexibility into missile operations which must be taken into account in their employment and the selection of compatible targets. The same consideration applies of course to manned bomber operations—except that bomber crews can frequently take corrective or alternate action in flight whereas missiles cannot.

To cope with these problems, it is important to assign missiles only to those missions which are within their capability at the prevailing stage of development. Some of the wide variety of strategic missions which SAC must be prepared to perform will permit the employment or assistance of ballistic missiles from the very start of their operational readiness. Other missions are still too far beyond present missile capabilities to make their employment feasible.

The first step, therefore, in exploiting SAC's Initial Operational Capability for ballistic missiles is to recognize and define their existing capabilities and deficiencies and to plan for their employment in such a manner as to make optimum use of the one and to minimize the other.

Solution of problems

The problems which have been described are so varied that many different approaches are needed for dealing with them. Some of the solutions may be temporary, especially in cases of technical deficiencies which can be expected to be alleviated in the near future. Other approaches may have to be indirect, such as in preventing the inadvertent launching of ballistic missiles. Lacking reliable technological safeguards to deal with these and related contingencies, ballistic missiles would probably not be launched until and unless there is definite proof of aggression—proof perhaps as drastic as the actual detonation of hostile bombs or missiles. This operational factor in turn generates the urgent requirement for the extensive deployment and hardening of missile sites. Conversely, SAC's alert force of manned bombers could be launched immediately upon receipt of tactical warning, since "fail-safe" provisions permit their recall in case the warning should prove unfounded.

Pending improvements in the three most critical deficiency areas in the first generation of ballistic missiles as compared to manned bombers—insufficient accuracy, yield, and reliability—the first characteristic which can be utilized in the Initial Operational Capability period is the missile's tremendous speed. With increasing experience in their maintenance and operation, ballistic missiles will soon permit the exploitation of an additional characteristic—their quick reaction capability.

To derive the maximum benefit from these two characteristics during the IOC period, it is necessary to analyze SAC's target system carefully and to use ballistic missiles only for those missions which stress quick reaction and speed but do not entail the stringent requirements for great accuracy and yields placed on manned bombers.

Mission analysis

The purpose of a strategic mission is to inflict a specified degree of damage upon a specified strategic target. Unless both of these conditions are met, the mission cannot be considered fully accomplished and may have to be repeated. SAC's Emergency War Plan (EWP) covers the target system assigned to SAC and in turn assigns the accomplishment of specified strategic missions to the various elements of SAC's strike forces.

At present all SAC missions are assigned to either medium or heavy bomber units in accordance with the relative locations of launch point and target, mission requirements, tanker coordination, and similar factors. The Emergency War Plan is constantly reviewed and modified as necessary, at the request or with the approval of higher headquarters.

There are two principal types of strategic targets, the Specified Point Target and the Specified Area Target. A third type, which is assuming increasing significance, is the Specified Mobile Target.

The Specified Point Target is a strategic target in SAC's Emergency War Plan which is relatively limited in size and has sharply defined boundaries (missile launch sites, factory complexes, power plants, large permanent structures or buildings, and the like).

The Specified Area Target is a strategic target in SAC's EWP which is fairly large in extent and normally has no clearly defined boundaries. The farthest reaches of the target area which are expected to suffer at least some predictable damage may, in the case of a high-yield weapon, be many miles from the Desired Ground Zero (DGZ) —that point within the target area above which the weapon has been programed to detonate. Examples of Specified Area Targets are airfield complexes, widely dispersed military or industrial installations, etc.

A Specified Mobile Target is a target in SAC's EWP which is, in effect, a point target but whose location is neither permanent nor always precisely known. Future targets of this nature could be mobile missile launching facilities mounted on a group of trucks, or possibly missile launching sites on ice floes.

Each of these general types of targets—specifically the first two—includes a great variety of categories, depending on the amount of hardening, size and shape of structures, concentration of built-up areas, nature and character of target, and many others.

Application of a weapon to any one of these many different targets is designed to achieve a specific objective. This objective could be the complete *destruction* of the target—normally a Specified Point Target—to the extent that it can no longer serve its military or industrial purpose and that its repair or rebuilding is not possible, at least during the decisive phase of the war.

Another objective of a strategic mission can be *disruption*—of communications, utilities, traffic, and similar activities or facilities essential to the continued conduct of the war. To be effective, disruption must be thorough enough to prevent resumption of useful operations for an adequate period of time.

A related objective is to *degrade*—that is, to reduce the effectiveness of—widely dispersed but coordinated military or industrial activities whose complete destructon is not possible or practicable. A typical example is the degrading, by means of missile salvos, of extended defenses against bombers in order to reduce the attrition rate in manned-bomber strikes.

Contamination of a large area by high-yield weapons can serve to *deny* that area to personnel who must use it in the performance of military or vital support duties. Finally the objective of a strategic mission can call for *devastation* of a large-area target, so as to weaken both the over-all warmaking capability of the enemy and his will to continue the war.

It is quite possible that a successful strategic mission may accomplish not only its specified objective but secondary objectives as well. For instance, a mission programed to disrupt the electric services in a particular area could at the same time deny a nearby airfield to its operating personnel and disrupt traffic over adjacent roads. A mission can be considered successful only if it has achieved its specified objective, regardless of what other objectives it may have achieved.

The large variety of strategic targets and of different objectives to be achieved in attacking these targets is indicative of the innumerable factors that must be considered in planning strategic missions. The factors of particular significance to this discussion are yield and number of warheads needed to attain specified objectives, and the vehicle or vehicles best suited to carry the weapons to the target. In the past SAC's choice of vehicles was limited to either medium or heavy bombers. The question, then, is what type of missions will be suitable for strategic missiles during both the initial and the advanced phases of their operational capability.

Mission effectiveness of missiles

The scope and number of strategic missions which can be assigned to ballistic missiles are initially limited, first, by the small quantity of operational missiles available, and, second, by their still unfavorable accuracy-yield characteristic as compared with that of today's manned jet bombers. The relatively low yield of the nuclear warhead of current ballistic missiles prevents their use not only for those missions which require a warhead of greater yield but also for missions where an otherwise adequate smaller yield would demand greater accuracy.

Even marked improvements in the electronic guidance systems of ballistic missiles may not suffice to ensure commensurate improvements in their mission effectiveness. There are several other seemingly unrelated problem areas which affect the probability of reaching the specified target and achieving the specified degree of damage. Following are some of the early problems which may have a bearing on the mission effectiveness of ballistic missiles:

- Human error, from the calculation of the trajectory to the "keying" of guidance instructions into the missile. Once the missile is launched, errors cannot be corrected.
- Geographic error, resulting from inadequate knowledge of the exact location of a target or errors in the datum position used as a reference point.
- Misinformation pertaining to a target, stemming from misinterpretation of intelligence data or the enemy's deliberate deception.
- Inaccuracies in the calculation of the ballistic trajectory, caused by insufficient or erroneous data pertaining to gravitational or magnetic anomalies, high-speed phenomena, elevation of the target, and similar factors.
- Effect of environmental conditions on the trajectory, such as extremes or unexpected variations in temperature and air density, meteoric dust, various types of radiation, etc.
- Malfunctioning during flight of one or more of the thousands of delicate components.
- Effect of missile defenses.

- Inaccurate or erroneous information on the degree of target hardening.

While these factors may in themselves be of minor or debatable significance, they combine to reduce the probability that a ballistic missile will accomplish its specified mission. With further improvements in missile technology, with increasing knowledge of the data needed to calculate precise trajectories, and with growing operational experience, most of these problems may warrant no further consideration. For the time being, however, missions whose success could be jeopardized by relying on missiles must be assigned to manned bombers. Manned aircraft are normally not subject to such unprecedented operating conditions and can correct minor inaccuracies and deficiencies in flight.

The mixed bomber-missile force concept

As pointed out before, the coordinated use of both manned bombers and missiles will provide SAC with an invaluable flexibility in the assignment of each specific mission to the weapon system or systems best suited for it. But this flexibility is reflected in improved combat capability only if there is an adequate choice of advanced weapon systems to meet satisfactorily the requirements of any strategic mission SAC may be called upon to perform.

At this writing ballistic missiles are not yet combat-ready, and SAC must still rely on its over 2700 bombers and tankers to accomplish its mission. However, the B-47 medium bombers are gradually becoming obsolescent and may possibly approach the obsolete stage before they can be replaced by adequate quantities of operational missiles. While there are still years of service life left in the B-52 heavy bomber, the ICBM will probably not be ready to entirely replace this aircraft by the time that bomber too reaches obsolescence and must be phased out.

To prevent a serious gap in our strategic strength during the transition period, it is essential to modernize our bomber force so as to keep step with the improvements in the Soviets' offensive and defensive capabilities. The B-47 and the B-52 must be followed by the higher-performance types like the B-58 and eventually by the highly advanced, hypersonic B-70 bomber. Concurrently, IRBMs and ICBMs will be phased into the SAC weapons inventory as rapidly as they become operationally available.

The Snark nonballistic, air-breathing missile, which is now in the final testing stages, will provide SAC with an intercontinental-missile capability even prior to the integration of the ICBM. Subsequently it will find use in long-range missile missions requiring evasive or deceptive tactics in support of, or in coordination with, bomber and ICBM strikes.

Just as the transition from propeller-driven to all-jet aircraft was a gradual one, so the transition from an all-bomber to a mixed bomber-missile force must be orderly and carefully programed. To achieve the maximum benefit from this combination, every effort must be made to reflect the latest technological advances in all operational weapon systems, both manned and unmanned. Also, great care must be exercised in the assignment of missions to those weapon systems which promise the greatest probability of success. The development of the optimum strategy and tactics in the employment of a mixed bomber-missile force is facilitated by electronic computers, which are used by SAC's planning staff to conduct war games based on the many varied sets of conditions incident to strategic operations.

With continued improvements in missile technology and operations, the percentage of missions which can be assigned to missiles will increase commensurately. However, indications are that for the foreseeable future missiles will not entirely replace the manned bomber but rather will supplement and complement it. The manned aircraft offer certain advantages that would be difficult, if not impossible, to achieve with missiles. This applies particularly to missions which must cope with unknown contingencies or which necessitate the observation and analysis of results before deciding on subsequent action. Manned bombers will also remain superior to missiles for the accurate application of nonnuclear weapons to a series of small, widely dispersed targets, or the use of weapons with very high yield.

Future aspects

There is little doubt that future developments will bring about rapid improvements in accuracy, yield, range, automaticity, maintainability, and similar areas in which early ballistic missiles are deficient. Technological advances will also engender spectacular improvements in some of those areas which constitute inherent rather than initial weaknesses of current missile designs.

One of the most far-reaching improvements, as far as operational employment is concerned, would be the conversion from liquid to dependable and stable solid rocket fuels. Use of solid propellants would greatly facilitate maintenance and logistics problems, enhance movability, permit more extensive dispersal and hardening, reduce requirements for skilled technicians, and allow for greater automaticity. The relative simplicity of solid-fuel power plants would increase reliability and improve reaction capability. Moreover, it is anticipated that over-all cost of procuring and maintaining solid-fuel missiles will be considerably below that for the liquid-fuel type. For all these reasons solid-fuel power plants will undoubtedly find increasing use in future generations of ballistic missiles.

Another improvement which appears technically feasible concerns means for permitting a missile to deviate from its normal ballistic trajectory. Once perfected, such a means would add immeasurably to protection against antimissile defenses which, at present, can be based on the fact that after a ballistic missile has been detected its trajectory can be predicted expeditiously and accurately.

A profound impact on SAC's future operations would also result from the development of an operational Strategic Reconnaissance Satellite (SRS). Such a satellite would minimize one of the principal inherent weaknesses of unmanned weapon systems—their inability to report whether and to what extent they have performed their assigned mission. The Strategic Reconnaissance Satellite would also assist in accurately locating targets, facilitate missile guidance, and, possibly, provide countermeasures against missile defenses. Moreover, it would permit early detection of hostile missiles and thereby enhance both SAC's alert posture and missile defense.

Obviously the Soviets would use satellites for similar purposes. This may create the need for developing antisatellite defenses. Thus the Air Force may have to extend its operations ever deeper into space, with the prospect of actual space warfare in the more distant future.

Nontechnical aspects of the future include those for growing cooperation with the other services and the military establishments of our allies in coordinating the assignment of ballistic-missile targets. The increasing availability of ballistic missiles, their tremendous scope of ranges, and their potential adaptability to mobile launching platforms on land, at sea, and in the air will eventually make the entire Soviet target system accessible to many organizations other than SAC. With adequate assignment of responsibilities and centralized control, the combined missile capability of the free world could represent a tremendous asset to its deterrent posture.

Consideration of Soviet missile capability

In the employment of ballistic missiles the Soviets must cope with problems and deficiencies similar to those affecting our own initial operational capability. The question whether or not the Soviets are currently ahead of us in their missile technology is rather academic. They would not launch an all-out missile attack unless and until they have enough operational missiles to ensure the immediate and complete success of such an attack by neutralizing our retaliatory forces. Indications are that the Soviets have not yet reached that capability. By the time they have accumulated what they would consider an adequate stockpile of ballistic missiles, our own stockpile can, with proper effort, have grown sufficiently to offset any technological advantages they might possess at present.

There are, however, some factors in missile employment which represent exclusive advantages to the Soviets. They have more accurate and detailed information concerning the location and nature of strategic targets in this country. Also these targets are more concentrated, with many major target areas within easy reach of submarine-launched missiles. As the potential aggressor they can select the most suitable time and circumstances for a surprise attack. Thus they can cause severe damage even if our subsequent retaliatory action led to their ultimate defeat.

But while successful attacks on large, highly concentrated target areas can be undertaken with relatively poor missile accuracies, much better accuracies are required to seriously weaken SAC's combat capability, even with a large number of missiles. The Soviets, too, recognize the mixed bomber-missile force as mandatory to achieve flexibility in the choice of weapon systems for a variety of missions.

There are two approaches the Soviets could and undoubtedly would use in trying to neutralize SAC's strike forces and thereby prevent unacceptable retaliation. The first approach would entail a surprise attack with both missiles and manned bombers, in which the missiles would be employed principally against area targets while the bombers would concentrate on SAC installations.

The success of such a surprise attack appears rather doubtful, at least at the present time. It is extremely difficult to time the attack in such a manner as to ensure the simultaneous arrival of all elements, manned and unmanned, and thereby to achieve a complete surprise. A small aggressive force would find it easier to delay detection but would not suffice to prevent retaliation. And the bigger the aggressive force, the less chance there is for a sneak attack. Radars have now been developed which can detect an ICBM at very great distances. Eventually they should be able to provide the minimum warning SAC will need to launch its manned alert forces before they could be hit on the ground. The previously mentioned hardening and deployment of missile sites will further enhance the survival of a missile capability adequate to retaliate effectively.

The Soviets' second approach in preventing decisive retaliation rests with continued improvements of their air defenses, especially against manned bombers. But as defenses become more sophisticated, they must rely increasingly on electronics, which, in turn, can be combated with electronics, generating a vicious spiral of countermeasures and counter-countermeasures of mounting complexity.

Future advances in missile technology and the techniques of missile employment will of course increase the Soviets' offensive capability and, therefore, the threat to us. However, as long as we grow with the threat and succeed in preserving our deterrent margin, we can at least maintain what is sometimes referred to as a "nuclear stalemate."

The concept of the nuclear stalemate seems to have a derogatory connotation which is not justified. As long as the Soviets threaten aggression, we must make every effort to prevent it, because in a nuclear war there are no winners, only different degrees of losers. The nuclear stalemate is preferable to open warfare even if we should eventually win the war, for we could win only at tremendous cost to ourselves. Therefore we must endeavor to maintain the critical balance in the hope that the fundamental issues can be resolved by future international and political developments which will, once and for all, end the threat to our security.

INTEGRATION OF MISSILES INTO THE SAC INVENTORY

SAC is well prepared to integrate missiles into its inventory. Throughout its existence, it has had to phase in a number of new weapon systems—B-29, B-50, B-36, B-47, B-52—and has gained considerable experience in adapting its operations, organization, personnel, and support activities to the different conditions created by new weapon systems.

This flexibility and adaptability will be exceedingly helpful in the integration of ballistic missiles. Their revolutionary nature will require some major modifications of present operational concepts, training approach, weapons selection and employment, and related areas. On the other hand, integration of missiles will be fairly gradual, permitting the well-planned and cohesive conversion of the existing organization and support functions to mixed bomber-missile operations.

Lack of previous experience in the operational employment of ballistic missiles and the integration of these missiles into a combat command while they are still in the research and development stage will cause many unprecedented problems. There will be continuous changes and modifications resulting from technical improvements and growing experience. For these reasons the conversion to a mixed bomber-missile force is divided into two broad phases, namely the Initial Operational Capability (IOC) and the Advanced Operational Capability (AOC).

The IOC covers the period from initial integration and transition to a limited but combat-ready missile capability. The AOC begins at that point which, in effect, concludes the "experimental" phase. While there will be continued improvements and subsequent changes, their effect on organization and operations will be more predictable and less drastic.

It would be futile to speak of an "Ultimate Operational Capability" as there are still too many unknowns to chart a path beyond the achievement of an Advanced Operational Capability. In fact it will be impossible to tell exactly when the IOC ends and the AOC begins, as there is bound to be a considerable overlap of the two phases, not only for different families of missiles but also for each individual type.

Organization

The decision to expedite the achievement of a missile capability by committing ballistic missiles to operational employment while they were still under development required the added decision as to whether the responsibility for the establishment of the IOC should be assigned to the developing command or the operating command. After a careful weighing of all factors involved, it was decided to assign this responsibility to the Air Research and Development Command. However, subsequent considerations indicated that the achievement of Advanced Operational Capability for SAC could be accelerated by getting SAC into ballistic missile operations at the earliest possible stage. Therefore the 1st Missile Division, with headquarters at Cooke Air Force Base, California, was transferred to SAC on 1 January 1958, together with the responsibility for the IOC phase of both the ICBM and IRBM programs. The commander of the 1st Missile Division, which now occupies a position equal to that of a numbered air force in SAC, is responsible for the training and expansion of the strategic ballistic missile force.

Further organizational changes included the establishment of a Headquarters SAC extension—"SAC Mike"—in ARDC's Ballistic Missile Division at Inglewood, California. The Ballistic Missile Division, which previously had the IOC responsibility, will continue to direct the ballistic missile research and development programs. SAC Mike, headed by a SAC "Assistant Commander in Chief," serves as direct contact for either conveying the latest requirements or requesting up-to-date technical information. This is expected to speed the solution of daily technical problems and otherwise shorten communications channels.

Also during January 1958, SAC activated its first two IRBM squadrons, one for the Thor and the other for the Jupiter. IRBM squadrons are slated for overseas deployment after completion of training.

The ballistic missile force will initially be integrated into the time-proven SAC organizational concept and formed into divisions, wings, and squadrons. Development of an organizational structure to meet all foreseeable contingencies in future missile operations is now in process, using the most advanced concepts of management engineering. Unpredictable technical factors and operational problems, political considerations, or other exigencies may require modified approaches which cannot be anticipated at this early stage.

Personnel

As weapons become more complex and potent, more and greater skills are needed to operate and maintain them properly. The many diverse skills required in the employment of ballistic missiles are so advanced that present military personnel at even the highest technical levels will barely meet entrance requirements for many ballistic missile specialties.

Estimates and the development of manning tables pinpointing functional areas and job requirements are essential to ensure the proper training in specialties which were nonexistent only a very short time ago. Also, the personal characteristics of personnel who are to man the ballistic missile units will probably be quite different from those who fly manned aircraft. To define these characteristics adequately is a problem that still lies ahead.

Added personnel problems may result from the conditions under which missile crews are expected to operate, such as isolation of launch sites, long hours of work underground, and the demanding alert status. These problems will aggravate already existing difficulties in retaining skilled personnel in the Air Force. Further reduction in the retention rate would be doubly harmful to ballistic missile operations because, unit for unit, missiles require one third more personnel in the electronics-technician category—the type most difficult to retain today—than does the manned bomber force.

Established SAC facilities and procedures for the selection and training of personnel to operate and maintain the advanced manned weapon systems can serve similar purposes in the ballistic missile area until sufficient empirical data have been accumulated to develop more specialized selection and training criteria. Initially emphasis will be on on-the-job training, both in the factories of the missile manufacturers and at the launch sites. More sophisticated training can be developed as soon as there is a nucleus of instructors with extensive operational experience, assisted by specialized training aids such as simulators.

On the brighter side of the personnel picture, SAC is in the position to select commanders for all echelons of missile operations from a large number of seasoned officers who are well versed in strategic operations and the employment of the highly complex, manned strategic weapon systems currently in use. Their versatility, experience, and familiarity with the concepts guiding SAC's mission will prove an invaluable asset to the early establishment of a combat-ready ballistic missile capability.

Support activities

SAC's existing support activities were developed over a period of years for the operation of weapon systems which in complexity, technological aspects, support requirements, and purposes are not very different from ballistic missiles. Therefore integration of the missiles requires little if any conversion of most support activities, rather their gradual expansion and addition of specialized functions. This applies in particular to three of SAC's most advanced and extensive support activities—logistics, communications, and intelligence.

SAC's logistics system was developed to provide adequate materiel support to installations scattered throughout the world, and, in turn, it must support the global operations of SAC's bomber and tanker forces. In spite of the huge quantities of diversified materials that must be moved over large distances, the system had to be designed for clocklike precision and immediate response to the widest fluctuations in demands so as to cope with any contingency.

This system is well suited for the logistic support of operational missile sites, although two aspects warrant special attention. As missile sites will normally be located in isolated areas, they must be quite self-sufficient. They must not only be capable of immediately dealing with any emergency but also be in continuous readiness to successively launch a given number of missiles. This requires a large stock of supplies and parts, tools, and other equipment whose exact specifications and quantity will have to be determined empirically for lack of any previous experience. As a result early operations of the first missile sites may be plagued by some materiel deficiencies affecting combat-readiness until adequate requirement data can be fed into the SAC logistics system.

Another problem will result from the location of the missile sites. While their wide dispersal in itself offers no unique difficulties, their isolated location may impede the steady flow of essential supplies and materiel, both over land and by air. This problem may have to be solved by the addition of helicopters to SAC's complement of cargo carriers.

Logistics for missile sites will be further enhanced by the availability of SAC's well-established, global communications network which is unequaled in scope, reliability, and reaction capability. Employing the latest advances in electronics, this foolproof communications system permits instantaneous and dependable contact with any SAC element in the air or on the ground throughout the world. The focal point is located in the vast underground control center of SAC's headquarters at Offutt Air Force Base, near Omaha, Nebraska.

From this control center the commander in chief of SAC and his staff direct the operations of the entire command. The communications network is in effect SAC's "nervous system" for the rapid transmission of information and action directives. Tied into this network, SAC's missile sites everywhere can be committed to action within a matter of seconds. Conversely, they can alert the entire SAC establishment just as rapidly in case they have been attacked.

Equally unique and indispensable to missile operations is SAC's highly developed intelligence organization. Its role is a vital one. Even the most perfect and potent strategic weapon system, whether manned or unmanned, is of little value unless it is applied effectively and expertly to the achievement of a military objective. This entails the capability to ascertain exactly what that objective is and how best to attain it. The purpose of strategic intelligence is to provide that capability.

The manifold responsibilities of SAC's intelligence organization begin with the establishment of the target system—that is, determination of those targets which contribute to the warmaking capability of a potential aggressor. The next step is to assign priorities, with top priority going to targets which in case of aggression would pose the most immediate threat to the United States.

Subsequent tasks serve to obtain all possible details concerning each individual target, such as precise location, size, shape, construction, defensive measures, vulnerability, and similar characteristics. While the Soviets' strategic intelligence can normally use overt sources to gather similar data in this country, SAC's counterpart must rely on experience, scientific methods, and much ingenuity in properly tying together bits and pieces of sometimes questionable information.

After the necessary target data have been obtained, another group must determine the specific objective to be attained in attacking a target. This information is then supplied to experts in nuclear weapons technology who must decide what number, type, and size of weapons to use and where to detonate them to achieve the specified mission objectives. Finally, recommendations must be made as to the type of vehicle or vehicles best suited to carry the weapon.

In addition to these tasks strategic intelligence must furnish detailed information concerning air defenses and, following a strike, must make the most rapid and accurate possible assessment of the damage inflicted.

It is obvious that these unparalleled intelligence facilities are not limited to the employment of manned weapon systems but are equally suitable for missile warfare. The only specialized functions that must be added are provisions for poststrike reconnaissance and facilities for the calculation of ballistic trajectories.

The latter requirement led to the recent activation by SAC of a Target-Trajectory Preparation Center whose personnel are presently undergoing intensive training. Equipped with the latest electronic computers to permit high-speed calculation of the complex trajectories, the Center will eventually be located at SAC headquarters and become an integral part of the intelligence organization. Availability of this organization for missile operations will permit achievement of a combat-ready status at a much earlier date than would otherwise have been possible.

Site operations

Several missile sites are now under construction in this country, and selection of additional sites is under way. Site selection is based on a number of criteria which are quite difficult to meet satisfactorily. Sites should be located in isolated areas for security and safety reasons, yet be close enough to active military installations which can provide administrative and related support. Added requirements include soil characteristics suitable for construction of hardened sites, climatic conditions permitting all-weather operations, a minimum of electric interference, and many other considerations.

Defensive measures for the protection of missile sites will in general parallel those taken for the protection of bomber bases. These measures include provisions for dealing with sabotage attempts designed to pin down SAC's retaliatory forces just prior to initiation of aggression, dispersal, and hardening of bases and missile sites against battle damage resulting from near misses.

Dispersal of missile sites can be more extensive than that of bomber bases, especially in the case of sites employing missiles with solid-fuel power plants. The primary purpose of dispersal is to extend the enemy's target system to the point where it exceeds his capacity for destroying our retaliatory strike forces to the extent required to ensure the success of a surprise attack.

Hardening of launch sites is not only more practical but also strategically more important than hardening of bomber bases. As mentioned before, missiles would normally not be launched until after the initial attack. Their sites must therefore be so deployed and protected as to ensure the survival of an adequate percentage. By their very nature, missile sites lend themselves quite readily to a fair degree of hardening.

Bomber bases are more difficult to harden effectively in view of their expanse. Also too much hardening would tend to adversely affect the reaction capability of the alert force. Hardening of bomber bases will generally be limited to communications, fuel storage, and the like. On the other hand survivability of SAC's manned strike forces is enhanced by an *offensive* measure for protection—the alert system. Under this system a certain percentage of the strike force is kept on continuous alert, ready to launch a counterattack within minutes after receipt of tactical warning. The size of this alert force and its quick-reaction capability are the very backbone of our deterrent strength and will continue to represent a most potent deterrent to aggression even after ballistic missiles have been integrated into the operational inventories of both sides.

Missile sites will be kept in a similar continuous alert status. Although tactical warning may not necessarily be the signal for launch, they must be ready at any time to launch their first missile within minutes after receipt of the strike order from Headquarters SAC. Improvements in automaticity should greatly enhance their quick-reaction capability.

Achievement of this capability is also contingent on further improvements in reliability and maintainability. As malfunctions cannot be corrected in flight, missile components must possess even greater reliability than the components of a manned bomber. Maintainability must permit missile crews to keep a maximum number of missiles in commission under the limitations imposed by the demands of self-sufficiency of missile sites. Equipment calibration, major repairs, and modifications will have to be accomplished by contractor or depot teams airlifted to missile sites.

Missile crews must also be trained and equipped to make replacements required by deterioration or obsolescence of components and to perform regular checks and tests. These tests must include periodic launches of missiles against known targets in isolated areas to ensure the over-all reliability and accuracy of the entire missile weapon system and to maintain crew proficiency at the high level required for actual combat operation.

As HAS been shown in this discussion, SAC is utilizing its entire organization, facilities, and experience in strategic operations for the earliest possible achievement of an Initial Operational Capability in the employment of ballistic missiles. SAC is rapidly approaching that capability and, thereby, a capability for retaliation and deterrence still more advanced than it has now.

As ballistic missiles will improve our deterrent posture, so will they improve the Soviets' offensive posture. As a result there will continue to be a precarious balance between aggressive intent and deterrence, which is the best we can expect under existing conditions.

Whether or not that balance will be maintained hinges on our ability and determination to grow with the threat, and on the Soviets' continued respect for our retaliatory strength. Still there is always the danger of a miscalculation on their part which would lead them to overestimate their strength or underestimate ours, or both. For this reason we must make absolutely sure that what we consider our deterrent strength is backed by our actual strength. For it is that strength which we must always be ready to apply decisively in fighting for our survival if deterrence fails.

Headquarters Strategic Air Command

APPENDICES

APPENDIX I

Notes on Technical Aspects of Ballistic Missiles

TECHNICAL TRAINING AND SCIENTIFIC RELATIONS GROUP
SPACE TECHNOLOGY LABORATORIES
THE RAMO-WOOLDRIDGE CORPORATION

These notes are intended to provide a brief introduction to the technical aspects of the USAF ballistic missile program. Particular emphasis is given to problems that are new or newly critical. Topics are covered in an order suggested by the relationships among them.

The Systems Concept

A ballistic missile system obviously consists of a tremendous number of components and detailed parts that must be designed, developed, and assembled into a working system. Less obvious, perhaps, is the fact that the *systems engineering* devoted to the study and planning of the over-all system is a significant and vital part of the program. Systems engineering is distinguished by its primary emphasis on the relationships of the various portions of a system to one another and to the over-all system performance.

In a systems engineering approach a missile is initially planned in broad outline, essentially in block diagram form, and the interactions of the different parts with one another are studied in detail before any hardware designs are committed to the missile. Necessarily the potentialities of detailed hardware must play an important part in the selection of possible systems for study and in their evaluation, but the emphasis is fundamentally on verifying that the system as a whole can be a practical, reliable, and sufficiently precise solution to the military problem.

In an alternate and less satisfactory initial approach various designs of engines, gyroscopes, airframe structures, and so on might be selected on the basis of their satisfactory performance in previous military developments, modified to meet the more obvious system requirements, and then committed to the new missile. An increasing effort might then be applied to working out further details of the system. Such an approach inevitably would lead to a prolonged schedule, and perhaps even to an inferior missile. As the program moved on, many decisions would have to be reversed or modified because of system requirements that were not understood at the beginning.

Systems engineering evidently must not be confined to the initial planning but must permeate the entire research and development phases, and even production. Although the initial researches must be as thorough as possible, many decisions must be made boldly on the basis of incomplete information. Investigation must continue so as to determine whether further data support the decisions. Any indications of the need for changes must be carefully weighed.

The system cannot be planned initially in complete detail. Within the subsystems the input-output relationships and general configuration of which have been tentatively established, more detailed systems engineering must be carried out. As the development progresses, it must receive continued monitoring from an over-all systems engineering point of view. This is especially important in times of apparent crisis such as may occur in any missile program, because a proposed change in propulsion, for example, might require accompanying radical changes in guidance or other areas. If the initial planning was sound within the limitations of available information and competent engineering is available at both system and more detailed levels, such an apparent crisis ordinarily is quickly resolved by a few minor changes.

Thus it is seen that systems engineering in a ballistic missile or any similar program requires employment of large numbers of specialists and also of an adequate number of competent administrators who can cement them together into a broad-visioned effective team. The over-all systems engineering effort for the present USAF program is carried out primarily in the Space Technology Laboratories of The Ramo-Wooldridge Corporation, in accordance with its responsibilities as technical director of the program and technical advisor to the Air Force Ballistic Missile Division of Headquarters Air Research and Development Command, USAF. The more detailed systems engineering within the various subsystems is primarily the responsibility of the corresponding contractors.

Systems and Subsystems of a Long-Range Ballistic Missile

A ballistic missile may be considered as an assemblage of a number of interconnected and interacting systems and subsystems that perform distinct functions in the accomplishment of the mission of the missile. In a military missile the payload is a *warhead*—high explosive, atomic, or thermonuclear in nature—that is to be delivered to and detonated at a predetermined target in enemy territory. The warhead, together with its auxiliary equipment, such as a fuzing system, is incorporated in the *nose cone* of the missile.

Delivery of the warhead to a predetermined target requires inclusion in the missile of a *guidance system*. This system regulates the position and velocity of the center of mass of the vehicle during powered flight, with the purpose of establishing a satisfactory trajectory prior to thrust cutoff. A *control system* is also necessary so as to maintain attitude stability of the missile during powered flight, to prevent undesirable responses when overriding guidance signals are introduced, and to correct deflections caused by winds, gusts, and other disturbances.

Electric power is required for the guidance and control systems. This power, as well as any required hydraulic or pneumatic power, is furnished by a subsystem, the *accessory power supply*.

For the *propulsion system*, present-day long-range ballistic missiles utilize rocket power plants with liquid oxidizer and liquid fuel as the propellant. The future may see the development of long-range missiles with solid-propellant rocket engines. The use of nuclear power also is an eventuality.

Flight monitoring equipment, part of which is carried by the missile, is needed to provide sufficient data for each test flight to justify the expense and effort of the firing.

Finally there is the *airframe,* the supporting structure for everything else in the missile. Each of the aforementioned systems or subsystems comprises a number of further subsystems, components, and component parts. For example, the liquid-propellant propulsion system includes not only the rocket engines and propellant tanks but also the turbopumps for forcing propellants into the engines, the propellant utilization system for monitoring and controlling the discharge rates from the propellant tanks, the ignition circuitry for starting the engines, and so on. However it must be emphasized that while all these subdivisions can be studied and discussed individually, their designers must give full consideration to the interactions between them if the missile is to operate successfully. Thus the missile, at every step of its development, must be considered as a complex of closely related and interacting mechanisms.

Powered Flight of the Missile

Power produced by rocket engines is applied to an ICBM or an IRBM only during the initial portion of its flight, from the *launch point* to the *thrust-cutoff* point *B* (Fig. 1). All necessary guidance and control of the missile must be accomplished during the powered flight, for the missile motion cannot be influenced when power is no longer available.

The ICBM and the IRBM are launched vertically, for this simplifies the launcher required for these large vehicles and also shortens the time that they are close to the ground during take-off. After this initial vertical climb the vehicle undergoes a programed turn toward the target. During this turn the guidance system begins to function and continues to do so until the desired altitude h, speed V, and angle γ are attained (at *B*, Fig. 1), whereupon it gives the signal for cutoff of the propulsive power. Perception and correction of vehicle attitude, exercised by the control system, are continuous during the powered flight. Both the attitude of the vehicle and the motion of its center of gravity relative to the required trajectory are adjusted by altering the direction of the thrust of the rocket engines, for instance, by putting jet vanes in the exhaust stream or by gimbaling the rocket thrust chambers.

There are many sets of values of the speed V, angle γ, and spatial position of B that will put the nose cone on a trajectory terminating at the desired target; but some sets are more favorable than others in respect to amount of propellant consumed by the engines or required precision of aim. It is the function of powered flight to impart to the

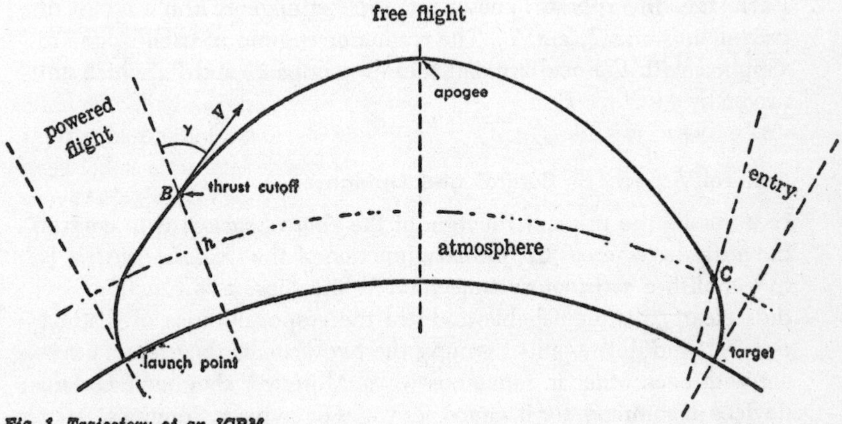

Fig. 1. Trajectory of an ICBM

nose cone, as accurately as possible, a favorable set of these parameters.

The energy expended in propelling the vehicle during the powered flight increases with the weight of the vehicle. Because both the kinetic and the potential energies are approximately proportional to the weight of the vehicle at thrust cutoff, it is desirable that this weight be as little as possible in excess of the weight of the nose cone. This objective is aided very materially by dividing the vehicle into two or more parts, or *stages,* with each stage containing a rocket propulsion system. Launching is accomplished by starting the engines of the first stage and, in some designs, also of other stages. At some time during the powered flight the first-stage engines are shut down, and this stage is jettisoned from the remainder of the vehicle. The engines of the next stage are then started, if they are not already operating, and they propel the vehicle on toward *B*. As the missile nears *B*, the engines on the last stage are shut down, and the final adjustment of the velocity needed to keep the nose cone on a trajectory that will reach the target is accomplished with rocket engines of comparatively small thrust, called *vernier engines*. Thus the term *thrust-cutoff point B* refers, accurately speaking, to the point where the vernier engines are shut down rather than to the shutdown point of the engines of the final stage.

In Fig. 2 is shown a possible configuration of a two-stage ICBM. Each stage incorporates one or more rocket engines E and a pair of propellant tanks T_o and T_f. The engine or engines of each stage are supplied with the oxidizer and fuel by pumps P_o and P_f, which are driven by a turbine T.

General Aspects of Control and Guidance

In a missile the primary function of the *control system* is to control the attitude, whereas the primary function of the *guidance system* is to establish a satisfactory trajectory. While these two functions are thus clearly distinguishable and are the responsibilities of distinct research and development groups, the two systems themselves interact with each other in numerous ways. Moreover they have certain devices in common, for instance, jet vanes or swiveling engines.

A ballistic missile is dependent on the control system for maintenance of a stable attitude, especially in the low-speed portion of the trajectory immediately after take-off. The control system must prevent the deflection of the missile during and after any disturbance, such as a gust, from becoming unacceptably large and must prevent wobbling in attitude after a guidance command. Because it is difficult to maintain sufficiently tight control without making the missile unstable at frequencies for which it readily vibrates, a significant portion of the control system engineering must be concerned with effects of airframe vibrations, propellant motions, and so forth on the control system. Solving the control problem is somewhat like trying to balance a four-foot length of garden hose on its end.

Although the possibility of instability resulting from interactions between the guidance and control systems needs some attention, most

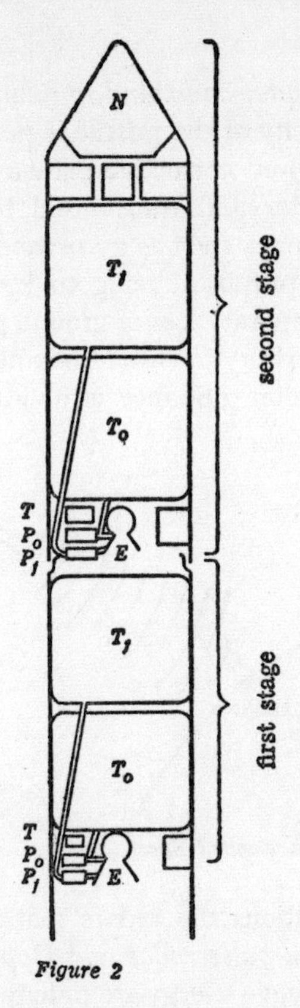

Figure 2

of the effort of planning the guidance in a ballistic missile program goes into investigations of the details of the powered and ballistic trajectories, the establishment of criteria to ensure that the missile will proceed from the thrust-cutoff point to the target, the design of a system for measuring position and velocity with sufficient precision, and the development of satisfactory computers for generating precise corrective maneuvers.

A choice of trajectory must be made that will ease the problems of propulsion and guidance as much as possible. If the ballistic trajectory is sufficiently understood and if measurements and corrective maneuvers can be made with sufficient precision during the powered flight, the missile will hit its target.

Radio-Inertial Guidance

In *radio-inertial,* or *radar-command, guidance* the measurement of the position and velocity of the missile is performed by one or more ground-based radars, and corrective maneuvers are computed by a ground-based computer and transmitted to the missile as "commands." Inertial elements, such as gyroscopes, may also be included in the missile, their purposes being to keep it approximately on course during any temporary loss of ground guidance and to prevent impact on friendly territory in case of complete loss of ground guidance. However precision guidance is obtained primarily from the ground.

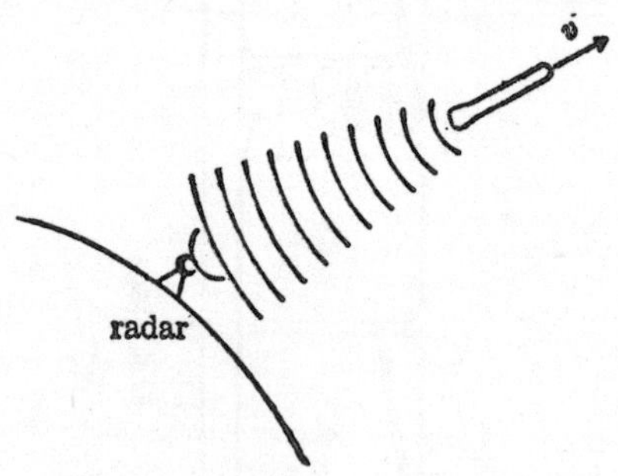

Fig. 3. Doppler Effect

As in other applications the radars that may be considered are primarily of two types, *pulse radar* and *Doppler radar.* In the pulse radar, pulses of microwave energy are radiated from a ground station, and the time lapses for return of signals from the missile are measured. This measurement provides direct determinations of the slant range, or line-of-sight distance, to the missile at any instant, within limitations imposed by the precision of practical time measurement and the precision with which the velocity of microwaves along the beam is known. The instantaneous velocity of the missile can then be computed in terms of the time-rate of change of slant range. In the Doppler radar, use is made of the fact that the return signal is shifted in carrier frequency by an amount proportional to the velocity with which the missile is moving away from the radar (Fig. 3). Thus measurement of this shift gives the velocity directly, within limitations similar to those for the pulse radar. Instantaneous slant range can be computed from the velocities or by counting the beats between the transmitted and returned signals. Either type of radar can also be designed to measure angles as well as range. Thus complete information on the instantaneous position of the missile may be obtained with one radar or by triangulation with three or more radars.

Refraction of microwaves in clouds. When a tracking radar is used for guidance of an ICBM or IRBM, or for evaluation of the guidance system, an error in apparent direction of the missile can be produced by refraction of the microwaves in clouds (Fig. 4). This problem is under experimental and theoretical investigation. In one of the most promising and convenient types of experiment, a radar and a microwave reflector are used to send beams out and back between stations in a valley and on a mountain in a region where intervening clouds are frequent. The variations in the apparent direction of the reflected beam as the clouds drift by can be studied and described in statistical terms.

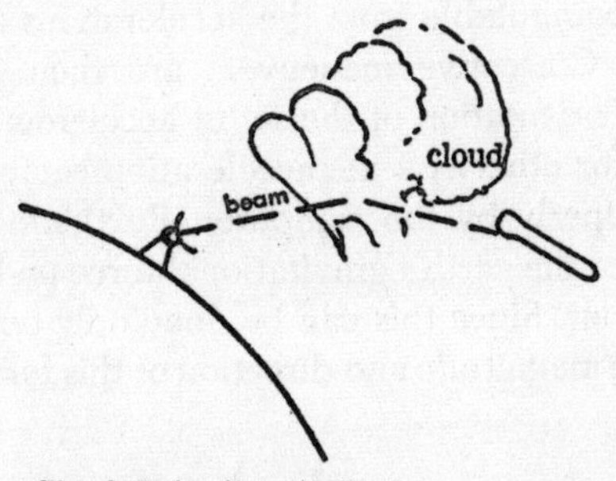

Fig. 4. Refraction in Clouds

Flame attenuation. At high altitudes the exhaust flame from the rocket engines spreads to a large angle. When radio communication

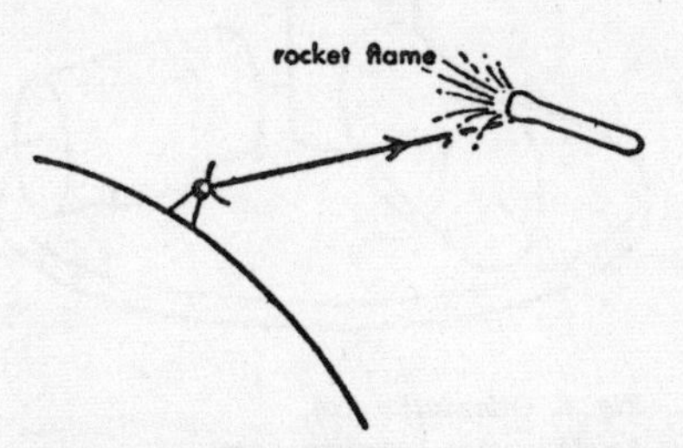

Fig. 5. Flame Attenuation.

between the missile and the ground is necessary, the transmission path may be through the flame, and the ionization of the gases in the flame may attenuate signals to such an extent that reception will be difficult (Fig. 5). This problem is under theoretical and experimental investigation.

Inertial Guidance

An *inertial guidance system* is a special sort of dead-reckoning system that, unlike radio guidance, operates independently of information received from outside the missile. Its computer and sensing instruments—a set of mutually perpendicular accelerometers mounted on a gyro-stabilized platform—furnish signals to the control system. These signals are based on data preset into the guidance system.

The set of accelerometers is used to measure the components of the vehicle acceleration along three mutually perpendicular axes (Fig. 6). Velocities are computable from the accelerations and positions from the velocities. Corrective maneuvers are then calculated by the computer. The orientation of the set of accelerometers must be precisely known, for otherwise the acceleration components will not be interpreted properly by the computer. Furthermore it is necessary that the effect of the earth's gravitational force on the accelerometers be subtracted out. Since this can be done only on the basis of prior estimates of the magnitude and direction of this force, the platform on

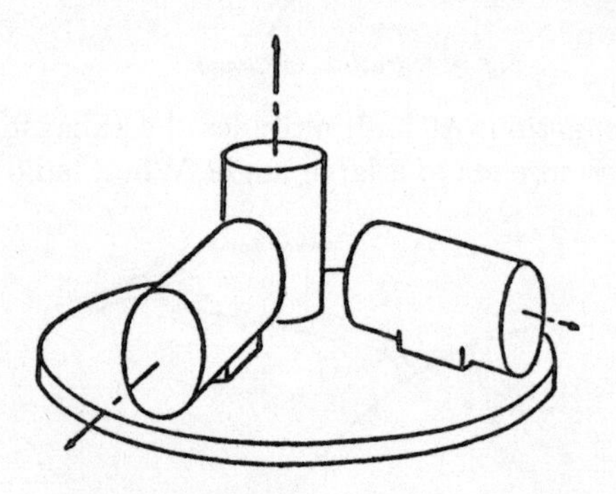

Fig. 6. Orientations of Accelerometer Sensitive Axes

which the accelerometers are mounted must be stabilized with respect to a known frame of reference by a set of precision gyroscopes and suitable servomechanisms. The reference frames that may be used range from those fixed in inertial space (*see below* "Theory of ballistic trajectories") to those fixed relative to the earth, but each possible reference frame imposes different requirements on the system components.

Inertial guidance has the obviously great advantage that interference with the operation of the sensing instruments cannot be accomplished by any means short of destruction by another missile.

Accelerometers

There are many accelerometer designs, but all reduce basically to an object of known mass that is subject to some precisely known restraint provided, for example, by a spring or a damper (Fig. 7). In response

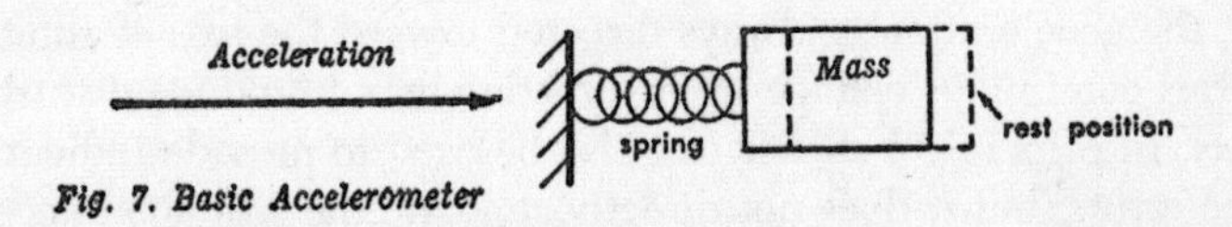

Fig. 7. Basic Accelerometer

to an acceleration in the direction of the sensitive axis, the object is displaced with respect to the case of the instrument. This relative displacement is proportional either to the acceleration or to the velocity of the missile, depending on the type of restraint.

One example of the velocity measuring type is the *gyroscopic-integrating accelerometer* (Fig. 8). This consists of a single-axis in-

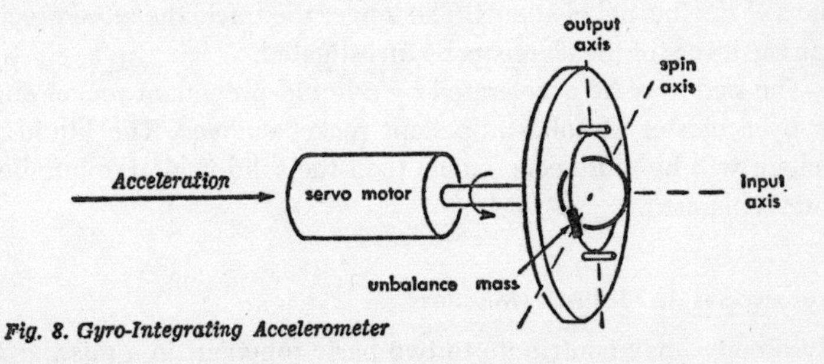

Fig. 8. Gyro-Integrating Accelerometer

tegrating gyroscope with an unbalance mass on the gimbal and rotatable by a suitable servomechanism. An acceleration along the input axis produces a torque about the output axis. In response to this torque the servomechanism rotates the assembly about the input axis so as to generate a torque of equal magnitude and opposite direction, thus preventing any deflection of the gimbal about the output axis. The angle of rotation about the input axis produced by the servomechanism is a measure of the instantaneous velocity. The restraint in this design is provided by the gyroscopic action, the output axis damping, and the servomechanism.

Sled Testing

Sled testing is desirable in the inertial guidance development program because of the difficulties encountered in trying to make laboratory measurements of the errors of accelerometers and gyroscopes under sustained accelerations. In a centrifuge, which may be used for such tests, the acceleration is always directed toward the axis of rotation, and this continuous change in its direction may introduce disturbing effects. In principle a shaker can also be used to provide indications of the errors, but it does not directly simulate the sustained accelerations that occur during powered flight.

The sled, which rides on two rails, is accelerated to a high velocity by rocket engines and then is slowed to a sliding stop by a water brake that picks up water from a channel between the rails; this deceleration can be controlled by presetting the water levels for various stations along the track. The successive positions and velocities of the sled are measured precisely during each run and compared with indications of the inertial elements. The longer the track, the more precisely can the errors of the elements be investigated.

The sled may be accelerated by a liquid-propellant rocket engine or by a cluster of solid-propellant rocket engines. The liquid propellant will be more economical than the solid if a large number of tests is planned.

Gyroscopes in Ballistic Missiles

Gyroscopes may contribute to two basic functions in a missile: control and inertial guidance. The selection of gyroscopes for either of these purposes must take account of the differences in operational characteristics of the various available designs.

A gyroscope consists basically of a wheel, or *rotor*, having a massive rim and capable of rapid rotation about its axis, called the *spin axis*. If the rotor is supported on a pair of *gimbals*, so that it is also free to rotate about the two axes perpendicular to the spin axis, the instrument is called a *two-axis displacement gyroscope* (Fig. 9). In this

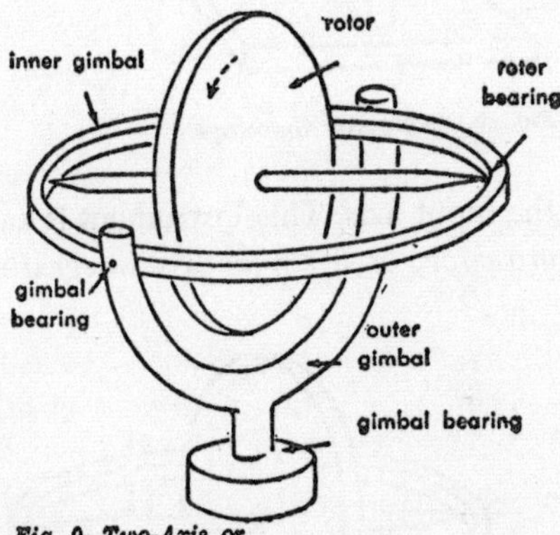

Fig. 9. Two-Axis or Two-Degree-of-Freedom Gyroscope

configuration the spin axis tends to maintain its original orientation, regardless of any maneuvers of the missile. Position indicators, such as potentiometers, can be attached to the gimbals to measure the gimbal angles and therefore the missile orientation with respect to the preselected, fixed direction of the spin axis.

In other designs there is only one gimbal. The axis of rotation is called the *output axis*. The supports for its bearings are rigidly attached to the missile airframe (Fig. 10). Thus the spin axis is constrained to follow the airframe when the latter rotates about a third axis called the *input axis*. This motion about the input axis is measured by applying to the deflecting gimbal a precisely known restraint provided by a damper or a spring. If a damper, such as a viscous liquid, is used as the rotational restraint, the deflection about the output axis provides a measure of the angular displacement of the

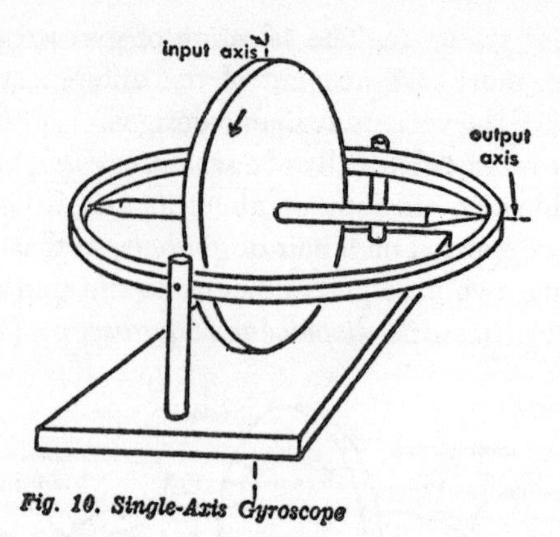

Fig. 10. Single-Axis Gyroscope

airframe about the input axis. This instrument is called a *single-axis displacement gyroscope,* or a *single-axis integrating gyroscope.* In

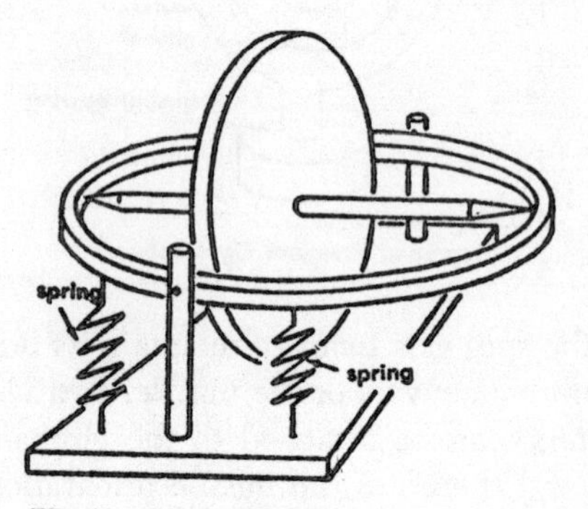

Fig. 11. Rate Gyroscope

event that a spring provides the major restraint, as in Fig. 11, the instrument measures the rate of rotation of the airframe about the input axis and is known as a *single-axis rate gyroscope,* or simply a *rate gyroscope.*

Control of a missile requires measurement of either the missile attitude or the rate of change of attitude, and the application of corrective torques. To achieve satisfactory attitude control, it is essential that the correcting torque for reducing unwanted oscillation in attitude after a gust be applied when the vehicle is actually in rotation rather than when the next extreme attitude error occurs. Thus the gyroscopes must be capable of rapid response and should provide some anticipation of any change in attitude that is occurring. Rate gyroscopes find good application here. If greater precision over a longer period is desired, integrating gyroscopes may be used to supplement rate gyroscopes or, with modification of the output signal, in place of them.

For inertial guidance of a missile the displacement gyroscopes may find application. Rapid measurement or anticipation is not necessary. But because the stabilized platform of the guidance system must be kept precisely fixed with respect to an inertial guidance frame of reference for a considerable time, the gyroscopes mounted on the platform must be extremely precise and capable of minimum drift over a long period of time.

Errors in gyroscopes. Because of the extreme precision required in gyroscopes for some of the ballistic missile applications, the possible errors of these instruments are of extreme importance. One of the first necessities is that the materials used in the gyroscope must be stable. Likewise any wear that occurs in bearings or rubbing surfaces must be such as not to introduce any play or significant mass unbalance.

The gimbal assemblies must be sufficiently stiff, free from excessive inertia, and precisely balanced about the gimbal axes so that no appreciable torque will be produced on them by gravitational, inertial, or frictional forces. The device for picking off signals must not exert significant torque on any gimbal and must be insensitive to stray fields in the vicinity. The motor used to position the gimbal must not exert any significant spurious torque.

The rotor must be precisely balanced so that its vibration is reduced to a minimum and so that no appreciable drift will result from externally applied vibration that is approximately in synchronism with the rotor.

The gyroscope must be designed for negligible wobbulation and nutation drifts, or else it must be isolated so that these drifts will not occur. Wobbulation drift occurs in a single-axis gyroscope when it is wobbled or vibrated so that its input axis describes a conical surface; this drift, which occurs basically because nonplanar angles do not add vectorially, can be influenced only to small extent by the design of the gyroscope. A wobbling two-axis gyroscope will not drift so long as the spin axis does not tend to follow the motion. However, this may initiate a similar motion of the spin axis, called *nutation,* that persists even after the original excitation ceases. Drift will then result except when the spin axis is precisely perpendicular to the gimbal axes.

Applications of Computers

The computers of interest in the ballistic missile programs are primarily electrical and are of two types, *analog* and *digital.* The *analog computer* receives its information in the form of voltages that are proportional to corresponding variables of interest, such as the angles expressing the missile attitude, and the forces or torques exerted by the atmosphere. These voltages are applied to a network of electrical elements that are analogous to the mechanical or other elements of the problem at hand or that perform mathematical operations that are analogous to the operations performed by these elements. The output signals of the computer provide the solutions to the problem. The *digital computer* receives its information in the form of counts that are related to the corresponding variables of interest and are made, for example, by analog-digital converters. The digital computer carries out arithmetic operations on these counts or numbers, except that it ordinarily uses a binary rather than a decimal system of numbers to simplify the requirements on its arithmetic circuits. The analog computer ordinarily finds its application where rapid approximate computations are required. The digital computer ordinarily is used where more precise computations must be made.

Computers find application in the systems engineering of the missile as well as in actual guidance. The analog computer finds more application in the study and planning of the control system, and the digital computer finds more in the study of the guidance systems, but there is no sharp dividing line. For extreme realism actual mechanical elements of the control system, such as servo valves or gyroscopes, may be substituted for portions of the computer. Computers may also be used in the study of the effects of various phenomena on the trajectory.

In the guidance of the missile the raw data yielded by its measuring devices are not necessarily expressed with reference to a convenient coordinate system, and so it may be advisable to have the computer perform a coordinate transformation. In addition, the computer must either compute the impact point of the missile or compare the data on the actual trajectory with that for a standard trajectory and decide on corrective maneuvers.

Accessory Power Supply

The accessory power supply (APS) of a modern ballistic missile is a system that furnishes electric, hydraulic, and pneumatic power to other systems of the vehicle on which it is installed. Specifically, on a long-range ballistic missile, the accessory power supply furnishes electric power to the guidance and the control systems during powered flight and, in some cases, during prelaunching and conceivably also after thrust cutoff. It may also furnish hydraulic and pneumatic power to these and other systems of the missile. Fig. 12 is a simplified diagram of a typical APS assembly.

The great need for minimizing weight in a long-range ballistic missile indicates the use of a lightweight gas turbine to supply the missile accessory power requirements. The APS would then consist of a hot-gas generator, a turbine with necessary gearing, alternating current and direct current generators, and any required hydraulic and

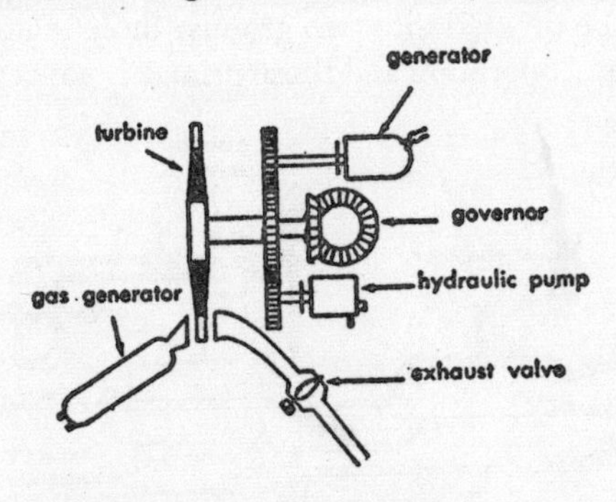

Fig. 12. Accessory Power Supply

pneumatic pumps. This power unit is installed in the final stage in the case of a multistaged vehicle.

In a multistaged missile it would not be practical to use power from the power plants of the various stages to drive the APS generators and pumps because this would require duplication of the generating equipment on each stage, thus increasing the weight. Furthermore such an arrangement would furnish accessory power only while the engines are operating. A separate APS, on the other hand, can be designed to furnish accessory power for any desired period. Separate liquid or solid propellant for the gas generator might be included in the APS. More commonly, however, the APS would draw propellant from the main tanks.

The well-known battery-inverter type of power supply could be used to supplement the gas-turbine type and conceivably might be developed sufficiently to replace it. Although improvements in batteries will make them more competitive with gas turbines as a primary power source, the choice between the two types still depends largely upon the amount of power to be generated and the duration of the operating cycle.

Problems Associated with Engine Development

The development of liquid-propellant rocket engines for long-range ballistic missiles poses both new problems and problems similar to those encountered on other programs, but now on a larger scale. These problems may be divided into two groups: those related primarily to engine design and operation and those primarily concerned with other

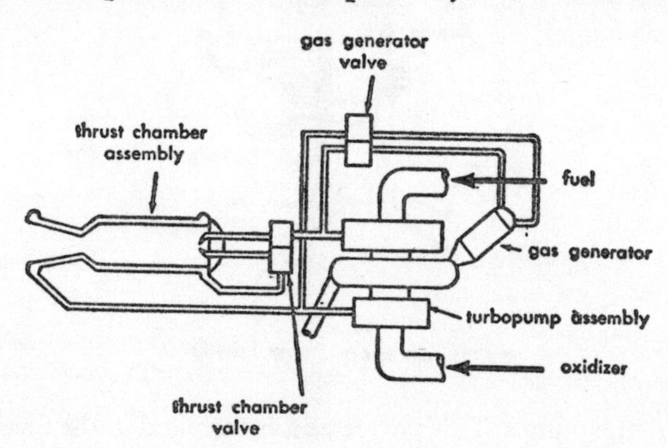

Fig. 13. Components of Liquid-Propellant Rocket Engine

systems on the vehicle. Fig. 13 shows the main components of a typical liquid-propellant rocket engine.

Among the first of the important engine design and operational problems to be solved is the selection of the proper propellant combination for the particular application. This problem is discussed in the following section, but is mentioned here because the characteristics of the propellants are factors in determining engine design, just as in the case of other reaction power plants. After selection of oxidizer and fuel, major design and developmental problems likely to be encountered are conditions of power-plant operation, for example chamber pressure, nozzle area ratio, and type of injection; cooling system for the thrust chambers and gas generators; provision of the necessary degree of thrust control, including shutdown operation; starting of the complete power plant, for example thrust buildup sequence after ignition, simultaneous starting of several chambers, and altitude-start; elimination or minimization of combustion instability; and mechanical design of major components such as the turbopump assembly.

Thrust control is required in a large rocket-propelled ballistic missile so that the thrust may be kept within specified limits during the powered flight and also terminated to achieve the precise thrust-cutoff velocity required to strike the desired target. Reduction of combustion instability presents a problem to the engine designer because such instability gives rise to severe vibrations, over a wide frequency spectrum, that can damage not only the engine but also the airframe and other components, resulting in malfunctions and failures of equipment. Lastly, in multistage missiles, special engine ignition problems result from the low ambient pressures and temperatures existing at the extreme altitudes where stagings occur.

In the second group are those problems of rocket engine development concerned with the entire power plant, with thrust steering, and with operational difficulties introduced by the use of more than one engine in a single stage. The problems of engine installation and steering are intimately related, for if the vehicle is to be steered by swiveling the thrust chambers, the method of mounting the engines will be quite different from that used when the steering is accomplished by other means such as movable vanes in the jet exhaust. The third item, operational difficulties, refers to such matters as the need for attaining full take-off thrust before the missile is launched and the proper apportionment of propellant flow to all the engines of each stage.

The advent of the ICBM class of weapon systems has given rise to several new design concepts, attended by their special problems. The major concepts are (i) the geared turbopump assembly (Fig. 14),

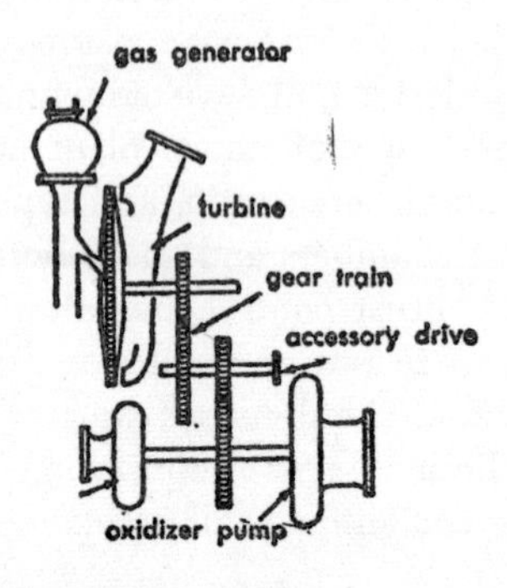

Fig. 14. Geared Turbopump

which introduced problems concerning gear-train design and a separate lubrication system; (ii) thrust-chamber nozzles with divergent sections of unusual length (Fig. 15) and unique configuration, causing a fabrication problem of considerable magnitude; (iii) propellant-control systems that ensure safe thrust-buildup, an electronics design problem; and (iv) multiengine power plants (Fig. 16). The geared turbopump is more efficient than the older single-shaft design and,

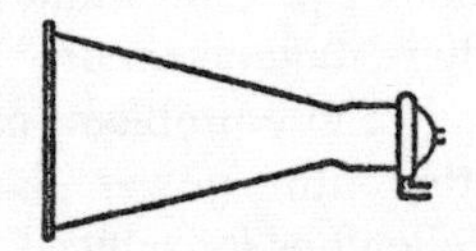

Fig. 15. High-Ratio Nozzle

in addition, provides extra drive shafts for accessories such as a small hydraulic pump. The need for rocket power plants of very large capacity, to operate at extreme altitudes, is the basis for design concepts (ii), (iii), and (iv). Bringing several complete rocket power plants together to obtain the required total thrust adversely affects reliability, missile control, costs, and reduction of aerodynamic drag.

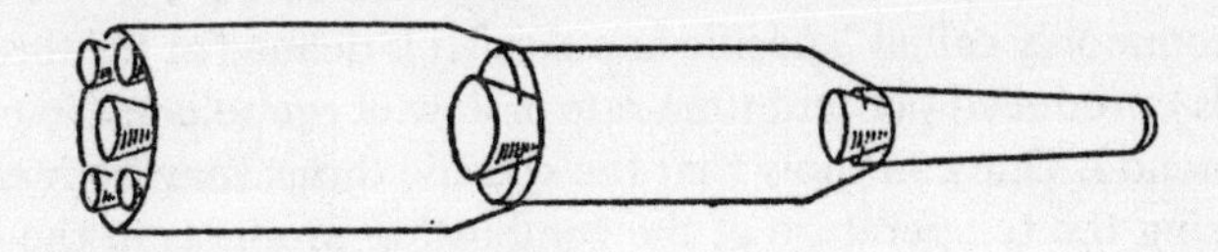

Fig. 16. Multiengine Power Plant

This listing of engine developmental problems is representative rather than complete; there are many other problems, both major and minor. However, progress in this relatively new propulsion field is rapid, and there are reasons to think that satisfactory solutions to the various problems involved will be forthcoming.

Selection of Liquid Propellants

In the choice of the propellant for a particular application, account must be taken not only of the properties of the propellant components, but also of the purpose of the vehicle to be propelled and the requirements on its power plant. For ballistic missiles, bipropellants—liquid *oxidizer* and liquid *fuel*—appear to be acceptable. Of the many available liquid combinations, however, only a few turn out to be satisfactory, and none is ideal in all respects.

Each propellant combination has its unique characteristics. These include performance characteristics, the physical properties of the component liquids and their end products, and such considerations as safety and ease of handling and storage, availability, and cost. Of primary importance are the performance characteristics; if they are inadequate, the propellant cannot be used, no matter how desirable its other characteristics may be. Furthermore the characteristics that do not directly affect performance can often be compensated for or modified. For instance if a liquid component has a high freezing temperature, thus complicating its use in low-temperature regions, it may be possible to add some substance that will lower the freezing point and yet not introduce unwanted side effects. Again, the corrosive action of a highly active propellant component may be rendered negligible by resorting to tanks and pipelines made of special materials.

One performance characteristic of major interest is *specific thrust*, more commonly called "specific impulse." It is defined as the thrust (in pounds) produced per unit time-rate of flow of propellant (in pounds per second). One can show that the specific thrust may be increased by raising the temperature of the combustion products in the chamber, by reducing the weighted average of their molecular weights, and, to a slight extent, by reducing the ratio of their specific heats at constant pressure and at constant volume. A high gas temperature can be obtained by using a propellant mixture that yields a large quantity of heat per pound of mixture. The average molecular weight of the combustion products is determined both by the nature of the oxidizer and the fuel and by the ratio in which they are mixed.

The specific thrust will also be lowered if the combustion gases dissociate into simpler molecules and atoms, because the dissociation requires energy and thus reduces the amount available for conversion into the translational kinetic energy of the exhaust stream. Where tests indicate that effects of dissociation are appreciable, a change can be made either to a propellant having more stable reaction products or to a lower gas temperature.

In addition to these basic requirements the densities of the propellants should be high, for the tank structure can then be made smaller and lighter and the liquids will also be easier to pump. Other desirable propellant properties include rapid and reliable ignition of the mixture, high rate of reaction, low vapor pressure, and low freezing point. Among the properties creating possible hazards are chemical instability, corrosivity, flammability, and toxicity. In view of these many restrictions, one can see why the search for suitable liquid combinations is a major problem of rocket research.

Significant advances with high-energy propellants may be forthcoming if solutions can be found for the engineering problems of adapting such propellants to rocket applications and of producing them on a commercial basis, at acceptable prices. For ICBM propulsion significant increases in performance and energy would result if reliable and practical rocket power plants could be developed for even the commonly known high-energy propellants, such as liquid fluorine and liquid hydrogen.

To reduce the rate of transfer of heat through the combustion-chamber walls, which is an acute problem in rocket engine design, several different methods have been devised and are in use. One scheme, still under investigation, is to employ an oxidizer-fuel combination that will deposit on the inner chamber wall an inert coating capable of providing good thermal insulation and also of withstanding the scouring action of the hot gas flow. The graph in Fig. 17 illus-

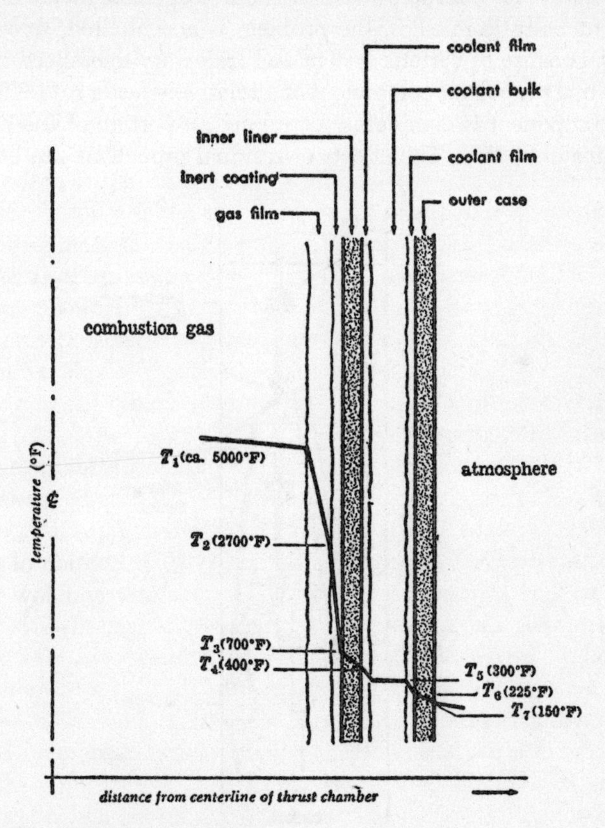

Fig. 17. Temperature Gradients

trates the temperature gradients to be expected in a regeneratively cooled thrust chamber provided with such an inert coating.

Propellant Utilization

Propellant utilization is a problem that becomes important when a missile is being fired for maximum range. The problem is (i) to ensure that the maximum amount of propellant available to the rocket engines is consumed by them and (ii) to design the propellant feed system so that a minimum amount of propellant is trapped and hence unavailable for consumption. For the bipropellant rocket engines of current ballistic missiles, the problem is accentuated, since the engines, because of various system and trajectory tolerances, may consume one propellant component at a relatively faster rate. Thus when this component is completely consumed, a portion of the other one remains unburned. The effects of residual propellant can be drastic.

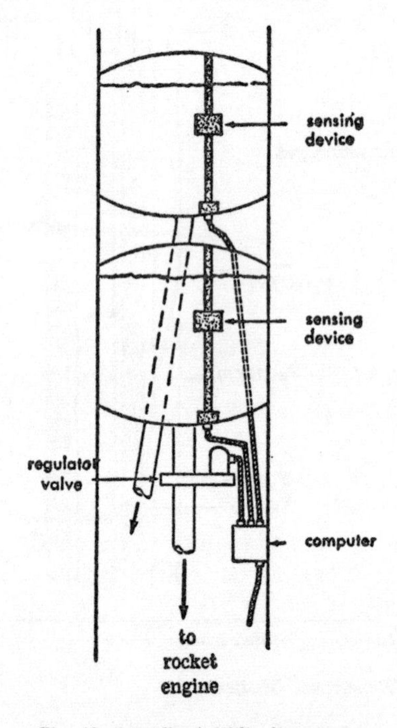

Fig. 18. Propellant Utilization System

For instance, a rough calculation shows that if one percent of the initial propellant weight remains unconsumed in a vehicle designed to have a thrust-cutoff speed of 25,000 ft/sec, the range will be reduced by about 600 nautical miles. Moreover to maintain this cutoff speed of 25,000 ft/sec when one percent is unconsumed, the weight of propellant needed initially would be almost doubled.

Figure 18 shows the main elements of a propellant utilization system. The most difficult problem is how to determine the amounts of oxidizer and fuel in the tanks at successive times during powered flight. When the vehicle is disturbed, as by a gust or by the control system, the resulting accelerations produce in the propellant liquids sloshing that may be appreciable even when the tanks are equipped with baffles or some other damping device. Thus the determination of propellant levels by conventional means is difficult, if not impossible. Measurements depending upon dielectric properties of the tank contents appear to be impracticable because of the severity of the liquid motions. However there are sensing methods that offer promise, and these are receiving extensive study and tests.

Vortices may form in a liquid that is flowing from a tank, and this can result in premature cutoff of the thrust. Thus studies must also be made to gain a better understanding of vortex formation and how it may be controlled.

The Airframe

The design of any airframe involves a continual struggle and compromise in satisfying requirements of both weight and strength. For a long-range ballistic missile, which must be power-accelerated all the way to thrust cutoff, excess weight is a critical problem, for it results in a drastic reduction of maximum range. Yet the airframe at the same time must have sufficient strength and rigidity to support the other components and the propellants without failing under normal static and flight loads. Included in these loads are the stresses caused by vibrations of the engines, propellant sloshing, maneuvers, and aerodynamic heating. The lift developed by the large missile body during a programed turn is an especially interesting problem.

A significant reduction in the mass that must be accelerated through the entire distance to thrust cutoff and also in the propellant weight at take-off is obtained by using a *multistage design,* in which one or more engine sections, with or without associated propellant tanks, are jettisoned during the powered flight. Advanced design techniques also permit reduction in airframe weight.

The development of new materials may offer opportunities for weight reduction. The designer must consider not only the physical properties of the materials, such as strength-to-weight ratio and corrosion resistance, but also such factors as availability and cost of the materials and their adaptability to standard fabrication techniques.

One effect needing thorough investigation is the shift of the center of gravity of the vehicle as the propellant is consumed. This shift relative to the center of pressure is a determining factor in missile stability. In the ICBM and IRBM account must also be taken of the rapid change in the relative positions of the centers of gravity and pressure when a stage with its rocket engines is jettisoned.

Aerodynamics of a Ballistic Missile

The ballistic missile is subject to aerodynamic forces, torques, and related effects during both the initial and the final portions of its flight. For the initial portion—from the launch point to the thrust-cutoff point *B* in Fig. 1—the aerodynamic calculations are conventional. Moreover the choice of aerodynamic characteristics is less critical for a ballistic missile than for other types. On the other hand these characteristics must be precisely known. Unless they are accounted for properly in the design of the control system, the missile may exhibit instability during a portion of the powered flight.

One unconventional aerodynamic investigation associated with multistage engines is concerned with the amounts of "hot drag" and "cold drag," that is, with the drags produced by the open end of the missile body when the rocket engines are firing and when they are inoperative, respectively. Different arrangements of engine clusters and different firing sequences of the exposed thrust chambers yield different values of hot drag. In some cases the low pressure in the engine compartment resulting from the "jet pump action" of the supersonic exhaust streams may create a structural problem.

During repassage through the atmosphere—from *C* to the target in Fig. 1—there are similar problems of stability that have required investigation, and heating effects occur that are not treated in ordinary aerodynamic theory.

The Nose Cone

The *nose cone* will contain, among other things, an atomic warhead and provision for arming and fuzing. On returning to the earth through the atmosphere the nose cone should be decelerated to reduce the possibility of burning up from aerodynamic heating. It must be contoured for the proper deceleration and for minimizing turbulence over its surface.

The rapid heating of the re-entry body on return to the earth through the atmosphere is under theoretical and experimental investigation. Since the conditions involved in the heating are beyond those readily produced in the laboratory, theory for such conditions must be extrapolated beyond any previous experimental confirmations. Some insight into the problem is provided by shock-tube studies. An instrumented model placed within the tube is momentarily subjected to conditions approaching those of re-entry by means of a shock wave propagated along the tube. Further insight is being obtained through flight tests in which models are accelerated by means of simple multistage rockets to conditions approaching those of re-entry.

In these experiments the important parameters are the atmospheric pressure, the mach number, and the Reynolds number. The experiments are planned to yield combinations of these parameters such that the desired information can be predicted from the data.

Encounters with Atmospheric Dust and Interplanetary Particles

Several independent lines of evidence have yielded approximate values for the probability of a collision between an ICBM and a meteoric particle and for the probable value of the meteoric mass encountered. For a single flight there appears to be about an even chance of a collision with a particle of diameter as large as about 0.0001 inch. The mass of particles of all sizes encountered by the surface of the vehicle during a half-hour flight would be roughly 4×10^{-11} lb/ft^2. If the vehicle should encounter a meteor shower, these figures of course would be larger, though still so small that the vehicle's course and range would not be affected appreciably. The damage would be confined to abrasion and pitting of the vehicle's skin. Such damage can also be produced by encounters with atmospheric dust during the initial and final portions of the flight. Pitting of the skin conceivably could result in abnormal heating during passage through the atmosphere, an eventuality that cannot be disregarded. As for the chance of collision with a meteor sufficiently massive to produce a catastrophic effect, this turns out to be so exceedingly small that it can be ignored. Incidentally there are practically no interplanetary particles of diameters less than about 0.0001 inch, for smaller particles are blown out of the solar system by radiation pressure.

The density of meteoric dust near the earth is approximately 3×10^{-19} lb/ft^3. This density has been determined by measurements of zodiacal light; the part due to scattering of sunlight by meteoric dust is found by separating from the measurements all other effects, such as scattering from the top of the atmosphere, scattering by electrons in interplanetary space (about 5000 per cubic inch), and the luminescence of the ionosphere. The density of meteoric dust has also been computed on the basis of the rate of accretion of the dust by the earth, 200 lb/sec. This rate of accretion is determined by three different, independent methods: pitting of recovered rockets and of acoustic devices carried on them; collection of micrometeorites and study of deep-sea nickel deposits; computations involving the determination of the optical density of atmospheric dust and the average diameter of the dust particles. The average diameter is found from time-correlation studies between meteor showers and the deposit of material on collecting plates, and between meteor showers and the size of the earth's shadow on the moon.

The values of the density of meteoric dust yielded by the aforementioned methods are about 10,000 times larger than that determined by reflecting radio waves from meteor paths and extrapolating to include particles which are too small—less than 0.0001 inch diameter—to produce reflection.

Exterior Ballistics of a Missile

The trajectory beyond the thrust-cutoff point B may be divided into two segments: the free-flight portion, from B to the point C of re-entry into the atmosphere; the re-entry portion, from C to the impact point T (*see* Fig.1). For a long-range missile the free-flight portion BC is above the sensible atmosphere; hence the missile during this phase is a freely falling body, the only force acting on it being gravitational attraction. During the re-entry portion *CT* aerodynamic forces also come into play, and these slow the missile and cause it to become heated.

The length and shape of the free-flight trajectory are determined by the speed *V* of the missile at thrust cutoff, the angle γ between the local vertical at *B* and the direction of *V*, the altitude *h* of *B*, and the values of the acceleration due to gravity *g* along the trajectory.

Considering a given point *B* and a given target *T*, one finds that for every thrust-cutoff speed *V* between the lowest and the highest values needed to reach the target, there are two values of the angle γ that yield trajectories connecting *B* and *T*. One of these trajectories is steep, of high apogee; the other is *flat*, of low apogee. As one decreases the thrust-cutoff speed *V*, these two possible trajectories approach each other, the steeper trajectory becoming flatter, and the flatter trajectory more arched. In the limit, when *V* attains the minimum value for which the missile will reach the target, the two trajectories merge into a single one of medium height (Fig. 19). Be-

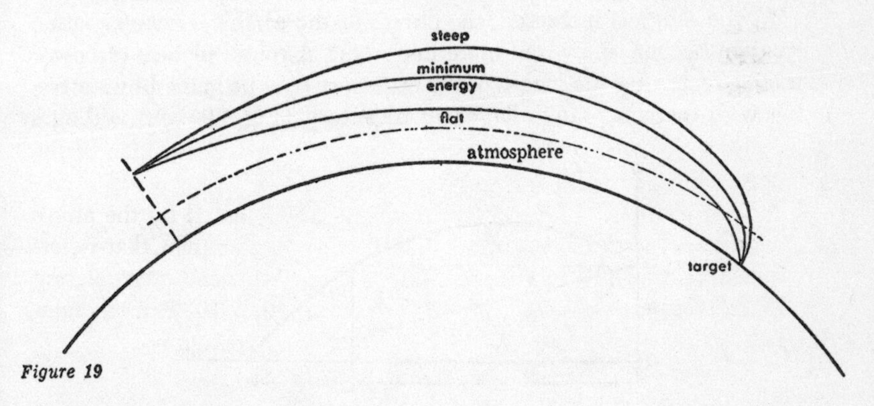

Figure 19

cause this medium trajectory requires the smallest speed *V*, and therefore minimum kinetic energy at thrust cutoff, it is optimum with respect to propellant requirements. It is also more favorable in other respects. For the steeper trajectory the re-entry speed is higher, thus presenting a more formidable heating problem. For the flatter trajectory the re-entry path through the atmosphere is longer. Both very steep and very flat trajectories require a more precise guidance system.

Effects of Earth's Spin and Curvature on Trajectory Length—A Qualitative Approach

A simple picture of a free-flight trajectory may be obtained by considering first the case where the range and time of flight are so small that the missile can be assumed to be traveling over a flat and motionless earth, above which the acceleration due to gravity g is at every point the same in magnitude and always directed normal to the flat surface (Fig. 20). For this *flat-earth* situation the horizontal range from thrust cutoff to impact is given by the expression,

$$\text{Range} = x + \Delta x = \frac{2V^2 \sin \gamma}{g} (\cos \gamma + \sin \gamma \tan \theta), \qquad (1)$$

where Δx is the additional range gained because thrust cutoff occurs at B instead of on the ground at O, and where θ is the angle between the horizontal and the straight line drawn from B to the point of impact.

As the range is increased, the effects of the earth's curvature and rotation become more and more important. A rough picture of how these effects alter the length of the trajectory may be gained by starting with the short-range flat-earth trajectory (Fig. 20) and adding

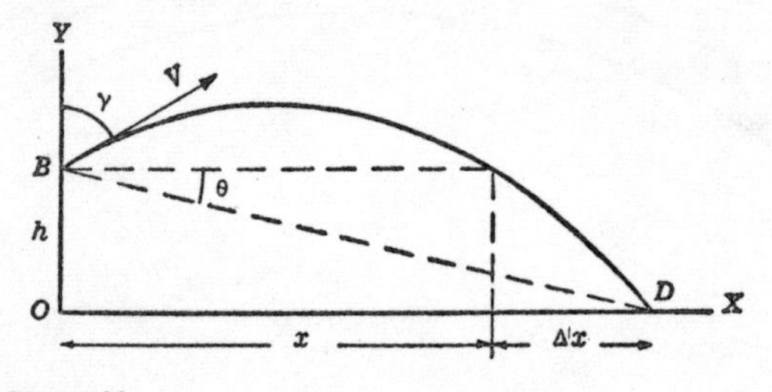

Figure 20

successive corrections to it. Only the simplest situation will be considered: namely, that of a missile moving in the plane of the equator. Moreover, since the interest here is in a qualitative picture, the mathematical expressions for most of the corrections will not be included.

However it is interesting to note that for so short a range as that of a shotput by an athlete at the equator, the range for eastward projection turns out to be about an inch greater than for westward projection, all else being equal. For a long-range missile the difference is proportionally still greater.

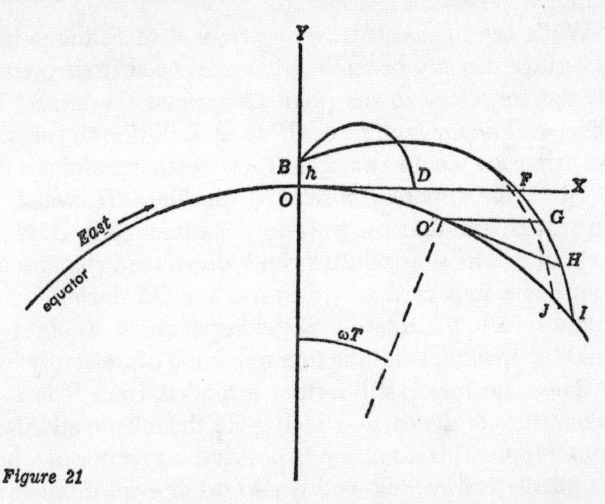

Figure 21

In Fig. 21 we are to imagine ourselves as being out in space, off the earth, at some point south of the earth's equator and looking in a northward direction, parallel to the earth's axis. If we could stop the earth from rotating, a missile leaving the thrust-cutoff point *B* would follow the same path as in Fig. 20, except that *OX* is now to be regarded as the tangent to the equator at *O*. Let us see how this path is changed because the earth actually is rotating and its surface is not flat. In Fig. 21 the coordinate system *XOY* is to be thought of as *fixed in space,* as not participating in the earth's motions. This means that the origin *O* does not move and that the missile leaves *B* at the moment when *B* is vertically above *O*.

(i) The trajectory is extended from *D* to *F* because the horizontal component of the missile's velocity at *B* is increased from the locally imparted value $V \sin \gamma$ to $V \sin \gamma + \omega R$, where ω is the earth's angular speed of rotation and *R* is the earth's radius. The circumferential speed ωR, which the missile has before it is launched and retains during flight, is about 1600 ft/sec eastward; this is a sizable correction even for missiles for which $V \sin \gamma$ might be as much as 20,000 ft/sec. Note that for westbound missiles, this effect of the earth's rotation would reduce the length of the trajectory. For motion along any parallel of latitude λ other than the equator, the correction would of course have the smaller value $\omega R \cos \lambda$ eastward.

(ii) While the missile is traveling from B to F, the point on the earth's surface directly beneath B has advanced from O to O'. This extends the trajectory to the point G because the impact area has been displaced downward, from OF to $O'G$, during the missile flight. Such an extension would also occur for a westbound missile.

(iii) At O' the apparent horizon is the line $O'H$, which cuts the trajectory at H, and thus the trajectory is extended to H. Notice that this particular extension results from a downward rotation or tilting of the apparent impact area with respect to OX during flight. For a westbound missile the rotation of the impact area, as observed from O', would be upward, resulting in a reduction of trajectory length.

(iv) The trajectory is still farther extended, from H to I, because of the curvature of the earth, which gives the missile additional time to acquire range. This extension is positive, no matter in what direction the missile is traveling, and would occur even if the earth were not rotating. The longer the range, the greater will be this extension, because the separation of the spherical surface from the plane OX occurs at an increasing rate as the distance from O increases.

(v) The missile would reach point I only if the gravitational force on it were at every point parallel to the Y-axis. Actually this force is directed toward the center of the earth at every instant of the flight. Consequently a backward component of gravitational force sets in as soon as the missile leaves the thrust-cutoff point B, and its magnitude increases steadily with the time since the missile left B. The net effect is to shorten the trajectory, so that impact occurs at some point J, rather than at I. Actually the backward component of the gravitational force is associated with two different factors. One is the displacement of the missile from the fixed point O as a result of its locally imparted velocity V. This part of the backward component increases with the duration of flight, decreases as the distance of the missile from the center of the earth increases, and would exist even if the earth were not rotating. The other factor is the departure of the missile from O because of its velocity ωR resulting from the earth's rotation. This part of the net backward component is always westward, thus reducing eastward ranges and extending westward ranges.

Although our interest has been mainly to show in a qualitative way how the rotation and curvature of the earth affect the range, it should be said that the method used here can be generalized to cover the case of a missile projected at any latitude and in a trajectory the plane of which is directed in any desired azimuth. For any case, however, the approximations involved in deriving the mathematical expressions for the various independent correction, or *perturbation*, terms are least objectionable for missiles having small velocities at thrust cutoff.

Theory of Ballistic Trajectories

Although the foregoing approach is useful for illustrative purposes, computations of trajectories of great length must of course be based on Newtonian dynamical and gravitational theory. One starts with the assumption that the earth is a homogenous sphere and therefore attracts a missile as if all the earth's mass M were concentrated at its center (Fig. 22). We have then a two-particle problem, that of a

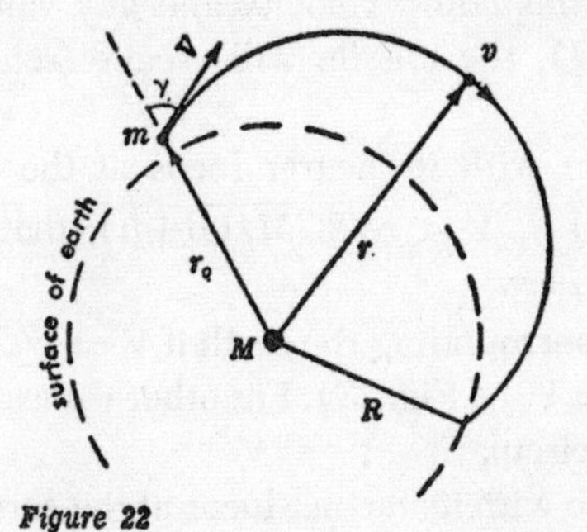

Figure 22

missile of relatively small mass m in free flight under the gravitational attraction of another particle, the earth, of exceedingly large mass M. Notice that the only role played here by the earth's surface is to provide launching and impact areas for the missile.

The trajectories to be used in coordinating the preliminary designs of the major subsystems of any particular type of missile are called *reference trajectories*. For this preliminary phase the trajectories will be sufficiently accurate if computed with respect to a nonrotating spherical earth. Thus the earth in Fig. 22 is to be thought of as motionless in an *inertial frame of reference*—a nonrotating set of coordinates in space that, for all present purposes, may be regarded as having its origin fixed with respect to the center of the sun. Newton's equations of motion then apply in their simplest form, and from them an equation for the various possible free-flight trajectories of a missile may be derived. This equation turns out to be the general equation of a conic section. The character of any particular trajectory as a parabola or an ellipse is found to depend on whether the ratio of the missile's kinetic energy to its potential energy at thrust cutoff is equal to unity or is less than unity. Knowing this, one can then show that the speed V of the missile at cutoff determines the type of path as follows:

(i) A parabola if $V=\sqrt{2GM/(R+h)}$, where G is the Newtonian constant of gravitation, M and R are the mass and the radius of the earth, respectively, and h is the altitude of the thrust-cutoff point. Inserting in this expression the known values of G, M, and R, and letting h be, for example, 100 miles, we find that V is approximately 6.9 mi/sec. For this cutoff velocity and any value of the projection angle γ (Fig. 22), the missile will escape from the earth along a parabolic path.

(ii) An ellipse with its nearer focus at the center of the earth if $\sqrt{GM/(R+h)} < V < \sqrt{2GM/(R+h)}$; that is, if V is between about 5 and 7 mi/sec.

(iii) A circle surrounding the earth if $V = \sqrt{GM / (R+h)}$, about 5 mi/sec, and $\gamma = 90°$ (Fig. 23). For other values of γ the path will be elliptic, but not circular.

(iv) An ellipse with its farther focus at the earth's center (Fig. 24) if $V < \sqrt{GM/(R+h)}$, that is, less than about 5 mi/sec.

It is Case (iv) that is of interest in the ballistic missile program. For this one can show that to obtain maximum range for any given thrust-cutoff speed V, the projection angle γ must exceed 45°. The maximum possible range is half way around the earth, this being obtained when γ is 90° (horizontal projection), regardless of the altitude h of the thrust-cutoff point. However ranges exceeding about four tenths of the way around become increasingly impractical because of the extreme sensitivity of the range to the angle γ and speed V. To get one

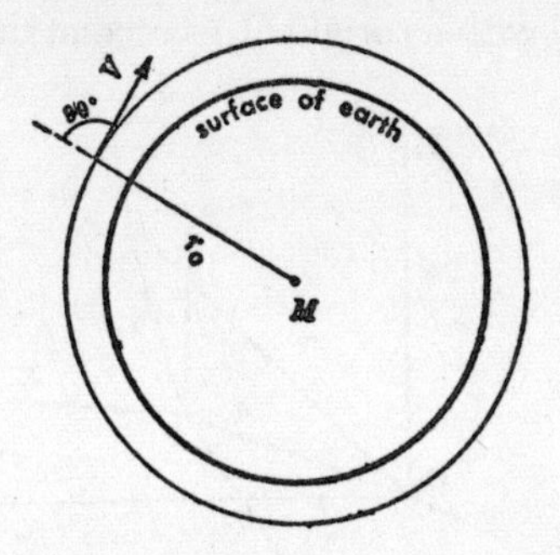

Figure 23

fourth of the way around the earth when h is 100 mi, the optimum values are roughly 70° for γ, 4 mi/sec for V, and 0.5 hr for the flight time.

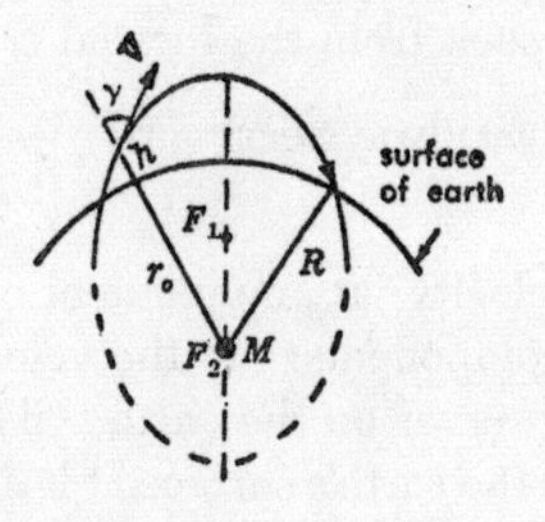

Figure 24

Effect of earth's motions. In computing accurate *flight test trajectories,* account must of course be taken of the effects of the earth's motions. This amounts to finding how velocities and accelerations measured on the earth, a noninertial frame of reference, can be transformed into data suitable for use in the basic Newtonian equations. Here we will be able to clarify some concepts—the Coriolis acceleration, the static vertical, and so on—that were of less importance a decade or so ago when air vehicle speeds were smaller and the accuracies of navigational instruments were just about equal to the magnitudes of some of the effects to be described.

In Fig. 25, let $X_iY_iZ_i$ represent a set of rigid coordinate axes fixed in inertial space and with its origin O_i located at the center of the sun;

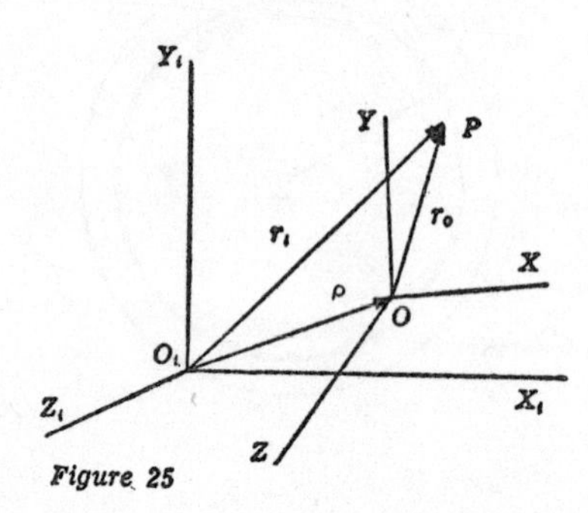

Figure 25

and let XYZ be a similar set of axes rigidly attached to the rotating earth and with its origin O at the earth's center. If V_i is the velocity (speed and direction of motion) of the missile m at any moment during its free flight, as seen from the inertial frame $X_iY_iZ_i$, then

$$V_i = V_{obs} + \omega R \cos\lambda \text{ (always eastward)} + V_{orb} \text{ (along earth's orbit)}. \quad (2)$$

In words, the "true velocity" at any moment can be expressed as the *vector sum* of three components: (i) the velocity V_{obs} of the missile as measured by an observer on the earth; (ii) the velocity $\omega R \cos\lambda$ with which a point on the earth's surface at latitude λ moves eastward in a circle about the earth's axis, where ω is the earth's angular velocity about its axis, and R is the earth's radius; (iii) the orbital velocity V_{orb} of the earth's center O about the sun, of average magnitude about 18 mi/sec and in a direction in space that varies with the time of year.

The expression for the "true acceleration" a_i of the missile relative to the inertial frame $X_iY_iZ_i$ is obtained by differentiating Eq. (2) with respect to the time. The result, omitting unimportant terms, is

$$a_i = a_{obs} + \omega^2 R \cos\lambda + a_{Cor} \quad (3)$$

that is, a_i is the vector sum of three components: (i) the acceleration a_{obs} of the missile as observed from the earth; (ii) the *centripetal ac-*

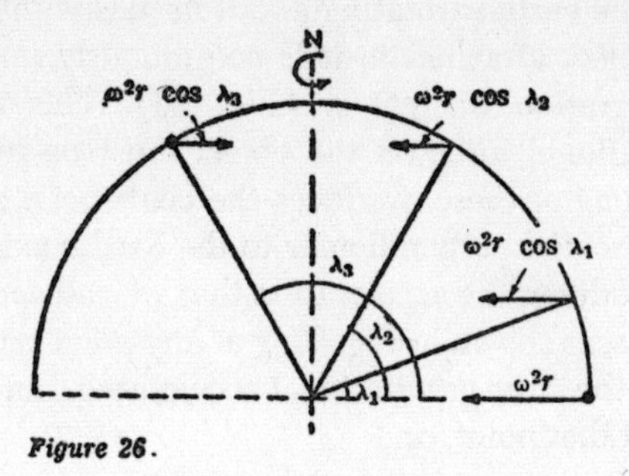

Figure 26.

celeration ω^2R cos λ, which is always directed toward and normal to the earth's axis, is possessed by the missile before launching, and is retained by it during flight (Fig. 26); (iii) the *Coriolis acceleration* a_{Cor}, which will be discussed in a subsequent section. Omitted from Eq. (3) are two additional components of acceleration that are negligibly small: one is the acceleration of the earth's center in its orbit about

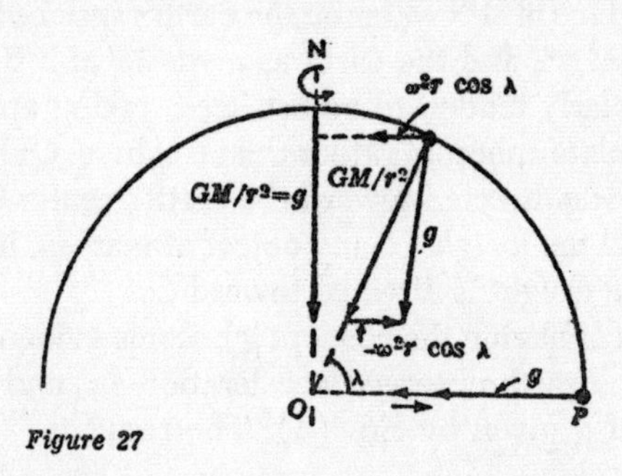

Figure 27

the sun; the other involves the angular acceleration of the earth about its axis.

The Acceleration g and the Static Vertical

If the earth did not rotate on its axis, there would be associated with every point on and above its surface a pure gravitational field of intensity (acceleration) a_i. Its magnitude at any point distant r from the center of the earth would be GM/r^2, from Newton's law of gravitation, and its direction would be toward the center O of the earth.

But actually the earth is rotating about its axis with angular velocity ω, and any object attached to it is continuously undergoing a centripetal acceleration $\omega^2 r \cos \lambda$ (Fig. 26). This means that the earth's gravitational force on the object must be resolved into two components: one of these produces the centripetal acceleration and is therefore directed perpendicular to the earth's axis; the remaining component produces the acceleration that we call *acceleration due to gravity* g. Thus, as shown in Fig. 27, g at any point is the *vector difference* between the "true gravitational acceleration" and the centripetal acceleration at that point, or

$$g = GM/r^2 \text{ (toward earth's center)} - \omega^2 r \cos \lambda \text{ (toward earth's axis)}. \quad (4)$$

This variation of g with r and λ obviously might be a matter of considerable importance for a missile trajectory of great length and height.

The direction of g at any point is called the *static vertical* at that point. The surface of still water on the earth's surface is perpendicular to g, not to GM/r^2; and the earth as a whole, at a time when it was not rigid, similarly tended to adjust itself, taking approximately the shape of an oblate spheroid rather than a sphere. Only at the equator and the poles is g directed toward the earth's center O; and since mg is what we call the *weight* of any object of mass m, it is only at these places that the weight is directed toward O.

Advantages of having the concept g become evident when we solve Eq. (3) for the earth-observed acceleration a_{obs} and then insert into it the value of g given by Eq. (4). The result is

$$a_{obs} = g - a_{Cor}. \quad (5)$$

In words, a_{obs} at any point of a missile's free-flight trajectory is equal simply to the vector difference between g and the Coriolis acceleration at that point; and g at any point can be determined experimentally by means of either a pendulum or a *gravimeter,* the latter being, in principle, an object of constant mass supported by a spring system, the change in elongation of which may be read with precision. Moreover, since Eq. (5) does not explicitly involve the position vector r, the origin O of the reference frame XYZ (Fig. 25) may go *at any point on the earth* rather than only at the earth's center.

The Coriolis Acceleration

The Coriolis acceleration a_{Cor}, which we encountered first in Eq. (3), is of magnitude $2\omega v_{obs} \sin \beta$, where β is the angle between ω, the earth's angular velocity, and v_{obs}, the earth-observed velocity of the missile; and the direction of a_{Cor} is perpendicular to the plane of ω and v_{obs} in the sense of advance of a right-handed screw imagined to be

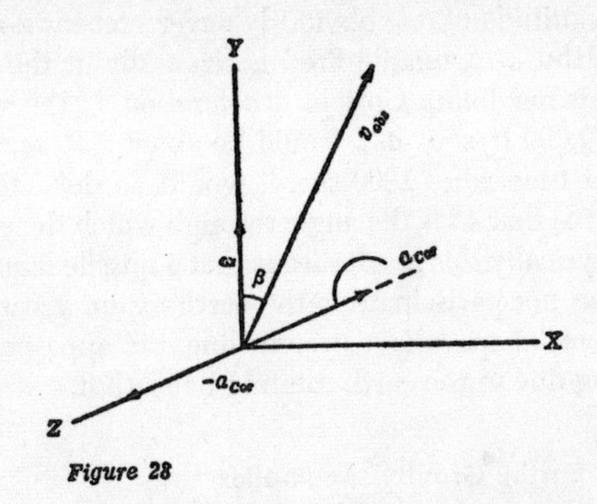

Figure 28

rotated from the first to the second of these vectors through the angle β (Fig. 28). In considering the following examples, remember that the vector ω is always parallel to the earth's axis and points in the direction from South Pole to North Pole.

(*a*) The Coriolis acceleration is zero at any point on a trajectory

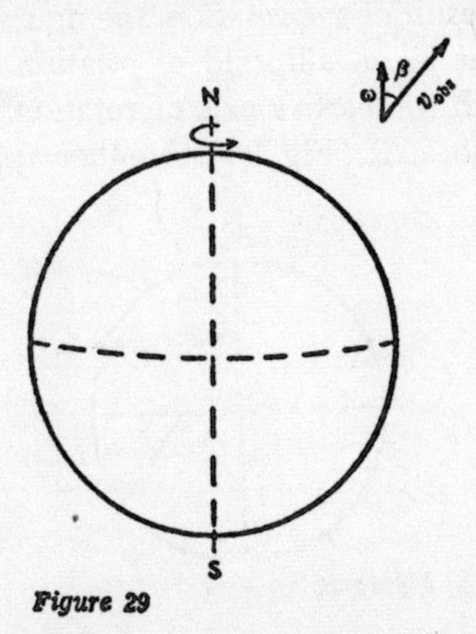

Figure 29

at which the missile's velocity v_{obs} is parallel to the earth's axis, for there $\sin \beta = 0$.

(b) When a missile is launched vertically upward from the earth's surface at any place in the northern hemisphere except the pole, a_{Cor} is eastward, into the page in Fig. 29. Therefore $-a_{Cor}$ in Eq. (5) is westward. Thus the missile, as observed from the earth, is deflected westward from the static vertical.

(c) The magnitude of a_{Cor} obviously never exceeds $2\omega v_{obs} \sin 90°$, or about $0.00015 v_{obs}$. A missile fired horizontally at the North Pole would have this maximum Coriolis acceleration. If the speed of the missile were 20,000 ft/sec, $-a_{Cor}$ would be about 3 ft/sec^2 westward; and if its flight time were 1000 sec, it would be deflected about 4° westward. Notice that 4° is the angle through which the earth rotates in 1000 sec. Physically this result means that a missile launched at the North Pole does not participate in the earth's spin, and therefore its trajectory in inertial space is a straight line, the apparent westward deflection being due to the earth rotating beneath it.

Figure of the Earth; Gravity Anomalies

A significant factor in the final computation of very-long-range missile trajectories and satellite orbits is the actual figure of the earth. By *figure of the earth* is meant the surface obtained by imagining the surface of the smooth sea to be extended through all the land areas of the world. If the earth were not rotating, this surface would be spherical. However, as a result of the rotation, the figure is more nearly an *oblate spheroid,* that is, an ellipsoid of rotation, the minor axis of which coincides with the earth's axis of rotation and is 13.35 miles shorter than the major axis (Fig. 30). Another approximation to the

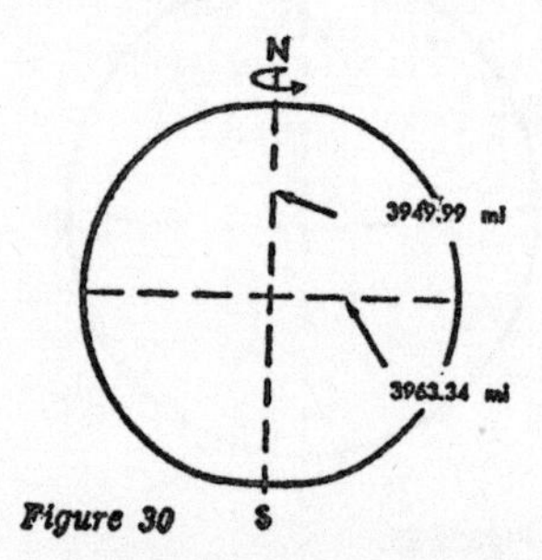

Figure 30

figure of the earth, useful for some measurements, is given by an ellipsoid with three unequal axes. Because any figure more plausible than the oblate spheroid presents computational difficulties, the latter is usually taken as a basis for computation. Its deviation from any more accurate figure has been shown by gravimetric measurements to be very small.

By making the additional assumption that the earth is composed of concentric ellipsoidal strata, each of which is homogenous as regards density, one can derive a theoretical expression for the gravitational force at any point on or above the surface of the oblate spheroid. This expression has long been available for computations of trajectories. Only recently, however, has the theory for elliptical orbits relative to an oblate, rotating earth been worked out. In the case of satellite orbits the theory shows, for example, that the *period*, or time required for one complete revolution, not only has the usual dependence on altitude but increases with the inclination of the orbit to the equator. For near-equatorial orbits the period is less than for orbits of the same altitude about a spherical earth, whereas for polar orbits the period is greater. As for ballistic missile trajectories, the obvious question of importance is the extent to which oblateness affects miss distances.

The assumption that the earth is an oblate spheroid permits the derivation of an improved formula for computing the magnitude of the acceleration due to gravity g at any point of latitude λ and altitude h. This formula of course yields more accurate values of g than those given by Eq. (4), which was derived on the assumption that the earth is spherical. However experimental determinations of g at different stations of the same latitude on the earth's surface generally do not agree with one another or with the theoretical value. These discordances of course arise because the earth is not an exact ellipsoid of revolution, as is assumed in the theoretical formula, and also because of local topographic and geologic conditions—the existence of mountains, valleys, oceans, and abnormally high or low densities of the materials near the gravity stations. Such departures from the expected values are called *gravity anomalies*. Although gravity anomalies are small in magnitude, varying in different localities from about zero to about ± 0.07 percent, they make possible refined determinations of important geodesic quantities: geodesic lines, deflections of the static vertical, and elevations of sea-level points with respect to the surface of the oblate spheroid used as a reference figure.

The Phases of Research, Development, and Production

Any missile program if successful, and in particular a ballistic missile program, involves the three definite but overlapping and blending phases of research, development, and production. There is more blending between research and development than between development and production. Ordinarily there is no abrupt transition between research and development. At the beginning of a program the proportion of research to development is high. Toward the end of the developmental phase, the research may taper off. Research and development are close together organizationally and require frequent and direct interchanges of information.

As in most military contracts, the research carried out is applied research. Its primary motivation is the fact that at the beginning of the program not everything is known that should be known to guarantee success. The scope of the required knowledge is not clear until the objectives and performance of the missile are defined. This usually involves specific advances beyond the state of the art. A secondary motivation derives from the fact that, even in explored areas, the technology on which missiles are dependent is in constant need of improvement. For these reasons a missile program profits by a vigorous and practical research effort at the beginning and a continued research effort to support the developmental phase.

Although it is wise to stay close to the state of the art wherever possible, any new program that promises major advances in military capability inevitably involves some corresponding advances in scientific knowledge and technology. The ICBM and IRBM have requirements of precision guidance that have not previously been reduced to practice in a complete operating system. The altitude attained is greater than that of any other military missile. This not only involves extensions of the current propulsion technology but raises questions about matter that may be encountered on the edge of interplanetary space. Further problems arise because of the wide ranges of temperature and vibration through which the vehicle must be designed to operate satisfactorily and reliably. There is a problem of safe return of the warhead through the atmosphere without overheating. Although a comprehensive discussion of such problems is not possible here, it appears safe to say that nothing has been found to date that would prevent the ultimate success of the USAF ballistic missile program.

If it were feasible for research men to foresee all problems and solve them before missiles were flown and if designers could always design correctly on first attempt, there would be no need for a developmental phase. In practice a missile necessarily must be developed as an extended series of designs, redesigns, tests, and measurements. Developmental hardware differs from research hardware not only in serving to prove out a principle but in being capable of practical use in the missile and adaptable to production with redesign only for changes in tooling or for easier assembly by workers of minimum skill.

The early portions of the research and developmental phases are centered on the attainment of one or more satisfactory designs. Eventually the emphasis shifts toward the demonstration through continued tests and firings that one or more designs are satisfactory. When a design is sufficiently proved out, the production phase begins, but evaluation of the design continues and some further improvements are made.

The production organization must prepare for the eventual full-scale production of the hardware by manufacturing it in gradually increasing quantities while perfecting the product and its method of manufacture. The operation must be relatively flexible at first, to permit necessary engineering changes that were not completed before production began. But the emphasis soon shifts to that of adapting the design as necessary for production tooling, for manufacture in sufficient quantity with plants of feasible size and without excessive demands of skilled labor and for manufacture at a lower cost per item, consistent with the other important requirements on the hardware.

Missile Reliability

The probability of hitting the target is influenced in part by the dispersion of those missiles whose flights have not been influenced by major malfunctions and in part by the number of missiles that fail because of some internal malfunction or some difficulty in the ground equipment. Although a reliability group is normally concerned with the monitoring of aspects of design and manufacture that contribute both to dispersion and to loss, the reliability of the weapon system in strictest sense is related to the second aspect.

The *reliability* is defined as the ratio of the number of successful firings, with only normal dispersion and no major malfunction, to the total number of firings. The ICBM and IRBM are neither the most complicated nor the simplest of missiles under development. The more complex the weapon system, the greater, in general, is the reliability needed in the various portions of the system. Thus reliability is one of the important considerations in the development of any missile. The absence of a human pilot suggests that the reliability which can be tolerated is somewhat smaller than that for an airplane; but to attain this reliability in an unmanned vehicle is more difficult.

A reliability program is largely a matter of monitoring to ensure that the design techniques applied and the component parts utilized are the best that are available, that the environmental conditions of the missile—temperature, altitude, humidity, corrosive air, vibration, and so forth—have been taken sufficiently into account in the design, that extensive testing is carried out to support the development program, that even more testing is incorporated into the manufacturing process than with hardware for other applications, that adequate control of quality of workmanship is maintained, and that a well-balanced record of environmental conditions and performance histories is obtained from the missile flights. It will be noted how heavily dependent the attainment of satisfactory reliability is on testing, both to ensure that the hardware is built as it was designed and as an aid in perfecting the design. However, as the design matures, it is important that the need for further testing be kept to a minimum.

Extensive testing of hardware will be carried out in environmental chambers. Vibration is notably an awkward environment to analyze and design to, but the most advanced techniques currently known for data reduction and for simulation of vibration will be used. Of special importance is an efficient process for gathering data on reliability problems and ensuring that the diagnoses are used to improve the design or the manufacture methods at the earliest date consistent with maintenance of an orderly schedule.

The Approach to Testing

Any missile development is heavily dependent on testing. The schedule and the success of the development are critically influenced by the planning for the tests. Of special importance are the order in which the various tests are carried out, the relative emphasis placed on them, the complexity of any supporting equipment needed for making each test, and the adequacy of the test facilities.

The approach used in the USAF ballistic missile program is one of parallel or overlapping tests with an orderly progression from simple test items to a complete system. Extensive testing of detail parts, subassemblies, and assemblies is being carried out in the laboratory. However, flight testing is scheduled to begin at the earliest possible date because the optimum conditions for the laboratory tests are never known until a number of flights have taken place. Early flights are also necessary to verify that no important aspect of the problem has been overlooked in the initial planning.

The test vehicles begin with the simplest version of the ultimate weapon that can profitably be flown and gradually progress to a complete system, with no radical redesigns along the way. The only vehicles primarily useful for research are a rocket sled for testing of inertial guidance components and some simple vehicles for obtaining fundamental data on the re-entry problem.

To ensure that the tests progress rapidly, special efforts have been made to provide adequate facilities for testing in the laboratory and in flight. Of particular importance are the elaborate facilities and equipment for static firings and flight tests that have been provided at various centers, especially at the Air Force Missile Test Center, Cape Canaveral, Florida.

Flight Monitoring Equipment

As is true of most other missiles, the USAF ballistic missiles are expendable and nonrecoverable. Since the nominal target for a test flight is in the open ocean, precise location of the impact point is possible only with special techniques. Consequently extensive monitoring equipment is necessary to provide sufficient data for each flight to justify the expense and effort of the firing.

The flight monitoring equipment may be divided into two classes:

the missile-borne sensing and radio telemetering equipment, together with the necessary ground-based receivers and recorders; and the ground-based radar and optical tracking devices located along the firing range. The telemetering systems respond to various voltages generated within the missile and transmit a corresponding code to ground receivers. The voltages may be signals of functional importance in themselves or may be generated by transducers as measures of temperatures, engine gimbal angles, vibrations, and so forth. A *transducer* is a device that is actuated by energy from one system—in the present case mechanical or thermal—and that supplies energy in the same or different form to another system—here electrical.

Unless special techniques are used, the information obtained by telemetry about the functioning of the various systems in the missile is only semiquantitative; it provides clues for the diagnosis of malfunctions but does not necessarily permit precise evaluation of performance. The optical tracking devices provide data on missile attitude as well as on position and velocity, but most of them operate only at short range in contrast to the radars. Some of the tracking equipment will have precision comparable to or better than that of the guidance systems, or at least have errors of somewhat different origin, so that a check on the precision of guidance can be made.

As with most missiles, the raw data provided by the telemetry and the tracking devices will not be in the most suitable form for study. Consequently an extensive *data reduction process* is necessary after each flight. This process, which consists of the conversion of the recorded data into meaningful form, such as curves or tables, will be carried on partly at the launch site and partly in contractors' laboratories.

Some Nonmilitary Advances

The effort expended in development of the ICBM will have benefits even when judged by peacetime standards. Significant advances in science and engineering will result.

The advances in science are primarily in those areas that are new or have become newly critical. For the most part they will remain of interest when ballistic missiles are no longer needed for military purposes. The supporting research and the test flights will contribute to geodesic methods and to more accurate geodesic data. Advances in celestial mechanics have been necessary, for instance, in the theory of elliptic trajectories relative to an oblate earth. Also in the general category of physics of the atmosphere and hyperatmosphere are problems associated with ion layers, properties of clouds (such as optical or microwave refraction), flame attenuation of radio signals, and the characteristics of atmospheric and meteoric dust. Extensive investigations have been made in hypersonics—the phenomena associated with motions at speeds large by comparison with the speed of sound—in radio wave propagation through a boundary layer generated by hypersonic flight, and in the properties of materials under extreme conditions of temperature and pressure. Advances have been made in fluid dynamics, especially in connection with vortex formation, and in connection with combustion phenomena and thermodynamics, especially combustion instability, dissociation and reassociation, nucleate boiling, and heat transfer.

Of necessity advances are occurring in engineering areas also, especially in connection with rocket power plants, structures (as in designs to reduce weight and to reduce stresses owing to thermal loads), guidance, control, and design of ground equipment. The development of unmanned vehicles for the purely scientific exploration of extraterrestrial, circumlunar, and interplanetary regions will be aided very materially by the work done in ballistic missile programs. For instance, no longer is it a matter of pure conjecture that eventually we may be able to land instruments on the surface of the moon capable of transmitting physical data back to the earth over a period of many days.

Some progress is being made too on the problems of reliability and operational safety, two areas that are of particular importance in relation to any future attempts at space flight. Reliability is an unwieldy engineering problem when one is dealing with advanced designs. However the efforts made on the ICBM to make it a practical and economical weapon will do much to improve our approaches to the reliability problem in general.

Los Angeles, California

APPENDIX II

Fundamental Equations of Force Survival

COLONEL ROBERT D. BOWERS, USAF

As a democracy dedicated to peace the United States has traditionally held the policy of fighting only in retaliation to blows struck against her by an enemy. So deeply rooted is this policy that we have clung to it even in this age of nuclear weapons and high-performance, globe-girdling delivery vehicles. We have acknowledged the high degree of national peril involved in this free choice by building and maintaining in peacetime large, combat-ready retaliatory forces. Deterrence, and the ability to retaliate effectively if the deterrence fails, are dependent on the ability of our retaliatory force to survive an initial attack and still have the capability to inflict an unacceptable degree of damage on the enemy.

Such a force must of course be developed, built, trained, and its employment planned long before the outbreak of war. Of the many new factors involved in this process one of the most critical is the computing of the portion of the retaliatory force that will survive the enemy's initial attack. All persons engaged in national defense may encounter this problem at one time or another. It is encountered often these days by the military planner. What factors are important in force survival? How do they interrelate? How much emphasis should be put on each?

Definition of Symbols

P_k = probability of destroying any one missile; also the expected fraction of the force that is destroyed.
P_s = probability of survival of any one missile; also the expected fraction of the force that survives.
P_I = probability that the enemy knows the location of U.S. missile(s) or that he knows there are missiles at any particular site.
P_L = probability that a U.S. missile is launched before arrival of enemy weapons.
$1 - P_L$ = probability that a U.S. missile is not launched before arrival of enemy weapons.
P_M = probability that weapon(s) will miss the target, i.e., the weapon(s) will all fall outside the lethal radius.
$1 - P_M$ = probability that weapon(s) will hit and destroy the target.
R = lethal radius (or radius of destruction) of an attacking weapon.
C = circular probable error (CEP) of attacking weapon.
n = number of enemy missiles impacting in each target area.
W = yield of attacking weapons in megatons (MT).
H = site hardness in pounds per square inch (psi) of overpressure.
E = number of enemy weapons assigned to attack the U.S. missile force.
r = over-all reliability of enemy weapons, i.e., the fraction of the enemy missiles that will function adequately so as to impact in the target areas.
a = attrition rate of enemy weapons by U.S. active defense.
N = number of missiles in U.S. force.
k = concentration of U.S. missiles, i.e., number per site.
NP_s = the number of U.S. missiles expected to survive.

Although there are professional operations analysts and study organizations such as RAND to turn to, planners are often faced with the necessity of estimating answers to questions such as these in advance of the completion of rigorous analyses. The equations developed here are the tools for making such estimates, and they can also be used to better understand and define problems preliminary to more detailed analyses.

The term "fundamental" is used to describe these equations because certain simplifying assumptions are made in the derivations. This procedure may not be sophisticated enough to satisfy the strictest mathematicians, but it is adequate to show the general relationships among the various survival factors. These in turn should be accurate enough for broad military planning where many of the parameters—particularly those under control of the enemy—can never be precisely known or controlled by the planner. Because the equations are somewhat bulky, they may appear formidable at first glance to those not normally confronted with mathematics in the exercise of their daily duty. Closer inspection will show that the terms

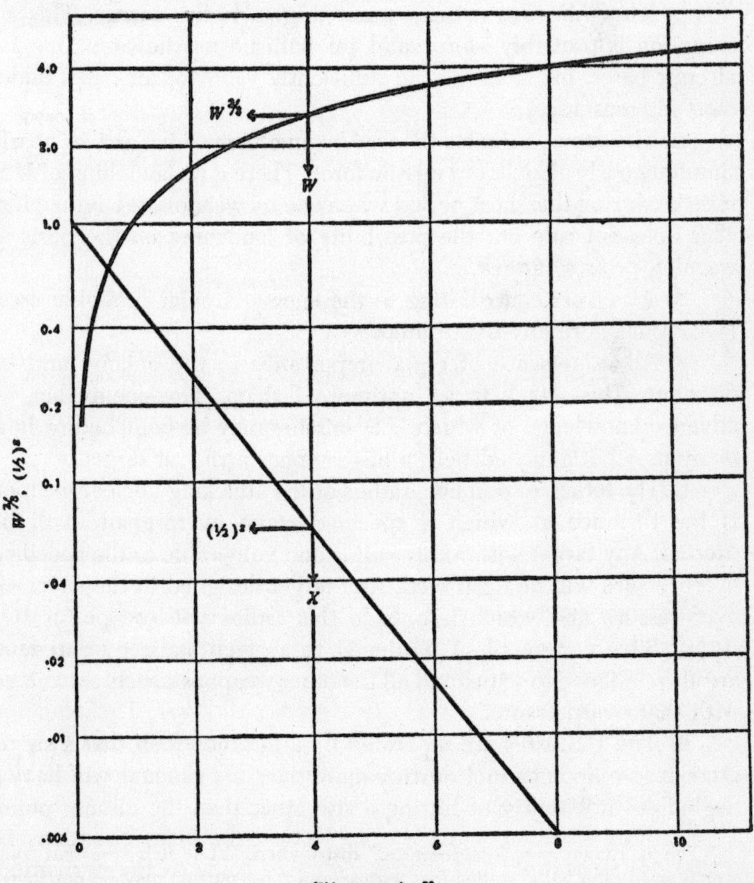

are easy to understand and that the equations can be solved by anyone familiar with slide-rule fundamentals. For those who are not, a graph is included which allows the equations to be solved by long-hand arithmetic.

The assumptions used in developing the equations are:

a. For purposes of terminology it is assumed that the target for enemy attack is the U.S. ballistic missile force. For application to the U.S. aircraft force, simply substitute "aircraft" for "missile" and "base" for "site" in the terminology.

b. The U.S. sites present point targets to the enemy. This assumption is probably more valid for ballistic missile sites than for aircraft bases, but it should be sufficiently valid for air bases under most circumstances.

c. The enemy initiates the war by an attack which arrives nearly simultaneously all over our missile force. There is no launching of U.S. missiles during this short period when enemy weapons are impacting. This does not rule out the possibility of launching on the basis of warning prior to attack.

d. All errors contributing to the enemy circular probable error (CEP) are normally distributed.

e. All targets are of equal importance to the enemy, and he distributes his attack in an optimum fashion. The enemy has no advance knowledge of which U.S. missiles may be launched or how many may be launched before his weapons arrive at target.

f. The lethal, or damage, radius of the attacking nuclear weapon is the distance at which a specified static overpressure will be exerted. Any target within this radius and vulnerable to the specified overpressure will be destroyed. Any target designed to the specified overpressure and which is outside this radius will escape.*

g. Sites (or missiles) hardened to a given static overpressure are also designed to withstand all the other weapons effects associated with that overpressure.

h. The U.S. sites are separated by a distance such that a single attacking weapon cannot destroy more than one site and will have a negligible probability of hitting a site other than the aiming point.

* This is known as a "cookie cutter" distribution. While it is true that some targets inside the lethal radius may escape and some outside may be destroyed, the approximation is adequate for our purposes.

This distance can easily be determined when yield, accuracy, and site hardness are known.

i. The enemy attacking weapon has no alternate target capability after it has been launched.

For a U.S. missile to be destroyed by enemy attack, all of the following conditions must obtain:

- The enemy must know the location of the U.S. missile at the time he launches his attack;
- The missile must not be launched prior to arrival of enemy attack; and
- The enemy weapons must impact within the lethal radius.

The probability that a missile will be destroyed is the product of the probabilities that each of the above conditions will obtain. Stated mathematically the probability that any one missile will be killed or destroyed by enemy attack is:*

$$P_k = P_I(1 - P_L)(1 - P_M) \qquad (1)$$

where P_I is the probability that the enemy knows where the missile is;

$(1 - P_L)$ is the probability that the missile is not launched prior to arrival of the attack; and

$(1 - P_M)$ is the probability that the attacking weapon(s) will destroy the target.

The probability that a missile will survive enemy attack is:

$$P_s = 1 - P_k$$

Substituting this expression into (1):

$$P_s = 1 - P_I(1 - P_L)(1 - P_M) \qquad (2)$$

The probability $(1 - P_M)$ that weapons aimed at a point target will hit it depends upon the lethal radius, accuracy, and number of attacking weapons.

If one enemy weapon impacts in the region of each site $(n = 1)$, the probability of site destruction is:

$$1 - P_M = 1 - (\tfrac{1}{2})^{R^2/C^2}$$

* See accompanying summary of symbol definitions.

When n is greater than 1, $(n > 1)$:*

$$1 - P_M = 1 - (\tfrac{1}{2})^{R^2 n/C^2} \qquad (3)$$

When n is less than 1, $(n < 1)$:

$$1 - P_M = n\left[1 - (\tfrac{1}{2})^{R^2/C^2}\right] \qquad (4)$$

The lethal radius (R) can be expressed in terms of the target hardness (H) and weapon yield (W) as follows:**

$$R = \frac{6W^{1/3}}{H^{1/3}} \qquad (5)$$

where R is nautical miles, W is megatons, and H is pounds per square inch (psi).

An expression for n in terms of the quantities previously defined can be derived as follows: The number of enemy weapons assigned to attack the U.S. missile force is E. The number of assigned enemy weapons successfully launched and functioning properly is Er. The number of assigned enemy weapons launched, functioning properly, surviving air defense action, and reaching the target is $Er(1 - a)$. The number of U.S. missiles is N. If these are concentrated with k missiles per site, then the number of sites (or targets to the enemy) is N/k. Therefore by definition:

$$n = \frac{Er(1 - a)}{N/k} = \frac{Er(1 - a)k}{N} \qquad (6)$$

The probability that any given missile in the U.S. force will survive (which is also the expected fraction of the force surviving) can now be found by substituting equations (3), (5), and (6) into equation (2). The result is:

$$P_s = 1 - P_I(1 - P_L)\left[1 - (\tfrac{1}{2})^{36W^{2/3}Er(1-a)k/C^2HN}\right] \qquad (7)$$

* This is mathematically precise only when n is an integer, but is an adequate approximation for any other value of n greater than 1.

** This expression is for a surface burst and has been derived empirically from the unclassified Department of Defense–Atomic Energy Commission publication "The Effects of Nuclear Weapons," June 1957 (AFP 136–1–3). Somewhat more precise expressions could be derived for limited ranges of hardness. For an airburst and 10 pounds per square inch (psi) or less hardness the expression $10\ W^{1/3} / H^{0.6}$ can be used.

Equation (7) is for the case where at least one attacking weapon reaches each site, i.e., the term $\frac{Er(1-a)k}{N}$ will be equal to or greater than 1.*

For the case where there are more sites than there are enemy weapons reaching the sites, (i.e., the term $\frac{Er(1-a)k}{N}$ is equal to or less than 1), equation (4), instead of (3), should be substituted into equation (2), resulting in the following expression:

$$P_s = 1 - P_I(1 - P_L)\frac{Er(1-a)k}{N}\left[1 - (\tfrac{1}{2})^{36W^{2/3}/C^2H}\right] \qquad (8)$$

All the major factors in force survival are now related in these expressions. By use of the appropriate one of the equations the expected fraction of the U.S. force surviving can be determined for any given set of the parameters. In using the equations the assumptions under which they are derived must be kept in mind and the survival probability modified to account for any change in the assumptions. For example, if the U.S. missiles are launched while enemy weapons are arriving (which is contrary to assumption "c"), the survival probability would tend to be raised because some missiles would be launched before being attacked; but at the same time the survival probability would tend to be lowered since the missiles (if initially in hardened sites) would be exposed and more vulnerable during the period preparatory to launch. These could be offsetting factors, but they would need further examination in any particular case to determine the effects on survival.

The equations are intentionally made general to cover all the major factors in force survival. In particular cases or under particular circumstances they can be considerably simplified. For example, if the force is based at fixed sites rather than mobile,**

* The form of equation (7) will vary with the assumptions as to how the enemy assigns targets to his missiles and the information the enemy has (and uses) about the reliability and survivability of his missiles after the launch operation begins. Equation (7) represents the best the enemy can do without bomb-damage assessment.

** In a mobile system the missiles would be moving from place to place so that the exact location of some fraction of the force is unknown to the enemy at any time. This may be good from a survival standpoint, but it has practical it can be assumed the enemy will know the location. Then the term P_I equals 1. If there is no launching prior to enemy ICBM attack* the term P_L equals 0. Equation (7) then reduces to:

$$P_s = (1/2)^{36W^{2/3}Er(1-a)k/C^2HN} \qquad (9)$$

and equation (8) reduces to:

$$P_s = 1 - \frac{Er(1-a)k}{N}\left[1 - (1/2)^{36W^{2/3}/C^2H}\right] \qquad (10)$$

As an example of the use of the survival equations and the accompanying graph, take the case where the number of assigned enemy weapons is equal to the number of U.S. missiles; the overall reliability of enemy weapons is 80%; there is no combat attrition of enemy weapons; there is no launching of U.S. missiles prior to enemy attack; the U.S. missiles are based at fixed sites hardened to 75 psi and dispersed to 5 missiles per site; the enemy CEP is 3 nautical miles and the yield is 1 megaton (MT).

The parameters then have the following values: $E = N$, $r = .80$, $a = 0$, $P_I = 1$, $P_L = 0$, $k = 5$, $H = 75$, $W = 1$, $C = 3$, $\frac{Er(1-a)k}{N} = 4$.

Since $\frac{Er(1-a)k}{N}$ is greater than 1 (each site is attacked by more than one enemy weapon) and since $P_I = 1$ and $P_L = 0$, equation (9) should be used.

When these figures are substituted, the numerical value of the exponent becomes:

---

logistic, operational, and reliability limitations, plus the fact that the fraction of the force on the move is not available for immediate retaliation.

* Launching missiles prior to manned bomber attack may be feasible, but launching prior to enemy ICBM attack has practical limitations of short warning time and national decision time. These limitations are more thoroughly discussed by Colonel H. W. C. Shelton, "Impact of the Ballistic Missile on Defense," *Air University Quarterly Review*, IX, 3 (Summer 1957), 131 ff. [reprinted on pages ff. above]. It should be pointed out that these limitations do not necessarily apply to launching manned bombers on warning of ICBM attack. The bombers can be called back if the warning turns out to be false.

$$\frac{36W^{2/3}Er(1-a)k}{C^2HN} = \frac{36 \times 1 \times 4}{9 \times 75} = .214$$

and from equation (9):

$$P_s = (\tfrac{1}{2})^{.214}$$

From the accompanying graph, when $x = .214$, then $(\frac{1}{2})^x = 0.86$. Therefore $P_s = 0.86$. Under these conditions 86% of the U.S. force would be expected to survive the enemy attack.

These calculations can be repeated for various values of the parameters to determine the alternatives between hardness (H), dispersal (k), active defense (a), reaction time (P_L), force size (N) and enemy capabilities (E, r, C, W) for fraction of force survival (P_s), or number of surviving missiles (NP_s).

When costs of the various alternatives are known, the particular combinations and degrees of hardness, dispersal, active defense, reaction time, and force size can be chosen that will provide maximum survival at given cost or given survival at least cost.

The question is often asked: Can our force survive highly accurate or high-yield weapons if it is based at fixed sites and makes no launchings prior to enemy attack? Further examination of equations (9) and (10) will throw some light on this problem. If the CEP becomes very low (approaches zero) or the yield becomes very high, then, for reasonable values of the other terms, the exponent in the equation becomes very large and the term containing the exponent vanishes. The survival according to equation (9) then becomes zero. But this is for the case where there is one or more attacking weapons per site. When there are fewer attacking weapons than sites, equation (10) is applicable and, under these circumstances, becomes:

$$P_s = 1 - \frac{Er(1-a)k}{N}$$

It is obvious from examination of this equation that a fraction of the force will still survive if the term $\frac{Er(1-a)k}{N}$ is less than 1. We have no control over the factors E and r, but we can make the whole term as small as possible by increasing air defense (a), decreasing concentration (k), or increasing force size (N).

A careful cost analysis would be required to determine what emphasis should be given to each of these measures. The extreme difficulties and high cost of air defense against ballistic missiles are also pointed out by Colonel Shelton in the previously referenced article. However, it is obvious that if a great number of missiles can be dispersed to no more than one or two missiles at a point, then, regardless of the air defense capability and limitations of mobility and fast reaction, it would be highly costly for the enemy to prevent the term $\frac{Er(1-a)k}{N}$ from becoming less than unity. Further it would then be highly unlikely that the enemy could attack all targets over a very short period of time and thus some launching of U. S. missiles could occur before arrival of attack ($P_L > 0$).

It can be concluded that by proper planning and design of the force configuration survival is possible against highly accurate and high-yield enemy weapons. In the case just considered, this survival might dictate smaller, simpler, and less costly missiles which can be more widely dispersed and can be procured and operated in greater numbers without excessive cost or manpower.

Another possibility not included above might be to harden our sites to the point when H in the equation is high enough to offset the low value of C, so that the term containing the exponent in the equations does not vanish. Here again the cost and feasibility of such a measure must be determined and carefully weighed against the other measures.

Another comparison that can be made by using the equations and substituting typical values is the relative cost and military value of hard and soft bases. A good measure of merit in designing a missile force is the cost per surviving missile rather than the cost per initial missile in the force. A force configuration which will give a low cost per surviving missile is obviously better than a configuration resulting in a high cost per surviving missile—other things such as logistics and operating simplicity being equal.

It would be useful to know how the cost of a hard base compares to that of a soft base if they have equal measures of merit (cost per surviving missile). The following steps will give an indication. Let D equal the dollar cost of a missile force. It does not matter here whether this is a yearly cost, ten-year cost, or cost on some other time basis, since the time factor cancels out. The cost per surviving missile is D / NP_s. For equal measures of merit:

$$\left(\frac{D}{NP_s}\right) \text{soft} = \left(\frac{D}{NP_s}\right) \text{hard}$$

If the number of initial missiles is assumed to be the same for the two configurations, then:

$$\left(\frac{D}{P_s}\right) \text{soft} = \left(\frac{D}{P_s}\right) \text{hard}$$

$$\frac{D(\text{soft})}{D(\text{hard})} = \frac{P_s(\text{soft})}{P_s(\text{hard})}$$

As a typical case, assume a fixed-base concept ($P_I = 1$) and a surprise attack ($P_L = 0$) of one weapon per target, $\frac{Er(1-a)k}{N} = 1.$

Then from equation (8):

$$P_s\ (\text{hard}) = (\tfrac{1}{2})^{36W^{2/3}/C^2H(\text{hard})}$$

$$P_s\ (\text{soft}) = (\tfrac{1}{2})^{36W^{2/3}/C^2H(\text{soft})}$$

The ratio of costs is:

$$\frac{D(\text{soft})}{D(\text{hard})} = \frac{P_s(\text{soft})}{P(\text{hard})} = (\tfrac{1}{2})^{36W^{2/3}/C^2(1/H\,\text{soft} - 1/H\,\text{hard})}$$

Substituting values from the previous example of $W = 1$, $C = 3$, $H(\text{hard}) = 75$ psi and taking $H(\text{soft}) = 3$ psi as a typical soft base:

$$\frac{D(\text{soft})}{D(\text{hard})} = (\tfrac{1}{2})^{\frac{36}{9}\left(\frac{1}{3} - \frac{1}{75}\right)} = (\tfrac{1}{2})^{1.28} = .41 = \frac{1}{2.44}$$

$$D(\text{hard}) = 2.44\ D(\text{soft})$$

or, under these conditions a 75-psi site would need to cost more than twice as much as a 3-psi site for equal measures of merit. In other words a 75-psi base would be better than a 3-psi base unless the

75-psi base cost more than twice as much as the soft base. Although no conclusions can be drawn from this one example, repeating the analyses and assigning various values to the parameters should provide a good feeling for the payoff in hardening missile sites.

Another way in which these expressions may be used is to determine the relationship between hardness and dispersal for given survival. For example, take the previous case where $P_I = 1$ and $P_L = 0$ and equation (9) applies. If the survival is to remain the same under two separate conditions of hardness and dispersal (call them conditions 1 and 2), then the value of the exponent of ½ must not change. If all the other terms in the exponent remain the same under the two conditions, then:

$$\frac{k_1}{H_1} = \frac{k_2}{H_2}$$

$$H_2 = H_1\left(\frac{k_2}{k_1}\right)$$

Thus if the first condition is 5 missiles per site ($k_1 = 5$) and the second condition is 10 missiles per site ($k_2 = 10$), then for equal survival:

$$H_2 = H_1\left(\frac{10}{5}\right)$$

$$H_2 = 2H_1$$

and, under these circumstances, a 10-missile site must be twice as hard as a 5-missile site for equal force survival.

Only a few examples of the application of these fundamental equations of force survival have been shown. The equations can be used in many other ways to produce an indication of the relationships and relative worth of the measures contributing to force survival. It is obvious that all the factors entering into force survival planning cannot be put into mathematical equations. But intelligent application of the relationships presented here will go a long way toward providing broad planning guidance.

Air Force Ballistic Missile Division, Hq ARDC

APPENDIX III

The Ballistic Missile and Its Elusive Targets

MAJOR KENNETH A. SMITH, USAF

For hundreds of years map makers have been attempting to pinpoint one given place in relation to others across the face of the earth. The slight inaccuracies have always been an annoyance to navigators, but until recently the slow speed of the means of transportation allowed ample time to correct for the errors. With the coming of high-speed, long-distance aircraft the difficulty became somewhat aggravated, but still there was some time to make computations and a crew was along to correct navigational errors by taking visual sightings. Even in bad weather the radarscope or radio and radar navigational aids were available to the crew. With all these checks available the error to worry about was the human error of the navigator rather than the reference errors in the maps.

But with the coming of the ballistic missile the problem has suddenly assumed critical importance. All traditional navigation devices for correcting map error have no use here. The only things that matter are the validity of the information set into the guidance system before launching and the faithfulness of the missile's guidance system in keeping the missile on its trajectory. Of course such a system assumes that the location of the target in relation to the launch pad can be plotted precisely. It is this assumption that we must make come true by finding means to link our North American Datum system to those for other continents. This is one more science in which we are operating under an informational handicap, for the details of the North American Datum have been available to the rest of the world, including Russia, while comparable detail from the Russian datum has not been available to us. Presumably the Russians have been able to tie their datum into ours and can now pinpoint targets on this continent. We do not necessarily have to have their information to achieve the same accuracy ourselves. We do need more geodetic data than we have as well as more detailed information on the location of targets. But with some additional geodetic data there are methods that will enable us to extend our own datum system to cover other continents.

What has been accomplished

Since World War II there have been considerable advances in the reduction of different national surveys into large, unified geodetic systems. This was done by readjustment of existing continuous surveys and by direct connection between different systems. In general the connection systems have been limited to continental boundaries because of difficulties imposed by large bodies of water that separate most of the continents and by certain borders that have been closed for political reasons. The relationship between the North American Datum, the European Datum, and the Russian datum can only be estimated when comparing plotted positions on the separate datums. Estimates of the amount of error vary from hundreds to thousands of feet. Errors can also be introduced when trying to tie two surveys together, even though they are on the same continent. The Russians attempted to join the Pulkovo and Svobodny Datums near Krasnoyarsk and found an error of about 2700 feet. Recently the Army Map Service reported a correction in the placement of the Palau Islands in the Pacific Ocean. The islands' position has been moved 4000 feet northwest of their previously recorded position.*

Problems of mapping and surveying the world

If the world were a perfect sphere, many of the mapping and

* *Military Engineer,* No. 332, November–December 1957, p. 469.

surveying problems would not exist. The facts remain that there are hills and valleys on the warped surface of the earth and that a slightly shorter axis runs through the earth pole to pole than through it at the equator. These odd qualities complicate our problem of referencing points accurately on the earth's surface. As a basis for starting a survey or datum, a sphere must be developed which is as representative as possible of the actual shape of the earth. For this purpose an ellipsoid is chosen, the equatorial axis measured, and the flattening effect introduced by the shorter pole-to-pole axis determined.

There are five quantities that must remain constant when developing a datum. There must be an initial point from which to start the survey. The ellipsoid must be defined by length of the equatorial axis and flattening effect on the meridian. The initial point coordinates and the azimuth direction from which to start the survey must remain the same throughout the development of the datum. Change one quantity and the whole datum will have to be recomputed.

North American Datum. The 1927 North American Datum is the result of readjusting the triangulation of the United States and then tying into it the geodetic datums of Mexico and Canada. The initial point is located near Meades Ranch in Kansas. The datum is referenced to the Clark Ellipsoid developed in 1866. Information from the North American Datum is available to all nations of the world.

Russian Geodetic Datum. Russia at one time had two independent geodetic datums in progress. An attempt was made to link the old Pulkovo Datum with the Svobodny Datum at several points near Krasnoyarsk. There was a discrepancy, as previously stated, in plotted positions on the two datums of about 2700 feet. Since each datum has a different initial point, the error was unavoidable. Investigation revealed that the error was caused by using separate initial points referenced to the Bessell Ellipsoid developed in 1841. In 1946 the Russians stated that a new datum called the 1942 Pulkovo Datum would be computed and referenced on an ellipsoid developed by Krassowiski and Izatov in 1938.*

Single world geodetic datum. A single world geodetic datum

* B. Szabo, *Geodetic Datums and an Estimate of Their Accuracy,* Aeronautical Chart and Information Center, April 1956, p. 28.

would certainly be the most ideal situation for computing the target coordinates for use in the ICBM guidance system. In order to establish accurate information between two or more geographical positions, the points must be referenced on the same geodetic datum using the same ellipsoid. The main difference between the various computed ellipsoids lies in the length of the equatorial axis and the flattening effect on the meridian. The following table lists most of the important earth ellipsoids:

author	*year*	*a*		*1/f*
Everest	1830	6,377,276	meters	1/300.8
Bessell	1841	6,377,397	"	1/299.15
Clark	1880	6,378,249	"	1/293.5
Bonsdorff	1888	6,378,444	"	1/298.6
Helmert	1907	6,378,200	"	1/298.3
Hayford	1910	6,378,388	"	1/297.0
Heiskanen	1926	6,378,397	"	1/297.0
Krassowiski/Izatov	1938	6,378,245	"	1/298.3
Jefferies	1948	6,378,099	"	1/297.1
Ledersteger	1951	6,378,315	"	1/297.0

Note: a = equatorial axis
1/f = fractional value for flattening of meridian

Of these ellipsoids, the Everest, Bessell, Clark, Hayford (now known as the International Ellipsoid), and Krassowiski/Izatov are the surfaces of the most important and extensive surveys.

Methods of extending geodetic control

There are several methods of extending geodetic control. These methods are capable of spanning large bodies of water and in some cases land areas that are otherwise inaccessible. The geodetic methods are:

The Hiran, or direct method;
The celestial, or semidirect method;
The gravimetric, or indirect method.

Each method of extending geodetic control has a definite use.

Each provides an acceptable accuracy—defined by the U. S. Coast and Geodetic Survey as error in line extension of less than one part in 50,000. The gravimetric method offers an excellent procedure for developing a world geodetic datum and can be used to establish geodetic controls in land areas that are closed for political reasons.

Hiran method. Hiran (High Precision Shoran) operates on the transponder-responder principle and can be considered a radar beacon system. The airborne transponder alternately transmits two groups of pulses at different frequencies in the 210–290 megacycle (mc) band. Ground stations tuned to the transmitted frequency respond independently to the pulses received from the airborne transmitter. The ground transmitter utilizes frequencies in the 290–330mc band. By measuring the difference in travel time of the signals from each ground station to the aircraft, we establish a known position of the aircraft at any one instant. The timed pulses are displayed on a cathode-ray tube in the aircraft and are superimposed on the marker pulses to determine the exact distance from each ground station.

The Hiran method also makes use of a technique called line crossings or trilateration to measure long lines with great accuracy. These lines can be used to form a net of high-order horizontal control over large areas inaccessible to land survey parties. Line measurements are made by flying the Hiran aircraft along a line between or past two Hiran ground stations. This method of position fix or line crossing is an excellent method of extending geodetic control into new areas of unmapped territory or it can be used to extend a line across water areas to establish new geodetic control.* The error in the Hiran method runs approximately one part in 120,000.

Celestial method. There are three different celestial methods for establishing a geodetic point—the solar eclipse, the occultation of a star, and the moon camera method. The solar eclipse method was developed for measuring distances across the oceans by Ilmari Bonsdorff, the late Director of the Finnish Geodetic Institute. He measured by the sound-film technique the exact moment when a total eclipse began and ended at two stations situated on different continents. The positions have to be along the path of the total

* *Communications and Electronics*, Air Force Manual 100–1, Vol. 2, Department of the Air Force, December 1952.

eclipse. This method was tried during the last four total eclipses in 1945, 1947, 1948, and 1954. Observation of the total eclipse must be made at both ends of the geodetic line. The weather did not cooperate too well. The 1954 eclipse provided the only successful sightings. These enabled a line to be extended across the Atlantic from the United States to Sweden. The error of the solar eclipse method could be in the realm of approximately one part in 75,000.*

In the occultation method the exact transit time when a star disappears behind the moon is recorded and again recorded when the star reappears. The exact distance of the moon must be known, and the points are then computed by the same method as in solar eclipse. Each station along the occultation track must be set up to record the time the star disappears and reappears.**

To use the moon camera method of William Markovitz, of the U. S. Naval Observatory, it is necessary to photograph the moon and surrounding stars from several distant points at the same exact time. By comparing the moon's position in relation to the surrounding stars and measuring the angular differences in position of the stars, then knowing the direction of the moon from the observatories, the distance between the observatories can be quite easily computed. According to Markovitz, the accuracy of 40 meters can be obtained for the positions.*** The over-all error of the celestial method is less than one part in 50,000.

Gravimetric method. The gravimetric method is essentially a procedure of reducing the shape of the earth geoid configuration to an ellipsoid shape so that we can measure distance and direction between any two points on the earth's surface. The undulations and the deflection of the vertical are determined by measuring the gravity anomalies which exist over the surface of the earth. The smoothing out of the undulations gives a more representative shape of the earth and the deflection of the vertical provides information needed to correct positions of latitude and longitude that have been determined astronomically and to reference these corrected values directly to the chosen ellipsoid without recourse to triangulation.

* W. A. Heiskanen, *Intercontinental Connection of Geodetic Systems,* Ohio State Research Foundation, May 1955, p. 8.

** *Ibid.*

*** *Ibid.*

Dr. Heiskanen of the Ohio State University Mapping and Charting Research Foundation has outlined a method for establishing a world geodetic datum using the gravimetric method.* In order to arrive at a world geodetic datum—or world system of coordinates—there must first be a reference ellipsoid that can be used world-wide. The International Ellipsoid, developed in 1910 by Hayford, seems to be one of the best available. Also there will have to be a suitable gravity formula with which to compare the representative gravity measurements. The international gravity formula suggested has the following value:

$$\gamma = 978.0490\ (1 - \phi.0052884 \sin^2 \phi - \phi.0000059 \sin^2 \phi).$$

In order to get the gravity values as representative as possible, the observed gravity reading must be reduced isostatically to sea level and compared to the above international value for theoretical gravity. From this comparison we get the needed value of gravity anomalies $\triangle g_1$ which can be used to calculate the deflection of the vertical plumb ξ and η. In addition to this method of calculating the value of ξ and η Dr. Heiskanen explained another method which was adaptable to short triangulation nets. The astronomical observation values of latitude ϕ', longitude λ', and azimuth A′ and the corresponding values of ϕ, λ, and A are computed geodetically and referred to the ellipsoid. From the observed values and the computed values, ξ and η are found by the following formula:

$$\xi = \phi' - \phi$$
$$\eta = (\lambda' - \lambda) \cos \phi, \text{ or}$$
$$\eta = (A' - A) \operatorname{cotan} \phi$$

This method of determining the value of ξ and η can be used over limited areas. The measured arcs cover only a relatively small part of the earth's surface, and such triangulation nets cannot be carried across oceans.

If the problem is turned upside down and the formula rewritten in the following manner, we can convert astronomically observed quantities of ϕ', λ', and A' to the quantities needed for a reference ellipsoid ϕ, λ, and A:

* W. A. Heiskanen, *The Geodetic Significance of World Wide Gravity Studies*, Ohio State Research Foundation, Technical Paper Number 124, November 1950, pp. 41–42.

$$\phi = \phi' - \xi$$
$$\lambda = \lambda' - \eta \sec \phi$$
$$A = A' - \eta \tan \phi$$

This gives the quantities of ϕ, λ, and A, which can be referenced directly to the ellipsoid selected without recourse to triangulation. Here indeed is a method of computing a world geodetic datum utilizing all the observations recorded to date regardless of the referenced datum or original ellipsoid used.

It must be remembered that the use of gravity anomalies to determine the value of the vertical deflections ξ and η is no magic method. It is an elastic tool in the hands of the geodesist. It is also possible to transfer the coordinates of latitude and longitude taken from an accurate map directly to the gravity datum by applying the recorded values of the vertical deflection for the mapped area. The mapped area must have a reliable grid of latitude and longitude. One additional advantage can be utilized in the gravimetric method of using isostatically reduced anomalies: it is possible to obtain an acceptable value of the gravity anomalies by using the average value to compute the needed vertical deflection ξ and η. While some error will be introduced, the error will not be large enough to prevent the calculation of the target position when using weapons of a large blast radius. Using the tools of gravimetric datum the following results can be obtained:

• The determination of a general world geodetic datum—or world system of coordinates—using the information of the many existing datum systems, such as the Russian, Swedish, and European, in the gravimetric datum without the task of recomputing all the datums.

• The computation, based on the world geodetic datum, of the geographic coordinates of any important point in the world where astronomical observations exist. It is also possible, using the coordinates of a point taken from a reliable map having an accurate grid, to compute the coordinates directly to the gravimetric datum if the gravity anomalies are available. The error between two points, computed gravimetrically using celestial observations and accurate vertical deflection measurements, should be no greater than 50 meters. This is well within the accuracy of Hiran or celestial methods.

• The accurate computation of the distance and direction between launch point and selected target of ICBMs.

Considerable work has been accomplished on the gravity measuring requirement. Some parts of the world have thousands upon thousands of gravity measurements recorded. Much of the world still remains to be worked, but certain parts of the world of interest to the ICBM program are well covered. In 1950 the Air Force Cambridge Research Center established a world-wide gravity measuring program. No less than 30 countries, many leading oil companies, and prominent geodesists from all over the world are cooperating in this program to solve the problem of gravity data collection.*

About one fourth of the world has been mapped accurately to the scale of 1/250,000. Approximately two fifths of the world has been mapped to the scale of 1/1,000,000 or larger. The areas that have been mapped and the gravimetric measurements offer an excellent source of information on which to base a datum computed gravimetrically. Celestial observations taken from available datums such as the Pulkovo, European, and others will furnish additional information.

The future

The Hiran method of extending geodetic control has been used extensively by the armed forces. Hiran is limited in its range over land areas, since United States aircraft are not allowed to fly over many parts of the world because of political differences. The celestial method has been used, but the observations of solar eclipse, star occultation, and moon camera methods are all dependent on visual sighting of the celestial bodies. The weather does not always cooperate. When using the celestial method, observers have to be in place at both ends of the line to be extended. Here again certain areas are inaccessible and cannot be covered by the celestial method. The gravimetric method of extending geodetic control presents the best method of developing a world geodetic system because it references any available geodetic information to the reference ellipsoid without recourse to triangulation. The gravimetric method is the only one that can extend geodetic control to areas that are now totally inaccessible to the United States.

* Heiskanen, *Intercontinental Connection of Geodetic Systems*, p. 16.

Can the ICBM hit the target? If we get the proper distribution and density of gravimetric readings and use the gravimetric method to establish a world geodetic datum—or world system of coordinates—for calculating the precise relationship between the launch point and the target, the answer can and must be yes.

Air Command and Staff College

APPENDIX IV

The USAF Reports to Congress

Compiled by

LT. COLONEL KENNETH F. GANTZ, USAF

In August 1957 the Soviet Union announced that it had an intercontinental ballistic missile. This claim created a ripple of interest. Reactions varied from mild alarm to scepticism. Two months later, in October, came the big shock. The Soviets put into orbit around the earth a satellite vehicle weighing 184 pounds. One only had to watch the night sky at the appointed time or tune in on the proper shortwave frequency to have proof of the basic fact that the satellite was there. The international debris was still settling a few weeks later, in November, when the second Russian satellite arced into orbit—this time one weighing 1100 pounds and carrying a live dog.

December sharpened the dismay of the free world when the U. S. Navy's much-publicized Vanguard rocket collapsed on take-off and its small, shiny satellite lay amidst the wreckage on the launch pad. January 1958 brought the first ray of sunshine. The Army succeeded with its Jupiter-C test vehicle and the first American satellite was in orbit—apparently better instrumented than the Russian ones but at

30 pounds a meager payload in the face of the Russian achievements.

In the United States public debate has been troubled and points of view have been many and varied. Still, out of the welter of opinion two facts have emerged as incontrovertible:

• the Soviet Union has gained a major technological and propaganda triumph through the launching of the first earth satellites;

• the state of the art which they represent constitutes an urgent technological and military challenge to the United States.

Estimates vary as to the relative positions in the race of the Soviet Union and the United States, from the more pessimistic ones of our being five to two years behind the Russians to claims that we are neck and neck. But since the first two sputniks no responsible voice has claimed that the United States is clearly in front. For impressive as the satellites themselves may be, behind them lurks the ever more impressive military implications of the powerful missiles that put the big satellites into orbit.

Of the many responses triggered by this situation one of the most important has been the inquiry into the status of the U.S. missile and satellite programs by the Preparedness Investigating Subcommittee, a standing subcommittee of the Committee on Armed Services of the United States Senate. Members of the subcommittee under the chairmanship of Senator Lyndon B. Johnson of Texas are Senators John C. Stennis (Mississippi), Stuart P. Symington (Missouri), Leverett Saltonstall (Massachusetts), Ralph E. Flanders (Vermont), Estes Kefauver (Tennessee), and Styles Bridges (New Hampshire). More popularly known as the Johnson Committee after its chairman, the subcommittee has been holding extensive hearings in an effort to determine what needs to be done to bolster the missile program and the related research and development programs on space vehicles and space weaponry.

In his opening statement Senator Johnson expressed his belief that the facts the hearing might disclose would not "invite our people either to a siesta or to a hysteria" but that they would "inspire Americans to the greatest effort in American history. And this committee seeks only to determine what can be done, what must be done now and for the long pull."

Many of the views expressed by leaders of the United States Air

Force in response to the questions of the subcommittee members and their Chief Counsel, Mr. Edwin L. Weisl, are of absorbing interest and importance to airmen. From the thousands of words of testimony representative passages and statements have been selected bearing on certain prominent issues of immediate concern to their professional understanding. These passages have been chosen wherever they were found throughout the unclassified portions of the testimony and have been assembled into a continuity with a minimum of summary in the hope of fairly representing the opinions of our own Air Force leaders on these topics of professional concern: the status of our Air Force programs, the quality of our incoming weapons, and our march forward into new weapon systems that bear on the exploration of and the capability to control space.

The cited remarks are in most instances brief selections from large blocks of direct testimony in the verbatim give-and-take of the questioning. To preserve both flavor and authenticity, editing has been limited to the process of selection in view of the space available and the voluminous transcript of the unclassified statements made during the sessions of 17 December 1957, and 8 and 9 January 1958. Only Air Force testimony is included.

First Priority—Maintain the Deterrent Force

The anchor view of the USAF testimony was an absolute need for a force capable of certain counterattack under which no enemy might hope to profit from his war or find victory in sudden attack. This force is the Strategic Air Command. At present its strength is in the manned bomber forces, which are, in professional opinion, currently quite capable of performing the counterattack mission. Missile forces are beginning to phase into the Strategic Air Command to supplement the manned bombers and diversify the counterattack capability. Ultimately astro forces will phase in for manned operations in space. But whatever weaponry and combinations of bombers, missiles, and spacecraft the Strategic Air Command may assume from year to year, its deterrent force must be kept strong year in and year out. It cannot be allowed to peak and slump as the new weapons and capabilities phase in and older weapons phase out of its operational units. This, said Lt. General Donald L. Putt, Deputy Chief of Staff for Research and Development, USAF, "it is essential that we do . . . we have got to take care of today's deterrent force. We have also got to do the things that need doing today so that when we get to tomorrow we have not slipped back then."

General Curtis E. LeMay, Vice Chief of Staff, USAF, concurred and commented on the ultimate superiority of manned systems in air-space warfare. In response to Committee Counsel:

Mr. Weisl. "Do you believe that our manned bombers with nuclear weapons today constitute the major military deterrent against Soviet aggression and our major weapon system of retaliation?"

General LeMay. "I don't think there is any doubt about that, Counsel.

"That is true."

Mr. Weisl. "How long have we got to keep that strength?"

General LeMay. "It is rather difficult to pick out a definite date when we could absolutely say that unmanned vehicles or weapon systems would take over the mission now performed by the manned vehicle.

"I expect it to be a gradual transition, and I have serious doubts whether we will ever see the time when there will be no manned vehicles in our weapons inventory.

"I believe that there will always be a place for them, and while they may not look like the airplanes that we now operate, they will be manned weapon systems nevertheless, and I think any force that has manned weapon systems at its disposal will certainly have the advantage over one that chose to go to an unmanned system."

Secretary of the Air Force James H. Douglas agreed: "Today, our principal concern is to maintain the military strength which provides an effective deterrent against an aggressor. . . . The Strategic Air Command is a main element of our deterrent force. With the swiftly moving technological development the maintenance of a deterrent force has required a rapid succession of new weapons, with the old phasing out as the new are phased in. SAC, for example, since World War II has gone successively from the B-29 to the B-50; B-36; B-47 and now to the B-52. Each one of these weapons followed a familiar evolutionary pattern—a first phase of limited operational usefulness caused by exasperating mechanical failures, a second phase of weapon maturity with improvements designed to increase effectiveness, and a third phase of gradual obsolescence as a more advanced weapon system became available.

"Ballistic missiles are viewed by the Air Force as continuations of this evolutionary process. Three principles must be constantly kept in mind.

"First, we must push the development and integration of the weapons of tomorrow at a pace which permits our scientists and technicians to operate effectively.

"Second, while a new weapon system is being phased in—whether it is the B-52, B-58, or a ballistic missile launched from the ground or an aircraft—we must maintain the deterrent force with the weapons of today.

"Third, we must press forward with projects for the weapons of day after tomorrow even though we cannot clearly see precisely how those weapons will operate."

To maintain the deterrent capability of the manned bomber forces of SAC will take bases, men, and new generations of aircraft. All are expensive to acquire and maintain, and funds will have to be found, if a strong and alert force is maintained.

. . . bases

Mr. Weisl. "General LeMay, . . . you have stated to the Subcommittee on Air Power of the Armed Services Committee * that you need a greater dispersal of SAC bases.

"Has anything resulted from that testimony?"

General LeMay. "Since I last appeared before the Committee, I believe there has been one more base assigned to the Strategic Air Command.

"However it is only capable of taking tankers at the present time and needs some more construction before bombers can move on it."

. . . men

General White. "We are definitely short of manpower in the coming year, and I have requested an increase of 10,000 personnel. . . .

* [In 1956. For a report on USAF testimony before this Committee see "U.S. Air Power Today," *Air University Quarterly Review,* VIII, 4 (Fall 1956), 60–78.]

850,000 is our present schedule end strength by 30 June 1958, and I have asked that that be raised to 860,000."

Senator Saltonstall. "If you have 860,000, will you have enough manpower to put crews on the Thors and the Jupiters?"

General White. "That is one of the major reasons for asking for the additional 10,000."

Senator Saltonstall. "If you put on additional manpower on the Thors and the missiles, how will your crews be on the B-52's and B-47's?"

General White. "You mean, as to numbers?"

Senator Saltonstall. "Yes."

General White. "We expect to be all right as to numbers."

Senator Saltonstall. "Will you have, what, 2½–"

General White. "1.6 crew ratio per aircraft."

Senator Saltonstall. "On B-52's?"

General White. "On all strategic aircraft."

Senator Saltonstall. "Will that be enough to keep–"

General White. "That is all strategic bombers."

Senator Saltonstall. "Will that be enough to keep your crews, to keep sufficient crews alert?"

General White. "That is the ratio required in order to keep alert."

Senator Saltonstall. "And how much of your force can you maintain on alert or keep on alert?"

General White. "That works out to one third of the force."

Senator Saltonstall. "One third of the force?" . . .

General White. . . . "It is not only a question of personnel, but you have to have the adequate runways, the taxiways, the alert shelters and the ground handling equipment and the ground crews to keep the aircraft in commission, and you have to have more flying time in order to compensate for the aircraft that are kept on the ground."

Senator Saltonstall. "And if you had your own way 100 per cent, would you have more on the alert than one third, or is that enough?"

General White. "I would think it would be highly advisable to have more. It gets exceedingly expensive in manpower and in aircraft. You have to have more aircraft, and a great many more crews."

Senator Saltonstall. "So that you have asked for 10,000 more men?"

General White. "Yes."

Senator Saltonstall. "And if you get those 10,000 more men in all different categories, that would carry you in a satisfactory or optimum way?"

General White. "It would carry us on a very austere basis."

Senator Saltonstall. "On a very austere basis?"

General White. "That is correct, sir."

. . . new generation aircraft

In a sense all weapons are interim weapons. All weapons in the inventory in quantity verge toward obsolescence in view of those under development. But the fight must be fought with the inventory, and the old and the new must overlap. General LeMay brought out that some SAC wings are still equipped with the B-36. General White agreed that the B-47 wings are losing their effectiveness in the face of improvements in aircraft and air defense. The 603 programed B-52's, better than 600-mph heavy bombers, are not yet all out of production and into inventory for "interim" modernization. The B-58, a medium bomber with speed approximating mach 2, is in final testing but not yet quite ready to enter quantity production. More KC-135 tankers will be needed for the full B-52 force. And looking immediately ahead, planners see the supersonic, very-high-altitude X-15 rocket plane, a forerunner of the spacecraft, and the chemical-fuel B-70 hypersonic bomber. The X-15 experimental plane Secretary Douglas characterized as one of the "radical" USAF projects: "It does include a man. It has a good many characteristics of the missile, and is able to reach altitudes of something like a hundred miles. It has almost all of the re-entry problems of the ballistic missile and ultimate problems of returning it, a satellite, to the earth after it has been on orbit.

"It really requires all the characteristics that one would find in a manned satellite to take care of the man. It does not require the propulsive force."

The Sputnik Acceleration—Programs Leading to the Missile Phase-in

Much of the Committee's inquiry centered on the adequacy of the post-Sputnik speed-up of the USAF missile program. The trend of

Air Force testimony called for a faster pace and amplification of funds.

Senator Johnson. "Do the present authorized plans for the development of the Thor, the Atlas, and the Titan represent the fastest rate of progress that you think can be made?"

General Schriever. "Does your question also include the operational force buildup?"

Senator Johnson. "Yes."

General Schriever. "The total program?"

Senator Johnson. "Yes, sir."

General Schriever. "The answer to that is no."

Senator Johnson. "Would you specify specifically in what respects you are dissatisfied with each of them, if that is so, for this permanent record?"

General Schriever. "In the Thor program we have complete authority to move as fast as we can possibly move insofar as completing the development.

"We have a much greater capability in building or producing Thors and building operational units faster and getting deployed faster."

Senator Johnson. "If there is nothing fundamentally wrong with the design, should not it be possible to step up the rate of development a great deal by working faster and longer and harder, and isn't that advisable in the light of the situation as we know it to be?"

General Schriever. "We are working as fast right now as far as the development program itself is concerned, putting together all of the pieces that are involved in the development. There is no restriction on overtime at the present time or multishift operations."

* * * *

Senator Johnson. "Have you got anything else you want to say about the Atlas and the Titan, General, so far as the present authorized plans for development are concerned?

"Are you making the fastest rate of progress that you think can be made and should be made?

"I want to tie you into this record for history to see what our expert told us ought to be done, and if you think more ought to be done, I think you will say so."

General Schriever. "In the Atlas program the development phase of it with all overtime restrictions now removed, . . . there is agreement I think between myself and Convair that we cannot accelerate the development program.

"There is also agreement that we can do more in terms of production and we can get more units, more groups in the same period. . . ."

Senator Johnson. "And your view is that we should?"

General Schriever. "We should at least—"

Senator Johnson. "And that we can?"

General Schriever. "Yes."

* * * *

General Schriever underscored the importance of bringing Titan along.

Senator Saltonstall. "May I ask a question on the Titan?

"The evidence was that there was no new money or no extra money put in for the Titan, is that correct?"

General Schriever. "That is correct."

Senator Saltonstall. "How far along in the development stage are you with the Titan?"

General Schriever. "The Titan is about a year behind the Atlas. . . ."

Senator Saltonstall. "In your opinion, General, is it more valuable to go forward faster with the Atlas in the stage that it has now reached than to perhaps speed up the Titan?"

General Schriever. "No, sir. I think that you have to go both ways.

"I think that the Atlas you can get into operational units sooner, . . .

"That actually increases the number of squadrons as compared to the present program . . . the Titan, as General White pointed out yesterday, the Air Force has recommended that instead of the . . . squadrons that are presently in the program, that we go to. . . ."

Senator Saltonstall. "In the Titan?"

General Schriever. "In the Titan in the same time period, and this we can also do.

"The Titan should go because it is built around the hard base, and I think you need to take the calculated risk now, because if we do this, we have to make the decisions now and select the site location and initiate our whole construction program because the hard base is a considerable construction program. . . ."

Senator Saltonstall. "May I ask you this: from the point of view of the defense of the United States and the United States security, is it in your opinion necessary, looking forward to the long range of 1961 and 1962, that we have both the Atlas and the Titan in operational stages?"

General Schriever. "Yes, sir, I think so.

"In the first place the Titan is a follow-on, it is a more sophisticated weapon. . . .

"Also looking into the space age and astronautics age, the Titan is a booster for astronautics development. . . ."

Senator Saltonstall. "So that the Titan is valuable not only as a missile for defense purposes but also as a booster for space programs."

General Schriever. "That is right."

Senator Saltonstall. "Satellites?"

General Schriever. "And so is the Atlas."

Lt. General Clarence S. Irvine pinpointed program obstacles in the Thor-Jupiter duplication and perhaps in overregard of the missile as an end in itself rather than a way stop to yet more sophisticated weapons.

Mr. Weisl. "Now, General Irvine, what bottlenecks can you tell the committee are present which impede or obstruct the acceleration of the development of ballistic missiles?"

General Irvine. "As I told you, on the Atlas, the program, I think, is pretty well on schedule. There it is really a question, at this point, of time. Maybe we could accelerate it a little with a little more money in key spots.

"The real question is how many do we want? We need to make that decision fairly soon.

"In the case of the Titan, there we are running essentially a development program. We are not ready for the production order yet. Since that is a real backup in that it is considerable improvement over the Atlas, I think we would be better off if we accelerated that weapon system.

"Again, in the case of the existing Thor and Jupiter, there is a question of getting authority for sites and really making a determination of the ultimate requirements that are necessary. . . ."

Mr. Weisl. "You were not consulted, either, were you?"

General Irvine. "No, I was not.

"However, I learned about fifty years ago from my Scotch father how to take orders and I have got orders and am carrying them out. . . ."

Mr. Weisl. "Are there any other obstacles?"

General Irvine. "In the missile, the ballistic missile area, I do not think that there is a sufficient awareness, outside of the long-haired types like General Putt and myself, that the ballistic missile is only a short step in the evolution of a weapon system; that we feel out of it comes things like a ballistically boosted manned machine, whether this is made as an airplane to not quite go in orbit, or whether it is a true orbital type machine.

"There is too much feeling, I think, in the people in this country and in government, that we are perhaps just a little bit crazy when we talk about this sort of machine. And as far as I am concerned, I have been accustomed to this, having been in engineering a little bit, that I think this is a very high compliment when a lot of people in this country think the Air Force is trying to go too far and too fast."

Mr. Weisl. "Well, according to General LeMay, we neither have gone too far nor too fast. Do you agree with General LeMay's testimony?"

General Irvine. "I do."

The Jupiter IRBM Weapon System Is Examined

The unqualified opinion of Air Force missilemen and production experts was forcefully expressed. The cost of putting two missiles into production and establishing the weapon systems to operate them is justified only by the insurance value of different designs, by sending the message to Garcia over two different routes. The Jupiter intermediate-range ballistic missile is similar in concept and design to Thor, unlike the pairing of the quite different designs of Atlas and Titan. Jupiter prospects are already available in Thor.

Mr. Weisl. "General Irvine, you know, of course, about the decision to manufacture both the Thor and the Jupiter?"

General Irvine. "Yes, sir."

Mr. Weisl. "Do you think there is any substantial difference from an operational standpoint between the Thor and the Jupiter?"

General Irvine. "They are about as alike as the Ford and the Chevrolet."

Mr. Weisl. "Do you think the Jupiter is the backup for the Thor?"

General Irvine. "No, not to any real engineering degree. The laws of nature are the same for the Army and the Air Force, and they have equally skilled people working on the job, except in this area I think the Air Force got started sooner with a more thorough understanding of what we are trying to do. And that was not just to build a missile, but to build a weapon system with a complete environment including the people, the operational concept, the fitting of this weapon system into the over-all SAC war plan, this last probably being the most important of all."

Mr. Weisl. "Has the Air Force sufficient facilities to manufacture as many Thors as can possibly be needed in the foreseeable future?"

General Irvine. "We are in the interesting position on this as we are in many other weapon systems of being able to build more than we could justify to meet military requirements or that we think the country ought to buy."

Mr. Weisl. "Since the Air Force will be charged with the responsibility of operating both the Thor and Jupiter, do you as an expert feel that you need both the Thor and the Jupiter?"

General Irvine. "This is a question of buying insurance. This to me is the difference between the 65-year-old man buying insurance to send his kid through school or buying insurance on the child. I mean you can pay a high price for insurance if you buy the wrong kind.

"If this were a missile which had an advanced engine, an advanced airframe—"

Mr. Weisl. "If you will pardon the interruption and will forgive me, does this have an advanced airframe? Does this have a different engine? Does this have a different propulsion?"

General Irvine. "It has the same engine, an Air Force-developed engine at North American, with somewhat different installation devices, but relatively the same installation procedures; so actually the facts of life in this case are that the accent on the development of the Jupiter has been toward developing a missile, not a complete weapon system. And this is perfectly understandable, because the people who are working on it did not have the entire environment and were not the people that had the problem of solving the entire military problem.

"Therefore, the ground environment and the operational concept and many other things are not—they do not quite fit. So that this to me—and I think if you have got some Fords coming out—this is like starting some Chevrolets, too. To meet our requirements it is going to be late, certainly after the middle of next year, before a missile that has all the apparent requirements in it to meet the Air Force mission—"

Mr. Weisl. "You are talking now of an intermediate missile?"

General Irvine. "Yes, I am talking about the IRBM. In other words, they have been flying prototype missiles and the work that has been done on them has been fine. The difference between that and the Air Force concept is like our feeling that new and modern high-performance airplanes we build on so-called hard tooling and we build enough of them so we have a production run.

"The Thor, built by Douglas with Air Force thinking behind it, was built on production tooling. So if you get a good one, we are in a position to go ahead and build a lot of them."

Mr. Weisl. "You have got a good one in your opinion in the Thor, have you not?"

General Irvine. "Yes, sir."

Mr. Weisl. "And you are in a position to build as many of them as the Air Force can possibly use in the foreseeable future?"

General Irvine. "More."

And General Schriever, answering assistant counsel:

Mr. Vance. "Speaking of backups, do you agree with General Irvine's testimony, as I understood it, that Thor and Jupiter are not necessarily backups for one another?"

General Schriever. "Yes, I agree that at this stage of the game I do not think that they are backups of the kind that we should pay that much insurance for."

. . . identical movability

Senator Flanders. "A fundamental difference, as I have observed it, between the two is that one is at least being used with the fixed launching platform, or is it, as it was explained to us, movable but not mobile launching platform, while the other is intended to have a mobile launching equipment mechanism.

"Now, is the Air Force sold on the notion of the fixed platform?"

General White. "The two weapons, as far as mobility—and that is, I think, an overstatement—movability, are identical, in our opinion, and there is no real difference between the Jupiter and Thor as far as their movability is concerned."

Senator Flanders. "Well, we saw fixed—we saw ground installations out in California which certainly were not mobile."

General White. "They can be, though. The same kind of a launching platform that one—on trucks, and so on, can be applied to the other. The real key—"

Senator Flanders. "Apparently it had not been developed. I did not know whether you had any feeling that there was a definite reason for the fixed platform."

General White. ". . . Even to move them even a few miles, they have to go over roads, and the narrow standard roads in Continental Europe are going to force a tremendous problem.

"I can only say the Air Force has an open mind upon it, and a great deal of the determination will be the desires of the nation to which these will eventually be turned over . . ."

Senator Flanders. ". . . Now, the ICBM is of necessity launched from a fixed launching spot."

General White. "Yes, sir."

Senator Flanders. "I have not heard of anybody who has suggested making that mobile, have you?"

General White. "Yes, sir, that is right, sir."

. . . quick reaction time vs. movability

Mr. Weisl. "General Irvine, you undoubtedly have either heard of or read the testimony of General Gavin and General Medaris to the mobility of the IRBM. Do you agree with their views as to mobility?

"Let me put it another way. You do agree that mobility is desirable, do you not?"

General Irvine. "We have—that is really a question—we had an inspection by our Secretary and Secretary Brucker from the Army out on the West Coast, a development engineering inspection of the ground handling equipment for the Thor. All the equipment was in place. The real material, not pictures, not ideas, but the material that would be used was set up in place and demonstrated. And this equipment is on wheels, and we are in a position to put this stuff on trucks and drive it around the country if that seems like a good idea.

"However, when you start talking about that sort of thing where you are going to move a train of 150 or 160 trucks around the country, I think some people ought to take a look at some World War II pictures of what—I was in a P-38 outfit a little while myself—is a demonstration of what you could do to a bunch of trucks on the road with a bunch of fighters, and the Russians have lots of fighters."

Mr. Weisl. "You heard or read the testimony of General Medaris, I believe, who said that this equipment is just as easy to move as an 8-inch gun."

General Irvine. "I have never experienced moving 8-inch guns, but I think the best answer to that question is, we design our materiel so that we can drive it around and set it up and tear it down and move it. We have five different plans which go from a completely mobile solution to where we would have a large number of sites, unoccupied sites, maybe some we would not use at all in time of peace, that we could move to, have our equipment so we could place all of it on wheels.

"From that through various gradations to a hardened site where there would be nothing for the enemy to look at if we decide to bring it out, shove the missile on a launcher, and shoot it.

"So we have those five different variations, and we feel they are necessary, from relatively thinly populated areas where the deployment plans could be carried out, to heavily populated areas where some places, anybody who has driven around some of the narrow roads in England, moving a 25-ton truck along, it sounds a little sporty.

"Should we decide to put this equipment in a place like Alaska, there it seems sort of sensible to dig in."

* * * *

General Irvine. "In the Air Force, we have some pretty big chunks we move around, and we think we know something about them.

"As I said before, the laws of nature are the same for everybody; whether it is an Army truck or an Air Force truck, it sinks in the sand just the same.

"If you set up a hundred-thousand-pound missile, we have the idea that maybe you ought to lay out a little piece of concrete about 20 feet square to put it on.

"But I would like to say one more thing about the real fundamental difference of opinion about the handling of these two missiles, the difference between Irvine and Gavin.

"Gavin is thinking in terms of equipment, quite properly, to chaperon an army in the field, as an extension of artillery. And with this concept there is nothing wrong with what he proposes to do.

"Our philosophy with these missiles, from the very beginning, was to create another weapon system which would fit into the SAC war plan; and therefore, among other things, we wanted fast reaction, the ability to shoot quickly, the same as in SAC we want an alert system to get the airplanes in the air quickly, while the people who fly them are still alive; and in the case of the missiles, while there is still a man there to push the button.

"This is the real difference in philosophy."

. . . cost

Senator Symington pointed out that "the principal extra cost of producing both Thor and Jupiter" had been stated to be the cost of "continuation of two research and development programs instead of one. Do you agree with that?" he asked General Putt.

General Putt. "No, sir."

Senator Symington. "Why not?"

General Putt. "Well, in addition to the added costs of two development programs, you have the additional cost of tooling up a different line, production line, a somewhat different set of ground handling equipment, the training of people in additional—not necessarily additional skills, but to handle different systems.

"The number of parts and pieces that go into your supply system are doubled, which is a headache in itself.

"So that I think there is considerably more than just the increased cost of two research and development programs."

Secretary Douglas estimated the extra cost of proceeding with Jupiter into operational units: "I think that it is reasonable to say that if we could proceed and were justified fully in proceeding with Thor at the present time without Jupiter, the present operational program could be accomplished for perhaps as much as $200 million, perhaps more, less than in going ahead to equip the presently planned units with both missiles. As the program increases in size, if it does, the difference will become relatively smaller, at least in relation to the whole program."

Air Force uses broad resources to pair development and production planning

Questioning of General Schriever brought out the Air Force concept of weapon development. Design-development contracts let to achieve performance specifications create a development-production team of experienced industrial organizations with regard to each of the component systems of a missile. Solution of tooling and production problems is an integral part of design development. Testing puts production facilities in being to manufacture the test missiles and readies them for quantity production. Over-all direction is provided by a contract systems manager under close technical supervision by the Air Force Ballistic Missile Division headed by General Schriever. In this regard Senator Bush brought up the much-publicized German scientists at the Army's Redstone Arsenal, who have done the research work on the Army's Redstone and Jupiter missiles. General Schriever was invited to comment on the "arsenal" system of weapon development as contrasted to the USAF concept.

Senator Bush. "Just as I was very much impressed at your establishment when we paid a visit to you recently, so I was very much impressed at Redstone by the people we met there and the operations which we viewed and I am sure you must agree there are wonderful people down there and they have done some wonderful things just as you have, too.

"Outstanding, I suppose, is this group of German scientists headed by Dr. von Braun who testified up here, and when one sees an organization like that, here is a man who has a team which has been engaged in rocket research and development for twenty years or close to it, I just wonder whether we are making all the use, getting all the use and value out of that kind of a team and that kind of a plan with his team, so to speak, that we should, in this very important work that is just going on in this country. . . .

"I don't want to embarrass you by asking you to answer any question that you don't think is appropriate and I won't insist on any answer from you on this but I wondered whether you would care to make any observation from your own experience and contact with the Von Braun group, and the Army arsenal work down there as to whether a good deal more value could not be gotten out of them at all levels of research and development in the rocket field or not, or do you have any general comment to make in connection with this broad question?"

General Schriever. "Well, first of all, I would certainly agree that they have a very competent group of people there.

"I think that the fact that they have a very competent group there, however, is sort of an accident.

"In other words, I don't go along with the arsenal philosophy of doing development and then turning it over to industry for production.

"I think the Air Force philosophy of having industry do development and having the capability of planning for production simultaneously is a much better way of doing it.

"The Air Force had quite a number of German scientists right after the war at Wright Field, and made, deliberately, the decision not to try to retain that group of scientists as a group, similar to what they have done at Redstone, and they have been, most of them have gone into American industry and a lot of them are in industry today; they are at Convair, they are at Bell, and a number of other companies, and although this is a matter of opinion, my feeling is that these people distributed to American industry, are doing equally as good a job for the United States. . . .

"I don't want to take any credit away from the group of people there [at Redstone]. . . ."

Senator Bush. ". . . In other words you don't feel that we are handicapping ourselves as a defense organization by not making broader use of the talents of the Von Braun group."

General Schriever. "Well, I think, as I say I think they are being used well up to the hilt now."

Senator Bush. "Yes, and you don't feel that there is a very much broader field in which they—to which their talents might be applied which would be the over-all field to affect not only the Army but the Navy and the Air Force too in the field of missiles.

"Are you getting as much benefit as you think you are entitled to from them or that you can use effectively?"

General Schriever. "Well, I think you have to put it this way: the group is in existence, it is a good group, so that is a fact."

Senator Bush. "Yes."

General Schriever. "And as far as whether my organization or the Air Force is getting as much use out of them as we could, I think we are getting as much benefit from what they are doing as is possible, as long as they are an agency under the control of another organization."

Senator Bush. "Oh, yes."

General Schriever. "Now we get complete information on their technical progress.

"We have a liaison office there and we get all information as to what they are doing technically."

Senator Saltonstall. "Is that mutual?"

General Schriever. "Yes, I have a couple of their officers right stationed with me and they get all of our reports."

Senator Bush. "Perhaps what I am getting at is this question, as to whether we could have a closer unification of effort in the missile field than we have right now, and that we have had in the recent years. It is a difficult question, I know."

General Schriever. "Yes, it is a difficult question to answer because fundamentally, I have, as I have said, I feel that as a country, we are better off by going to industry for our development. I don't think we should have Governmental agencies carrying out development in the manner that Redstone does.

"I don't mean to say we should not test and evaluate them."

Senator Bush. "I mean right up to the point where it is tested and manufactured."

General Schriever. "They actually assemble and test—they get the engines from North American, they get their guidance from Ford

Instrument Company, which is part of Sperry, but they do all of the detailed engineering, of assembling the total missile, and they actually carry out the test firings, they prepare the over-all drawings and specifications and finally turn them over to a company say like Chrysler to do the final assembling and production."

Senator Bush. "There appears to be a difference of opinion between yours, let's say, and General Medaris?"

General Schriever. "That is right, there is."

Senator Bush. "As to the economic philosophy or the efficiency of these respective approaches. He appears to be quite as convinced that theirs is better as you are that yours is better; that is very interesting, and I am sure you and he must know that you differ on that."

General Schriever. "Oh, yes. He knows what I think and I know what he thinks."

Senator Bush. "Yes. Well, that is pretty difficult for an amateur to get into it and decide who is right."

Senator Saltonstall. "Would the Senator yield on that?"

Senator Bush. "Just for a question."

Senator Saltonstall. "Is that not based, General Schriever, on history, the Army is the oldest in existence, they had to build their rifles and everything else in arsenals, so they adopted the arsenal theory.

"You fellows came along later with the airplanes and you adopted the industry theory."

General Schriever. "Yes. In the early days it actually was tried, the business of building airplanes in the government arsenal type of arrangement, and it did not work very well, and you can get all kinds of pros and cons on this, but I think that philosophically it is true that regardless of party, the policy of this country is to have private enterprise do the job for the government instead of having the government do the job; and I think if private enterprise can do it, and I think they can, in the case of developing these weapons, then we ought to tend to that direction."

Application of Air Force missiles to space operations

Most significant of all the facts emerging from the hundreds of thousands of words of testimony heard by the Johnson Committee was the readiness, now, of the Air Force to begin major space operations. The reconnaissance of lunar and interplanetary space is possible with the Air Force missile power now in existence, with Thor, Atlas, and Titan. Added to the manned space experiments now beginning with the X-15 rocket plane and to long-standing Air Force research in the physiology of space travel were capabilities for the attainment of the moon within months, the dispatch of reconnaissance probes to Venus and to Mars, and manned flight around the moon and back to Earth. These ventures became, under the weighed testimony of Air Force leaders, ventures of today's devices and today's work. Involved is control of space.

. . . control of outer space

Senator Johnson. "Now would you give the committee what things you believe are essential to control outer space?"

General White. "Well, I think the number one thing is to get some things in outer space, sir.

"The first thing you have to have is the means for firing objects into space.

"One of the most important, I say, projectors in this case in that field is the Titan, and that is one of the reasons not only because of its operational value to the ballistic missile inventory but because of the future growth in that booster for outer space projection, I am anxious to have the Titan expedited. It is a more sophisticated booster than the Atlas. It is a more rigid construction, and is the prime vehicle in the hands of the United States today for getting large vehicles and apparatus into outer space.

"You have to start with the booster and in my opinion the Titan is just over the horizon in that field."

* * * *

Senator Johnson. "Do you want to go ahead and discuss some other things?"

General White. "The human factors, if you want to get a man into space, we certainly do that, and we have done a great many experiments in the Air Force with that sort of thing. We have space suits actually developed to enable a man actually to live in getting to and from the moon.

"We will undoubtedly have to develop all sorts of communications equipment, guidance equipment.

"I actually foresee the use of weapons in space, both on offensive and defensive.

"I can imagine a satellite being a missile launching platform. It is possible to put one of those things in space, and have it go over any given spot on earth and at a given signal, and mind you of course this is not a simple proposition but I am told that it is possible, have that fire a missile at a given point on the earth, a certain city, for example.

"I think that if that is possible, that concomitantly there should be developed a defense against that kind of a satellite.

"The reconnaissance is one of the—probably one of the earlier developments that will take place.

"You will have a vehicle that will map enormous areas of the earth frequently and perhaps by television and other means get the actual photographs down on earth.

"Another way to do observation would be to put a vehicle in space which would be motionless with respect to the earth's surface, because if you fired high enough, and under certain conditions, the speed of that vehicle at the greater radius from the center of the earth can be made to equal the rate of rotation of the earth so in effect it relatively—relative to the earth's rotation it is stationary, and that can be used for many things, for observation of all the earth within the range, sight range of that particular vehicle, for communications purposes, and so on.

"I think you can even go on further, and I think it is within the realm of possibility that we can reach the moon within a very short time, by relatively short, two, three, four years.

"I think it is possible that man can go there. I am told, and I certainly have no personal knowledge or have any personal expertness in the matter, that by various combinations of stages with boosters such as that of the Titan it would be possible to actually reach one of the other planets in our solar system.

* * * *

"We have done a great many developments in this area.

"The Titan itself, the rocket engines for practically all of the ballistic missiles are Air Force engines.

"We have sent many instruments into the high altitudes to study cosmic rays, temperatures. We have sent people in balloons to very high altitudes to learn all we can about the reaction of the outer space, as near as we can reach it, on the human body. There are just an enormous number of such experiments we have done, sir."

. . . an extension of Air Force mission

Senator Johnson. "I want to ask you, what about the Air Force role of putting the Air Force into outer space?"

General Schriever. "Well, my feeling is this: that from a mission point of view, there is a great similarity in operating in the air, in the atmosphere above the earth, and in operating in space, and so that is No. 1.

"I think that it normally follows mission-wise.

"No. 2, from a technical standpoint, these ballistic missiles you see here, and what they represent in terms of resources, facilities, know-how, people, is the platform for going into space, not only the boosters but the guidance, the re-entry, all parts of it.

"I made a statement a year ago that at least 90 per cent of what we are doing in the Air Force ballistic missile program, 90 per cent of all of this work can be directly applied to an astronautics or space program.

"And so, from a technological standpoint, it is, I think, a normal transition to step from these ballistic missiles into satellites, moon rockets, going to planets.

"Of course, from a personnel standpoint, physiological standpoint, we have had the department* at Randolph Field for quite a long

*[Department of Space Medicine, School of Aviation Medicine, USAF, Air University, located at Randolph Air Force Base, Texas. The Department is headed by Dr. Hubertus Strughold, famous pioneer in the physiology of the space man. Dr. Strughold was Director of Aeromedical Research Institute and Professor of Physiology at the University of Berlin, 1935–1945, and Director of The Physiological Institute, University of Heidelberg, 1947–1949, before coming to America in 1949 to assist in establishing the Air Force Department of Space Medicine. He is the author of an excellent study, *The Green and Red Planet* (Albuquerque, University of New Mexico Press, 1953), concerning the possibility of living forms on Mars.]

time. Dr. Strughold has been working there on manned space flight. You are familiar with the balloon flights we have had, high-altitude aircraft. We are practically operating in a space environment when we get up to altitudes of 100,000 feet or so."

Senator Johnson. "And you consider control of outer space extremely important to the free world, do you not?"

General Schriever. "Well, I certainly do, although I would not be able to give you exactly why in tangible terms, again, a year ago, that I thought perhaps the future battles would be space battles instead of air battles, and I still feel that way about it."

. . . the reconnaissance satellite

General Schriever disclosed plans to use the Thor as a booster for a satellite with a recoverable reconnaissance device.

General Schriever. "Let me say this, that there was a lot of interest at different sources in the government for an advanced reconnaissance system. . . .

"Now since sputniks, there has been of course a desire to accelerate this program, and we have been looking at means for accelerating it and I have given verbal instructions and this will be carried out in contractual terms, to bring into this program the Thor as a booster to expedite getting orbiting vehicles and we think, based on our studies to date, and we have made rather exhaustive studies both in house and in Lockheed, that we can get before the end of this year, say some time around perhaps as early as July, but more likely about October, we can get an orbiting vehicle with the Thor as a booster, which would be a boost to this program here, in other words, we would be getting experience, we would be getting some of the components in flight and so forth, . . .

"Now the actual system that would be orbiting, the dry weight of that after you have used the fuel would be about . . . pounds, and there are several different existing engines that you could use for a second stage.

"One of them is the present Vanguard second-stage engine.

"Another one is the Bell engine that we are using for this particular program now, it was used for the Hustler air-to-surface missile. . . ."

Senator Symington. "So you could make and by what date do you think you could have a functioning weapon as a satellite?"

General Schriever. "I think that we could have a reconnaissance capability, using the Thor booster, by the spring of next year, with a recoverable capsule."

Senator Bush. "Spring of what?"

General Schriever. "Spring of next year, 1959."

Senator Carroll and General Irvine discussed photo reconnaissance by satellite, with ICBM power for the booster.

Senator Carroll. "Can you have under planning—you do not have to answer this if it is classified—did you, as sort of the production manager of the Air Force, did you have under consideration a sort of a reconnaissance satellite?"

General Irvine. "We have been working toward that end in General Putt's department for a long time, and in this area we have been interested in that problem because we knew in the engine required for the ICBM, we had the fundamental element required for the first step in the satellite."

Senator Carroll. "In other words, the ICBM engine—"

General Irvine. "Yes, sir."

Senator Carroll. (continuing) "—could be used to launch this reconnaissance satellite?"

General Irvine. "Yes, sir."

Senator Carroll. "Mr. Chairman, I have had brought to my office about—a while ago, a photograph, and this is certainly not classified, taken by the Boston University Physical Research Laboratory, which I understand is doing some research work for the Air Force, a picture taken from Pike's Peak of Denver, Colorado, 63 miles away, and taken evidently by a mirror camera, photographed with a red filter, and I am able to pick out with my eye, without the aid of a magnifying glass, the State Capitol, the Martin plant that is doing some military work, and many military installations.

"The thought occurred to me whether or not, if you take a picture with a camera on a horizontal plane at 63 miles, is it classified, can you tell us how far you can photograph down?"

General Irvine. "I think there again that Mr. Horner* can tell you

* [Honorable Richard E. Horner, Assistant Secretary of the Air Force for Research and Development.]

more positively about this than I can, but we have cameras that will take pictures from a satellite in orbit."

Senator Carroll. "Pictures from a satellite in orbit?"

General Irvine. "Yes, sir."

Senator Carroll. "Well, there has been some talk, as I remember, that—"

General Irvine. "A lot of work on it."

* * * *

Senator Carroll. "If we could launch such a satellite, reconnaissance satellite, I assume the Russians, being ahead of us, could launch one, too, and—"

General Irvine. "Yes, sir."

Senator Carroll. "And by having such photographic cameras functioning, perhaps each of us would know what each other is doing; is that possible?"

General Irvine. "I think this would be very healthy. This is the first step toward peace."

Senator Carroll. "Is that what you meant when you said a little while ago, if we would use some of our money or devote our money to some of the research programs, is this one of the programs you have in mind?"

General Irvine. "We have three Air Force programs with three different companies, one of which we have recommended for implementation."

. . . the manned satellite

General Schriever. "There is no manned satellite program authorized at this time. I would prefer not to say anything more about the program that has been under discussion, which Mr. Horner covered, because of its classification."

Mr. Weisl. "I think the Senator is talking about the X-15 which was discussed."

General Schriever. "Oh, this is not a satellite. This is a rocket-propelled experimental airplane."

Senator Barrett. "Yes, I understand that, General, but I was thinking about an extension of the X-15, and it would be perfectly agreeable to wait for executive session."

General Schriever. "Well, I think I can say something about certain things that appear possible in the not too distant future with the hardware that is now in the ballistic missile programs."

Senator Barrett. "That is what I had in mind."

General Schriever. "You can take the Thor, the Jupiter, the Atlas, and the Titan, and they all make perfect boosters, some of them better than others, and there is existing hardware for second stages available today that would put into orbit considerably greater weights than we are talking about in our current satellite programs.

"And these could then be followed by experimental recovery flights initially. You could even get to the moon by 1959."

. . . costs of astronautic research

Mr. Horner pointed out that the program of astronautic research disclosed by testimony to be within Air Force capabilities was not enormously costly: "I noticed throughout all of the testimony a thread which seems to indicate to me the general opinion that what we have called our astronautics program, what might be called space exploration, is something that is really quite expensive, and really relatively expensive.

"Relative to the efforts we now have in other fields, and specifically in the ballistic field, it can be really quite cheap, quite reasonable indeed.

"I say this because we have a large part of the industrial plant that is needed. We have a large part of the test facilities that are needed. We have a lot of the techniques fairly well in hand.

"What is left to do now is to put these things together, and there are any number of different things that can be accomplished, a list that would be truly challenging, for a relatively small investment over the next few years."

. . . the ten years ahead

The big investment for the first generation of space vehicles has already been made, General Schriever said. The exploitation of this generation of vehicles in space flight is ample for a wide range of projects over the next ten years. Sizably increased power is not presently needed.

General Schriever. "Present Atlas, Titan, and Thor provide booster capacity for space missions of primary interest for the next ten years. Principal investment in first-generation space vehicles has already been made.

"Two. The development of a few added stages of small size, as building blocks, can provide, in proper combination with the boosters, vehicles for all space missions for the next ten years. . . .

"Three. The guidance systems for the present and second generation ICBM and IRBM are basically adequate to perform the space missions, in other words to hit these, the moon, . . . planets; you need a guidance system to do it.

"Four. The development of payloads for some of the various missions, including payloads for animals and manned experiments, can be defined and initiated now. In other words, we can start work on these things now.

"Five. Research and technical development required on critical problems and on basic space phenomena can be defined and initiated now for the second generation of space vehicles and space missions.

"In other words, we are not just groping around. We can actually specify things."

Senator Saltonstall. "Are these your conclusions or conclusions of people who have submitted them to you?"

General Schriever. "These are the conclusions we have reached after many months of study in my organization where there have also been inputs by industry.

"These have been reviewed just a couple of weeks ago by the Ballistic Missiles Scientific Advisory Committee, headed by Dr. Millikan. They essentially agree with all of the major conclusions we have reached."

Senator Saltonstall. "And you believe in them personally?"

General Schriever. "I believe in them personally, yes. . . . "

Mr. Vance. "General, General Medaris testified that unless we developed an engine of a million-pound thrust by 1961 we would be out of the race.

"Do you agree with that?"

General Schriever. "No, I do not. I think that we need to develop larger engines, and I do not disagree that we should not develop a million-pound engine, mind you, but I do not agree we would be out of the race if we have not got one developed by 1963."

Mr. Weisl. "You do agree we should be working on such an engine?"

General Schriever. "Yes, I agree."

Mr. Vance. "Have you so recommended it?"

General Schriever. "No, I have not recommended it. . . ."

Senator Stennis. "I want to be sure we understand it. You really think we ought to be building this large engine?"

General Schriever. "I think we should be developing this large engine; yes, sir."

Senator Stennis. "With a million pounds' thrust, anyway?"

General Schriever. "In the order of a million pounds."

Senator Stennis. "But you do look upon it as kind of secondary necessity, that is, something to fall back on, rather than a primary necessity; is that right?"

General Schriever. "I think we need these kinds of engines. We need to have them by 1965 or so for the next generation of space vehicles.

"I have carried you through 1965 with basically the boosters we now have, plus these . . . second stages which, I think, will do everything that you want to do for the next ten years."

THE COMING OF ASTRO POWER

At the conclusion of his testimony General Bernard Schriever made a formal prepared statement to the Committee. The few typewritten pages he read for the record make up one of the prime documents of our age. Passing through the intermediate realm of the ballistic missile weapon systems to look forward into the dawning age of manned space operations, General Schriever dealt America her first hand as an astro power. These are the cards we have to draw to. This is the probable play. Facing war, the stakes are high; and in peace the adventure is on into a new age of man. We stand therefore at a time for "bold decision."

Statement of Major General Bernard A. Schriever
Before the Senate Preparedness Investigating Subcommittee
9 January 1958

My purpose here today is to assist your subcommittee in defining and evaluating the kind of future performance and programs which are required if we are to give our country undisputed leadership in the fields of ballistic missiles and astronautics.

As I see it, we face two challenges: one immediate, the other long-range. Meeting each one successfully is vital to the maintenance and strengthening of our national security.

In seeking to provide you with what in my opinion are concrete answers to these questions, I am not going back over past history. The concern we all share now is with history in the making—and what we can do to make that history lead us toward the security we require.

In looking now to the future, the immediate question is, what can be done to further compress the time within which we will achieve significant operational forces of intermediate-range and intercontinental ballistic missiles? How can we close the gap that now exists between our country and the Soviet Union with respect to the availability of these weapon systems?

. . . our ballistic missile potential

The Thor IRBM will be the earliest operational ballistic missile. Our planning now stipulates 15 missiles per squadron.

The present Department of Defense directive, which calls for both Jupiter and Thor squadrons, does not achieve at the earliest date the deterrent power which is well within our capabilities. If a decision is made immediately to increase our rate of production over the currently approved maximum rate, by early 1960 we can deploy twice as many operational IRBM squadrons, all Thor-equipped. The first two Thor squadrons would be overseas by the end of calendar year 1958.

The next addition to our ballistic missile force will be the Atlas ICBM, on which research and development has been, and is, proceeding about as rapidly as possible. We expect to equip our first Atlas operational complex in the near future. The force buildup beyond that first unit, however, can be appreciably accelerated beyond current plans. This can be accomplished by an immediate decision to double the currently approved maximum rate of production of Atlas missiles. This will permit us to equip almost double the total Atlas squadrons called for in the next few years. This also is well within our capabilities.

The third, and most advanced ballistic missile in our force of the immediate future will be the Titan ICBM. Here again our research and development is progressing at a rapid rate. Our most recent assessment, however, shows that we have the capability to equip twice the number of Titan squadrons indicated by currently approved schedules.

. . . the cost of these accelerations

Our estimates show that the additional strength provided by these accelerations of our missile systems can be accomplished by means of relatively small increases in the expenditure of funds allocated for the remainder of FY 58. However appropriation of considerable additional funds over those presently budgeted for FY 59 would be required.

It would be a colossal blunder if we were not to plan beyond the point of matching every Soviet ballistic missile with one of our own. We must continue to refine and improve this first generation of ballistic missiles, in effect progressing to a next generation of missiles. We can provide in the slightly more distant future greater accuracy, greater destructive potential, greater range, greater simplicity, greater mobility, but at less cost. All of this we can do and are now planning, and all of this demonstrates once again that there is no fixed, final and frozen solution to the problem of national defense, any more than there is any ultimate weapon.

. . . our astronautics potential

The second challenge, as I analyze the future, is in the longer-range field of astronautics. Here the military requirements are at present less clearly defined, but are no less demanding of an immediate, vigorous program designed to surpass Soviet capabilities in this field.

Fortunately we are already a long way down the road. The original investment for preliminary projects in space flight has already been made in our present Air Force ballistic missile programs.

We have already provided for approximately 500 million dollars worth of new facilities designed for development, testing, and production of ballistic missiles—facilities nonexistent only three years ago. We have a vast military, scientific and industrial organization experienced in the design, development, testing and production of ballistic missiles. Moreover, this organization is staffed by personnel of the greatest competence who have mastered many new fields of knowledge which can be springboards to substantial short cuts in our mastery of astronautics.

In my opinion, these presently existing assets provide our best steppingstones for every advance we can expect to make into this new age of space science and technology. Our studies have shown that by using our presently existing rocket engines and missiles, we can provide both at the earliest date and at the greatest economy not only unmanned reconnaissance of the moon, but also a basic vehicle for manned space flight. I believe that any program to develop a separate astronautics agency would result in duplication of capabilities already existing in the Air Force ballistic missile programs, and at a cost in funds and time similar to that already expended on these programs.*

* Following the prepared statement, further questioning took place in which General Schriever's position relative to the proposed new Department of Defense Space Agency was clarified:

Senator Saltonstall. "General Schriever, may I first say that this is an awfully interesting and important statement, and I certainly appreciate, as one member of the committee, you appearing as a witness today. Certainly, it is comforting to have men like you around.

"My question is this: You were critical in that statement just now of a new satellite agency, so to speak."

General Schriever. "Yes, sir."

Senator Saltonstall. "As I understand it, if they set up a new satellite agency in the Department of Defense, that would not mean that the present Air Force facilities, the Air Force personnel and the Air Force research could not, under the direction of that agency, go forward and go forward along the lines that you are saying.

"I would not interpret a new agency to mean that you would put on the shelf and throw away all, discard all, that you people have done, discard your efforts.

"Now, isn't that your understanding?"

General Schriever. "Yes.

"Let me clarify that point. I will read that again where I say that a separate

If we are to take full advantage of our present astronautics potential, these are some of the projects we can immediately initiate:

1. Our present Thor missile with existing second-stage hardware can place a satellite in orbit with a respectable payload.

2. By adding existing third-stage hardware, this vehicle can perform unmanned reconnaissance of the moon at a relatively early date.

3. A slightly modified Thor plus a high-energy fuel stage which we have been developing can make possible initial unmanned reconnaissance of Mars and Venus.

4. The Titan booster when developed plus high-energy second and third stages could put much greater weights into orbit and could provide extended manned satellite missions. This vehicle could provide manned flight around the moon and back to the earth.

Many far-reaching potential capabilities are apparent as we look more into the future and develop the possibilities of thermonuclear propulsion and payloads up to hundreds of tons. These few specific examples of capabilities now at hand and their times of realization, however, strongly emphasize the requirement for initiating these projects immediately if we are to have any chance of leading in space technology in the 1965–1970 time period.

The entire astronautics development program which I have touched upon can be initiated at once with no dilution or diversion of our ballistic missile programs.

As I analyze the future, if we are to meet the challenging requirements of either ballistic missile acceleration or of astronautics, we

---

astronautics management agency, and by that I want to clarify the word 'management,' I mean an operating management organization which has a large technical staff, and has its own procurement agency.

"I think we do need an agency which will formulate policy and approve total program for the Defense Department, and give direction."

Senator Stennis. "And give you the job to do; is that right?"

General Schriever. "But I think the existing—that is right, in part. I am not saying I should have it all."

Senator Stennis. "I know. But hand it down to you, and you take it from there."

General Schriever. "That is right. But we will be directed by that agency; I expect that.

"I think earlier I said we ought to have a strong direction agency that makes decisions . . . if that is the way it is set up, I am all 100 per cent for it.

"But if it attempts to set up a procurement staff and do the contracting out of the Pentagon and set up a big technical staff there and make all the technical decisions, I say you are not going to set up a very good thing."

must recognize where our strongest capabilities lie today, and make certain decisions now. The decisions we make today will exert momentous influence on where we stand tomorrow, and must point to well-planned, clearly-defined objectives. Today's situation calls for bold decision and calculated risk and funds.

Air University Quarterly Review

APPENDIX V

A Glossary of Terms Related to the Ballistic Missile

Compiled by

LT. COLONEL KENNETH F. GANTZ, USAF

AAMA. Middletown Air Materiel Area. See **AMA.**

abort. Failure of the missile to reach its target or accomplish its purpose for reasons other than enemy action, such as a malfunction in flight or an intentional destruction by the Range Safety Officer to prevent mishap during a flight test.

activated. To make a planned organization (see) "active" by assigning personnel to it. To make an establishment or installation such as a missile base operative.

AEC. Atomic Energy Commission. A Government agency established by Congress in 1946 to supervise and control the production of nuclear-fissionable materials in the U.S.

AEDC. Arnold Engineering Development Center. An Air Force installation for engineering development at Tullahoma, Tennessee, named for General of the Air Force Henry H. Arnold, Commanding General of the Air Forces in World War II. See **ARDC center.**

aerodynamic heating. The rise in the skin temperature of a missile due to the friction of the air at high speed. A severe problem with the long-range ballistic missile re-entering the atmosphere at a high mach number. Aerodynamic heating reinforced by heat from the missile components can also cause excessive internal temperatures and affect operation of the components. See **re-entry.**

Aero Medical Laboratory. A laboratory at Wright-Patterson Air Force Base, near Dayton, Ohio, for the conduct of research in aviation medicine.

AFAC. Air Force Armament Center at Eglin Air Force Base, Florida, does research and development testing of Air Force armament; provides test resources and services for contractors and other government agencies; operates the primary Air Force armament engineering test facility. See **ARDC center.**

AFCRC. Air Force Cambridge Research Center at Laurence G. Hanscom Field, Massachusetts conducts research in electronics, geophysical sciences, balloon technology, human engineering. See **ARDC center.**

AFFTC. Air Force Flight Test Center at Edwards Air Force Base, California accomplishes functional (as distinct from engineering) flight tests of complete, manned aircraft weapon systems; conducts engineering evaluation flight tests of aircraft and power plants; makes static firing tests of missile power plants, etc. See **ARDC center.**

AFMTC. Air Force Missile Test Center at Patrick Air Force Base, Florida, operates the Florida Missile Test Range for collecting test data on ballistic and guided missiles, controlled targets, drones, etc. See **ARDC center.**

AFPTRC. Air Force Personnel and Training Research Center based at Lackland Air Force Base, Texas. Its mission is to improve the operation and maintenance of weapon systems, to develop estimates of the qualitative personnel requirements of new weapon systems, to conduct social science research. See **ARDC center.**

AFSWC. Air Force Special Weapons Center, based at Kirtland Air Force Base, New Mexico, develops and tests atomic weapons and systems components; evaluates personnel hazards associated with such developing and testing. See **ARDC center.**

air-breathing missile. A missile with an engine requiring the intake of air for combustion of its fuel, as in a ramjet or turbojet. To be contrasted with the rocket missile, which carries its own oxidizer and can operate beyond the atmosphere.

airfoil. The contour or shape of the vertical cross section of an airplane wing.

Air Force Ballistic Missile Division. A division of Headquarters Air Research and Development Command established as a field organization to command and control the development of an operational intercontinental ballistic missile. Headquarters AFBMD is located at Inglewood, California.

airframe. The framework and envelope of the missile. The supporting structure for everything else in the missile. The airframe may be divided into several component parts with regard to the aerodynamic forces that act upon it: the forebody or nose, the midsection, the boattail, the base, and the aerodynamic surfaces.

Air Materiel Command. A major air command of the USAF that provides logistic support to the Air Force. This support includes research and development, procurement and industrial planning, and supply and maintenance. AMC provides service units for air depots and furnishes technical instruction and information as required. Headquarters AMC is at Wright-Patterson Air Force Base, near Dayton, Ohio. See **major air command.**

Air Research and Development Command. A major air command in the USAF that carries out the research and development activities required for the accomplishment of Air Force missions. See **major air command.**

AMA. Air Materiel Area. Any one of the several areas of the U.S. set up by the Air Materiel Command for expediting Air Force maintenance and the supply of Air Force organizations and installations within these areas. A principal subdivision of Air Materiel Command that operates any one of these areas directly subordinate to Headquarters AMC. Air materiel area headquarters are located at Middletown, Pa., Mobile, Ala., Oklahoma City, Okla., Ogden, Utah, San Antonio, Tex., San Bernardino, Cal., Sacramento, Cal., and Robins Air Force Base, near Macon, Ga.

AMC. Air Materiel Command. See.

anti-g suit. A tight flying suit that covers parts of body below the heart and is designed to retard the flow of blood to the lower body in reaction to acceleration or deceleration. An antiblackout suit. Bladders or other devices may be incorporated to inflate and increase bodily constriction as the "g" force increases.

apogee. The highest point of a trajectory.

APS. Accessory power supply.

ARDC. Air Research and Development Command. See.

ARDC center. Any of the several principal subdivisions of Air Research and Development Command and directly subordinate to Headquarters ARDC.

aspect ratio. The ratio of the airplane wing span to the chord.

Atlas. An Air Force intercontinental multistage ballistic missile of 5500 miles range with inertial guidance. Developing thousands of tons of thrust with liquid propellant, Atlas reaches a thrust-cutoff velocity near the escape velocity. The apogee of its trajectory is in the region of 800 miles, and its re-entry velocity is on the order of mach 25 at the very high atmospheric altitude of 250,000 feet. Time of flight to target at full range is 30 minutes.

attenuation. The diminution of effectiveness of an emission of radiant energy, such as a radio signal. Attenuation may be caused by distance, passage of the emitted wave through the exhaust flame of the rocket engine, etc.

attitude. The in-flight position of a missile as described by giving the inclinations of its axes to the earth or other specified frame of reference.

ballistic condition. Any one of the conditions affecting the motion or behavior of a missile in flight. Ballistic conditions may include velocity, weight, shape, and size of the missile, rotation of the earth, density of the surrounding air, etc.

ballistic missile. A missile propelled and guided during the first portion of its flight but later traveling a natural and uncontrolled trajectory. Although the rifle bullet and the artillery shell are simple ballistic missiles, the term currently implies the rocket missile designed to be impelled into the upper reaches of the atmosphere or beyond into space before plunging downward toward its target. The principles of scoring an accurate hit with the rocket missile are akin to those of aiming the aircraft bomb rather than the bullet or the shell. As temporarily a part of the airplane, the bomb must be steered to a precise point near and above its target for release from the propulsion and guidance imparted by the airplane, so that it will fall through the necessary ballistic trajectory to reach the desired point of impact on the earth. This trajectory is determined by the momentum imparted by the flight of the airplane, its direction and altitude, and the pull of gravity. It is subject during free fall of the bomb to modification by the forces of nature, such as wind, atmospheric pressure, and temperature.

Ballistic Missiles Office. Established by Air Materiel Command at Inglewood, California, location of the Air Force Ballistic Missile Division, as a separate organization element of Headquarters AMC. The Chief of the Ballistic Missiles Office acts as a manager for ballistic missile logistics, charged with setting up and maintaining a streamlined ICBM/IRBM logistics system. He is responsible directly to the Commander, AMC.

ballistics. The branch of science that deals with the motion, behavior, appearance, or modification of missiles acted upon by any condition or force. The art of designing missiles for efficient flight behavior in accord with their purpose.

ballistic trajectory. That part of the trajectory of a missile that is traveled after propulsive force is cut off.

bird. Slang term for a missile.

blip. A spot of light or other indicator on a radarscope indicating the relative position of a reflecting object such as a missile in flight. **Hypersonic blip:** indication of a reflecting object traveling at hypersonic speed.

blockhouse. A building, usually heavily reinforced, that houses the electronic equipment and controls for preparing and firing a missile, together with auxiliary apparatus.

BMD. Air Force Ballistic Missile Division. See.

BMO. Ballistic Missiles Office. See.

boattail. A cylindrical section of the missile body, the diameter of which continually decreases toward the rear. Its principal purpose is to reduce over-all aerodynamic drag of the airframe.

Bomarc. An Air Force surface-to-air long-range interceptor guided missile designed to operate at high altitude and at very rapid rate of fire. The Bomarc IM-99 is powered by two supersonic ramjet units, assisted by a rocket engine for take-off. It is launched vertically and is guided electronically to its target at supersonic speed. Its range enables it to destroy enemy aircraft at a greater distance than any other missile available for air defense. Successfully tested, Bomarc is now in quantity production.

booster. A rocket engine that assists the normal propulsive system of a missile or rocket vehicle. A booster rocket may be incorporated in the first stage of a missile to give more power for take-off.

B-70. A projected manned supersonic bombardment aircraft expected to operate at speeds of mach 3 and to be capable of sustained flight for several days at altitudes above 75,000 feet.

burnout. The time at which a rocket engine exhausts its fuel. Burnout is distinguished from thrust cutoff, which implies a cessation of burning upon intentional command signal or from self-control. See "Notes on Technical Aspects," Figure 13.

Cape Canaveral. A barren, once-untenanted sandspit on the mid-Florida Atlantic Coast. The cape was chosen as the launch site of the Air Force long-range missile proving ground that extends southeastward into the Atlantic over the five thousand miles to Ascension Island. The range is operated by the Air Force Missile Test Center (see **AFMTC**), with headquarters at nearby Patrick Air Force Base.

captive test. As distinguished from a flight test. A static or "hold-down" test in which a rocket engine or a missile is fired on a test stand to which it remains fixed.

case-bonded grain. See **grain.**

celestial guidance. A system for correcting deflection of a missile from its precalculated and preset trajectory. A device in the missile observes predetermined bright stars in relation to the coordinates of the frame of reference in which the missile is placed. If the angular computation of missile position in relation to the observed stars registers deviation from trajectory, error signals are fed from the computer to the servomechanisms that alter control surfaces, thrust, or rocket engine angle.

CEP. Circular error probability. The radius of the circle within which half the missiles aimed at the center may be expected to fall.

circular error. See **cep.**

cold-flow test. A hydraulic test of the operation and performance of a complete rocket propulsion unit or its major subsystems. Water is used instead of hazardous liquids to simulate propellant flow through the complete firing action on any individual action such as observed flow through the injector.

command. A radio transmission of data to a missile in flight to correct its position and velocity. See "Radio-Inertial Guidance," in "Notes on Technical Aspects."

command-destruct signal. A radio signal that operates intentionally the destruction device carried in the missile.

configuration. The organization and disposition of parts to make a whole, as for a military force. The figure, contour, or pattern produced by such a disposition, as for a missile. Shape. Appearance.

control system. A control system is necessary in the missile to maintain it in stable attitude (see), to prevent undesirable responses to overriding guidance signals, and to correct deflections caused by wind, gusts, and other disturbances. See also **guidance.**

Coriolis acceleration. The result of a force due to the earth's rotation acting upon a body in motion, such as a missile in flight. It results in the eastward deviation of a falling body. If a missile is fired vertically, it will fall to the west of its launching point. As the missile moves upward, its distance from the center of the earth's rotation increases. As its launching point moves east in the earth's rotation, the eastward motion of the missile would have to increase in velocity for the missile to keep pace, since the measure of circumference it must travel is greater than that of the launching point on the earth below. But its eastward velocity is limited to that imparted at the surface of the earth at launching (by rotation). This missile must consequently lag behind and fall west of the launching point, by the amount $x = 4/3\ \omega g t^3 \cos \phi$, when X is the duration, ω the angular velocity of the rotating earth, g the effective gravity, t the time fall, and ϕ the latitude. A missile moving horizontally with respect to the earth moves in a curved path with respect to space by reason of the rotation of the earth. Since a missile is fired at an angle to the horizontal, its trajectory will have a horizontal component of velocity. The Coriolis acceleration will impel the missile to deviate from a great circle trajectory, the direction of the acceleration being always to the right in the Northern Hemisphere and to the left in the Southern Hemisphere, regardless of the direction of flight. Appropriate correction must be made, with regard to latitude and the horizontal velocity of the missile.

countdown. The step-by-step process leading to a missile launching, performed in accordance with a predesignated time schedule. Also the method of counting off minutes and seconds remaining before firing a missile.

countermeasures. The employment of devices or techniques to impair the operational effectiveness of enemy activity. Electronic countermeasures involve the use of electronics to reduce the effectiveness of enemy equipment or tactics which employ or may be affected by electromagnetic radiation.

development. The process of working out and extending the theoretical, practical, and useful applications of a basic design, idea, or scientific discovery. The design, building, modification, or improvement of the prototype of a missile, engine, instrument or the like as determined by the basic idea or concept.

Dew line. A defensive line of radar stations at about the 70th parallel on the North American continent.

dispersion. The scatter of a set of missile trajectories about a particular aiming point.

Doppler radar. See "Radio-Inertial Guidance" in "Notes on Technical Aspects."

DO Rating. The Defense Order rating giving the Department of Defense a priority over commercial orders and purchases in private industry.

drag. The aerodynamic force in a direction opposite to that of flight and due to the resistance of the body to motion in air.

drift. Drift error is a change in the output of an instrument over a period of time. It is usually caused by random wander or by condition of the environment.

DX Rating. The Defense Department overriding priority given on ballistic missile orders and purchases to ensure top priority for the ballistic missile program.

EDP center. Electronic-data-processing center.

escape velocity. The speed a body must attain to overcome a gravitational field, such as that of Earth, and thus theoretically travel on to infinity. The velocity of escape at the Earth's surface is 36,700 feet per second, or approximately seven miles per second. A practical manned spacecraft would travel the atmosphere at a lower velocity and accelerate to escape velocity beyond in order to avoid unacceptably rapid initial acceleration and high skin temperature from aerodynamic heating.

1st Missile Division. The 1st Missile Division, formerly the 1st Bombardment Division (WWII) and later the 1st Air Division of the Strategic Air Command, was activated 15 April 1957 at Los Angeles, California, under the operational control of Air Force Ballistic Missile Division, Headquarters ARDC. On 16 April 1957, Headquarters 1st Missile Division was relocated at Cooke Air Force Base, Lompoc, California. Current mission of the 1st Missile Division is to train IRBM and ICBM crews to combat capability. On 1 January 1958 this Division was transferred to the control of the Strategic Air Command with no change in mission.

ft/sec. A foot-second. A unit of velocity, one lineal foot per second, used to measure the speed of a missile at a given instant during its flight.

frame of reference. The walls, floor, and ceiling of a room may be considered to establish, as an example, the coordinates of a frame of reference. A ball thrown within that room will have, for an observer in that room, a trajectory in relation to this coordinate system.

frequency spectrum. Range of frequencies from a low to a high in terms of the number of vibrations or cycles in a unit of time.

gantry crane. A large crane operating from a frame structure raised on side supports and usually traveling on rails for erecting and servicing large, vertically mounted missiles. The gantry can be placed directly over the launching site and then be rolled away just before the missile is fired.

Gapa. An early rocket-propelled Air Force test missile named for its contemporary type, a "ground-to-air pilotless aircraft." Design and construction began in 1945, and over a hundred Gapa had been fired when the project closed in 1949. The slim antiaircraft Gapa achieved speeds of more than 1500 mph and was homed to its enemy aircraft target by its guidance device. The Gapa series of firings led to the Bomarc missile.

grain. The physical mass of a solid propellant (see), the texture and compactness of its constituent particles. A well-designed grain burns smoothly on its exposed surface without excessive surging or detonation. The same propellant can be made in many grains. A **case-bonded grain** clings to the combustion-chamber wall or a liner; thus the rate of burning is restricted by reduction of the exposed surface of the propellant to its nozzle end.

gravity anomalies. Deviations between theoretical gravity and actual gravity due to local topographic and geologic conditions, such as the existence of mountains, valleys, oceans, or abnormally high or low density of the materials near the place of measurement. If a large body of material much denser than the surrounding material lies near the point of measurement, it will cause a deflection of a plumb line toward it. Although small in magnitude, gravity anomalies must be included in refined determinations of geodesic lines, the static vertical, and sea-level elevations. Gravity anomalies vary in magnitude from about zero to plus or minus 0.07 per cent.

guidance. The means and action of regulating the position and velocity of a missile during its powered flight in order to place it in a satisfactory trajectory before its power is cut off. Delivery of the warhead to its predetermined target requires inclusion of a guidance system in the missile.

guided missile. An unmanned vehicle with trajectory or flight path capable of being altered by a guidance system within the missile. The families of guided missiles are air to air, air to surface, air to underwater, surface to air, surface to surface, surface to underwater, underwater to air, and underwater to surface. The ballistic missile is a guided missile during the powered phase of its flight.

HADC. Holloman Air Defense Center, New Mexico, conducts research and development of guided missile subsystems and components; tests and evaluates missile weapon systems, missile operational techniques; and conducts aeromedical research and development. See **ARDC center.**

hardness. The property of an installation, facility, or equipment that will prevent an unacceptable level of damage resulting from aerial bombardment.

hard site. A missile launching installation designed to withstand nuclear weapon strikes of a stated magnitude.

hardware. The physical object, as distinguished from its capability or function. The actual engines, case, pumps, guidance system, or other components of the missile. Often used in regard to the stage of development, as in the passage of a device or component from the design or planning stage into the hardware stage as the finished object.

heat barrier. See **thermal barrier.**

heat exchanger. A power-plant unit installed in the exhaust system of the turbopump assembly. The hot exhaust from the turbine is passed over one or more coils of tubing in the heat exchanger to expand gas or to convert liquid oxygen into hot gaseous oxygen for pressurizing the liquid oxygen tank.

heat transfer. As in the transfer of heat across the combustion-chamber walls of a rocket engine, an acute design problem.

hypersonic. Mach 5 or greater. High-speed velocities five or more times the speed of sound. See **speed of sound.**

ICBM. Intercontinental ballistic missile.

IRBM. Intermediate-range ballistic missile. The 1500-mile-range missile as contrasted with the intercontinental or 5000-mile range missile.

inertial force. The force produced by the reaction of a body to an accelerating force, equal in magnitude and opposite in direction to the accelerating force. Inertial force endures only so long as the accelerating force endures.

inertial guidance. A kind of guidance effected by means of gyroscopic devices and mechanisms that automatically adjust the missile after its launching to follow a given flight path, the mechanisms reacting to inertial forces during flight. See "Notes on Technical Aspects of Ballistic Missiles."

inertial guidance system. A dead-reckoning missile guidance system that employs sensitive devices which respond to the earth's gravitational field and to inertial effects in accordance with the Newtonian laws of motion. The system is therefore not dependent on information obtained from radio transmitters outside the missile.

intelligence. The knowledge resulting from the collection, evaluation, integration, and interpretation of all available information that concerns the capabilities, limitations, vulnerabilities, and probable intentions of the enemy or potential enemy.

interference. Electrical or electromagnetic disturbance arousing undesirable response in electronic equipment.

IOC. Initial operational capability.

ion layer. See **ionosphere.**

ionosphere. An outer belt of the earth's atmosphere in which radiations from the sun ionize, or excite electrically, the atoms and molecules of the atmospheric gases. The height of the ionosphere varies with the time of day and the season, but its lower limit is generally considered to lie between twenty-five and fifty miles. It is divided into several layers with respect to radiation and reflective properties, the D-layer, the E-layer, etc. A characteristic phenomenon is its reflection of certain radio waves.

isostatic. Under equal pressure from every side.

jet. A jet engine, a kind of reaction engine that takes in air from outside as an oxidizer to burn fuel and ejects a jet of hot gases backward to create thrust, the gases being generated by the combustion within the engine. The jet engine differs from the rocket engine in its dependence upon air taken in from outside. The rocket engine carries its own oxidizer and is therefore capable of operation in outer space.

jamming. Interference with the reception of radio or radar signals, as by countertransmissions to distort or prevent the guidance of a missile.

JPL. Jet Propulsion Laboratory of the California Institute of Technology.

Jupiter. An Army-developed IRBM of 1500-mile range to be operationally employed by the Air Force as a companion missile to the

Air Force–developed Thor.

Jupiter-C. A multistage adaptation of the Army Redstone rocket tactical ballistic missile, used as an experimental vehicle and for putting the U.S. satellite 1958 Alpha (Explorer) into orbit. The satellite launching version of Jupiter-C had four stages: (1) a modified Redstone missile; (2) a ring of eleven scaled-down versions of the Sergeant, a 100-mile solid rocket tactical missile; (3) a ring of five more scaled-down Sergeants; (4) a final Sergeant and an instrument package. The Jupiter-C should not be confused with the Jupiter IRBM (see).

kill. The achievement of the desired effect against a target.

launch base area. A geographic area encompassing numerous command posts, launch stations and guidance stations, a control center, and a support base.

launching. The launching is the portion of missile flight between initial firing and the time when the missile reaches velocity at which it responds to normal control.

launching tower. A tower of steel girders for positioning and servicing certain missiles.

leveled thrust. A rocket power plant equipped with a programer or engine-control unit that maintains the output at a relatively constant thrust against variations in tank pressures, head-on pump inlets, turbopump output, and thrust-chamber performance.

line of sight. The straight line between the eye and a target or other observed point. Thus the straight line from a transmitting radar antenna in the direction of the beam.

liquid-propellant rocket. A rocket employing liquid propellant fed under pressure from tanks into the combustion chamber of the rocket engine.

liquid rocket. The liquid-propellant rocket.

Logair. A scheduled cargo airlift operated over established routes by commercial air carriers under contract to the United States Air Force.

logistics. That part of military activity concerned with the buildup and supply of a military force by providing for supplies, equipment, transportation, maintenance, construction and operation of facilities, movement and evacuation of personnel, and other similar services in order to render the military force efficient and effective.

logistic concept. A plan or idea for the buildup and support of a military force by providing supplies, equipment, maintenance, transportation, etc. The general statement of an approved Air Force policy on logistics for a particular weapon system, based on the requirements of the weapon system presented by the concept for its employment in operations.

low-order detonation. A partial or slow explosion, usually accidental.

LOX. Liquid oxygen, explosive.

mach. The speed of a moving body measured in units equal to the speed of sound in the air through which the body moves. This speed is indicated by a mach number designating the number of such units. Thus a speed of mach 1 is a speed equal to that of sound; mach .5 a speed equal to one half that of sound; mach 5 a speed equal to five times that of sound. The speed of sound in dry air at 32° Fahrenheit at sea level is 741 miles per hour.

mach number. A number expressing the ratio of the speed of a moving body through the air to the speed of sound in the air. Thus the speed represented by this number. See **mach**.

major air command. Any of the several principal subdivisions of the United States Air Force directly subordinate to Headquarters USAF. Among the major air commands are Air Defense Command, Air Materiel Command, Military Air Transport Service, Air University, Strategic Air Command, Tactical Air Command, U. S. Air Forces in Europe, Pacific Air Forces, and Air Training Command. The Commands are familiarly referred to by their initials, as ADC, MATS, SAC, which are pronounced in some cases as letters, "A-D-C," and in others as syllables, "Mats," "Sac."

mass ratio. The ratio of the initial take-off weight and the empty or final weight of the missile after consumption of the propellant.

Matador. An Air Force surface-to-surface winged guided missile for tactical use at ranges up to 500 miles, specifications for which were posted in 1946. Propulsion is by turbojet engines with missile speed of 650 mph and ceiling of 35,000 feet. The missile is transported on a truck bearing a zero-length launcher from which it is boosted by a solid-propellant rocket. The Matador TM-61 received its first flight in 1950 and was the Air Force's first operational missile. It has a wing span of 28.7 feet and a length of 39.6 feet. The first Matador tactical missile group was formed in 1951, and now at least five groups employ the missile, three of which are deployed in Europe. A newer Matador, the TM-76A, features a self-contained navigation system and range of 650 miles. Flight testing began in September 1957.

MOAMA. Mobile Air Materiel Area. See **AMA.**

multistage rocket. A number of rocket units assembled so that each successive unit fires as the preceding stages burn out.

NACA. National Advisory Committee for Aeronautics. A Government committee created by act of Congress in 1915 to study the problems of flight and to conduct aeronautical research and experiment. Its 17 members are appointed by the President and include two from the Air Force. The committee operates three principal aeronautical laboratories.

Navaho. A 5500-mile, ramjet-powered surface-to-surface Air Force guided missile with celestial guidance. The Navaho has been canceled.

Nike. An Army surface-to-air antiaircraft guided missile in operational use. Nike-Ajax, a liquid-propellant rocket, has a range of 25 miles; Nike-Hercules, a solid-propellant rocket, a range of 85 miles.

nitric acid–hydrocarbon rocket. Employs a rocket engine using liquid propellants, the oxidizer being nitric acid and the fuel being a hydrocarbon, such as jet engine fuel or furfuryl alcohol ($C_2H_3OCH_2OH$).

nitric acid rocket techniques. Several types of nitric acid mixtures are used for oxidizers.

nose cone. The cone-shaped cap at the forward extremity of a missile. In a military missile the warhead (see) to be delivered and detonated at the target, together with its auxiliary equipment, such as a fuzing system, is incorporated in the nose cone.

no-thrust point. A condition reached when friction and the compressor heat the air flowing through a jet engine to a temperature so high that combustion of the fuel would cause structural failure.

NOTS. Naval Ordnance Test Station at China Lake, California.

numbered air force. A United States Air Force unit designated by an assigned number and on an organizational level between a major air command and an air division. It is composed of Air Force wings or air divisions, together with appropriate support units. E.g., Fifth Air Force.

OCAMA. Oklahoma City Air Materiel Area. See **AMA.**

occultation. Shutting of the light from one celestial body by another intervening between it and the observer, especially the eclipses of stars by the moon. The apparent disappearance of a star behind the oncoming edge of the moon's disc.

OOAMA. Ogden Air Materiel Area. See **AMA.**

operational. Ready to carry out a mission. Actually operating.

operational missile. A missile that, in contrast to a research or test missile, can be used to attack an enemy target.

orbital speed. Orbital velocity.

orbital velocity. The speed a "circling" body (mass) must attain at right angle to the centripetal pull of a gravitational field in order to counterbalance it by inertial force and thus stay in orbit rather than escape the field or fall toward its center. For a circular orbit at any level in a gravitational field the orbital velocity is equal to 0.707 the escape velocity (see) for that level, applied in a direction at right angle to the radius of the orbit. The closer a satellite to the Earth, the higher its orbital velocity. Orbital velocity is 18,000 miles per hour (24,200 feet per second) for a circular orbit at 300 miles altitude. Orbital velocity of the Moon at a mean distance of 253,000 miles in its elliptical orbit around the Earth is 3100 feet per second. Many factors bearing on the placing of an artificial satellite in orbit indicate that it will assume an elliptical orbit, as the orbit of U.S. satellite 1958 Alpha (Explorer), which surges around the Earth from a perigee (low point) of 214 miles to an apogee (high point) of 1850 miles in a rotation period of 114 minutes. Since orbital velocity varies with distance from the Earth, a satellite in an elliptical orbit is at maximum velocity in perigee position and at minimum velocity in apogee position. A simple example of the calculation of the velocity required to maintain a satellite in its path around the earth is offered by the case of a circular orbit. Since the velocity needed must serve to equate the gravitational attraction at the radius of the orbit, then $V = \sqrt{g_o R^2 / r}$, where g_o is the acceleration of gravity at the earth's surface, R is the earth's radius, and r is the radius of the circular orbit. The time period of the satellite's revolution, once around its orbit, is found from $T = \frac{2\pi\sqrt{r^3/g_o}}{R}$.

organization. A designated group of persons, such as a squadron or a missile division, established by higher authority and formed as a unified whole, with a commander or director at its head and with specific mission and responsibilities.

OSAF. Office of the Secretary of the Air Force.

OSD. Office of the Secretary of Defense.

oxidant. An oxidizer. In a rocket propellant a substance such as liquid oxygen, nitric acid, or the like that yields oxygen for burning the fuel.

oxygen-hydrocarbon engine. A rocket engine that operates on propellant of liquid oxygen as oxidizer and a hydrocarbon fuel, such as the petroleum derivatives. See **nitric acid–hydrocarbon rocket.**

pad. A thick concrete base from which a missile is fired.

payload. The warhead or other useful load a missile carries.

pound of thrust. A measurement unit of the reaction force generated in a jet or rocket engine and available for propulsion.

propellant. The oxidant and fuel expended in a rocket to produce propulsion.

prototype. A model of a missile or other equipment that is suitable for complete evaluation of form, design, and performance. The prototype uses approved parts and is representative of the final item. It follows the experimental model and precedes the production model.

QPI. Qualitative personnel information.

QPRI. Qualitative personnel requirements information.

radar. Radio detection and ranging. A method of using beamed and reflected radio-frequency energy (radio waves) for detecting and locating objects, for measuring distance or altitude. The electronic equipment, sets, or devices used.

RADC. Rome Development Center at Griffiss Air Force Base, New York, accomplishes operational development and test of electronic supporting systems, subsystems, and components and operates an electronic countermeasures test facility to support ARDC centers. See **ARDC center.**

radio-inertial guidance system. A command type of guidance system. The system includes (1) a radar tracking unit composed of radar equipment on the ground, one or more transponders (an electronic device that receives a challenging signal and automatically transmits a response) in the missile, and necessary communication links to the guidance station; (2) a computer that accepts missile position and velocity information from the tracking unit and furnishes the command link appropriate signal to steer the missiles; (3) the command link consisting of a transmitter on the ground and an antenna and receiver on the missile (actually the command link is built into the tracking unit); (4) an inertial system for partial guidance in the event of radio failure.

ramjet. A ramjet engine. A kind of jet engine consisting essentially of a tube open at both ends in which fuel is burned continuously to create a jet thrust. The ramjet has neither compressor nor turbine, the air necessary for oxydizing the fuel being taken in and compressed, or "rammed in," by the high-speed velocity of the engine as the engine moves forward.

RAND Corporation. A non-Governmental, nonprofit organization for research relating to the national security and welfare of the United States. It developed from an organization created in 1946 to provide background research for certain Air Force projects and was reorganized as the RAND Corporation in 1948 under a grant from the Ford Foundation. The primary activity of RAND is the conduct of Project RAND, a continuing program to study strategy, tactics, instrumentalities, and techniques for the purpose of providing analytical information to assist the Air Force in formulating development plans and improved operational and logistical concepts for air warfare. The RAND Corporation also conducts research with its own funds and under sponsorship of other Governmental agencies.

Rascal. A long-range Air Force air-to-ground guided missile. This liquid rocket-powered missile may be carried in the bomb bay of a strategic bomber such as the B-47 and will permit the bomber to stand as much as 100 miles outside a ground-defended target area and dispatch the missile itself to penetrate to the target. Speed of the missile is mach 2.5, guidance is preset and by radar, Rascal may be released at 50,000 feet altitude and climb to 100,000 feet to increase the difficulty of interception before starting its plunge. The missile is 32 feet long and four feet in diameter. Strategic Air Command is activating operational Rascal squadrons.

rate transmitter and rate receiver. A special purpose radio transmitter and receiver combination used to determine the rate of change in missile range during flight.

Razon. An Air Force glide bomb controlled in both azimuth and range by movable control surfaces in the tail which may be adjusted by radio signals from the bomb-dropping plane. Development of Razon and Tarzon, a six-ton razon-type bomb, was begun early in World War II, but the two bombs did not reach the combat stage. The Tarzon project was abandoned in 1946 and picked up again in 1948, and the Tarzon was used successfully in the Korean War. The glide bomb, fitted with airfoils to provide for lift and control, was carried and dropped in the direction of the target by a bombardment airplane.

Redstone. An Army surface-to-surface tactical missile for use at ranges up to 200 miles. A development of the German V-2. It is inertially guided and is controlled by jet and air vanes. The Redstone was test fired in 1953 after ten years of development. Redstone, with power increase, is the basic rocket of the Jupiter-C rocket vehicle used to put the U.S. satellite 1958 Alpha (Explorer) in orbit.

re-entry. The entry of Earth's atmosphere by a missile on trajectory through space above. Re-entry poses formidable problems of aerodynamic heating effects from the extremely high speed at which the re-entry body penetrates the air. See **aerodynamic heating.**

refractory ceramics. As a possible coating or outer surface for the re-entry body of a missile. Refractory ceramics, such as the oxides of aluminum, silicon, and zirconium, resist oxidation and retain strength until near their melting points around 2700° C.

reliability. See "Missile Reliability," in "Notes on Technical Aspects."

Reynolds number. A dimensionless ratio used in predicting changes in flow character of fluid, *e.g.*, air. As air passes along the body of a missile in flight, the adjacent particles cling to the missile skin and thus have essentially a velocity of zero in relation to the surface of the body. The relative velocity of the air over the surface then increases with distance from the surface. This rate of increase depends upon distance along the body from its "leading edge," or point of penetration, and upon the density, velocity, and viscosity of the air. These last factors may be combined into a ratio known as the Reynolds number. The thickness of the boundary layer of air increases with the body length and changes the effective contour of the surface and resulting pressure on it.

rocket. A missile propelled by hot gases ejected rearward to create forward thrust. The gases are generated from fuel and oxidizer carried in the rocket. Since no intake of air is required, the rocket is capable of operation in outer space.

rubber-base propellant. A solid-propellant mixture in which the oxygen supply is obtained from a perchlorate and the fuel is provided by a synthetic rubber latex. The mixture is then cured into a charge that has the appearance of rubber tire material.

SAAMA. San Antonio Air Materiel Area. See **AMA.**

SBAMA. San Bernardino Air Materiel Area. See **AMA.**

SAC. Strategic Air Command (see).

shock tube. A device in which scale models can be subjected to a momentary gas flow at supersonic and hypersonic velocities. A "blast" of hot gas is sent down a long narrow tube to the test model, held in an evacuated section. A diaphragm at the forward end of the shock tube prevents a pressurized combustible gas mixture in the upstream section from spilling into the evacuated section. A spark ignites the mixture, the diaphragm ruptures, and the mass of hot gas rushes down the tube to the model. High-speed motion picture cameras record the aerodynamic phenomena through a transparent test section.

sloshing. Of the propellant liquids in their tanks, thus creating stresses and a difficult problem of determining the amounts in the tanks during the powered flight.

SM. Strategic Missile.

SMAMA. Sacramento Air Materiel Area. See **AMA.**

Snark. The Air Force Snark SM-62 is essentially a long-range winged pilotless aircraft designed as a strategic surface-to-surface guided missile. It was the first U.S. long-range missile to be test flown and is now in production for assignment to SAC units. The subsonic Snark is powered by a turbojet engine and is considered to have a range of 5500 miles and accuracy (celestial guidance) at least equal to the ballistic missile types.

soft structure. A structure relatively vulnerable to bombing attack. Usually located on the surface of the ground.

solid propellant. A rocket propellant in solid state, as distinguished from liquid propellant. A fast-burning, compound of fuel and oxidizer mixed to produce desired chemical and physical properties. Solid propellants are usually in plastic-like, caked form. They burn on their exposed surface, generating hot exhaust gases to produce a reaction force.

solid-propellant rocket. A rocket using solid propellant. All the propellant, which itself contains all the chemical elements for complete burning, is contained within the rocket engine combustion chamber, where it burns at a nearly constant rate at its exposed surface. Solid-propellant rockets are the oldest and simplest of rockets. No separate tanks, lines, and pumps are required. A disadvantage is the large and heavy combustion chamber. Gunpowder is a primitive form of solid-rocket propellant.

solid rocket. The solid-propellant rocket.

SOP. Standing operating procedure.

sounding rocket. A research rocket bearing instruments for the investigation of the upper altitudes or space.

specific impulse. Used in reference to a solid-propellant rocket, specific impulse is the total impulse divided by the weight of the propellant. The total impulse is the product of thrust and the duration of burning. For liquid-propellant rockets the term **specific thrust** (see) is used to denote the similar performance characteristic. The two terms are frequently used synonymously for the concept.

specific pump. A fuel or an oxidizer pump with a high-suction specific speed.

specific thrust. A performance characteristic of a rocket engine. Specific thrust is the thrust in pounds produced per unit time-rate of flow of propellant in pounds per second. Specific thrust may also be stated as the thrust developed for a unit weight of propellant ejected per second, or again, as the thrust in pounds divided by the propellant consumption rate per second. The term is used commonly, with liquid-propellant rockets in distinction from the usage of specific impulse (see) with solid-propellant rockets.

speed of sound. The speed at which sound travels through a medium such as air or water. The speed of sound through air under certain conditions is used as a measure of velocity of high-speed airplanes and missiles. Sound travels at different speeds through different mediums and at different speeds through the same medium under different conditions of temperature, pressure, etc. In air under "standard sea level" conditions, sound travels at approximately 1100 feet per second or about 750 miles per hour. See **mach.**

stage. One of two or more divisions of a missile, each of which contains a rocket propulsion system. In some designs launching is accomplished by the engines of the first stage. After some portion of powered flight, the first-stage engines are shut off and the stage jettisoned. The second-stage engines are then started. The object of multistage design and jettisoning the stages is to reduce the mass that must be accelerated through the entire powered flight to thrust cutoff and then to free the missile at the beginning of free flight of as much weight in excess of that of the nose cone as possible.

staging. The act of jettisoning at a predetermined trajectory point missile components no longer needed (engines, tanks, and associated equipment).

stagnation temperature. The temperature of air that has been brought to rest from a given velocity or mach number (M). At this temperature all the kinetic energy has been converted to heat energy. Also referred to as total temperature, stagnation temperature (T_o) varies with the ambient temperature (T) in the following relation: $T_o/T = 1 + 0.2M^2$.

standing operating procedure. A fixed and approved method or procedure for accomplishing something. A set of instructions prescribed to attain a standardized procedure.

starting transient. The series of events that take place when a modern liquid-propellant power plant is started. This sequence includes: starting the gas generator, bringing the turbopump up to full speed, firing the main pyrotechnic igniters in the thrust chambers, switching over from external feed, initial combustion of a limited propellant flow to the thrust chambers, building up of main thrust in a series of steps or by a timed increase, and stabilizing the output of the power plant at the specified thrust.

star tracking. See **celestial guidance.**

static overpressure. The pressure, added to the normal atmospheric pressure, that exerts a crushing effect on objects. It is usually measured in pounds per square inch (psi). Static overpressure is synonymous with "shock overpressure," as distinguished from "dynamic" pressure, which exerts a wind effect or toppling effect on objects.

static testing. Ground testing of missiles or parts under simulated flight conditions.

step-approach testing. A method of missile testing to reduce the costly flight tests of a complete missile. The testing proceeds through a series of "steps." First the component parts of the missile are tested until found satisfactory. Next full assemblies of component parts are tested, followed by "hold-down" static firing tests of the propulsion system and airframe. Static tests of complete missiles finally precede the actual flight testing. Each step thus permits checking of the reliability of components and systems at the lowest possible level of over-all assembly, and the interaction of the missile assemblies and systems can be checked as subassemblies and subsystems are mated.

Strategic Air Command. A major air command in the United States Air Force, the units of which are in a constant state of readiness to permit immediate operations of strategic reconnaissance or strategic bombardment, either unilaterally or jointly with the operation of other forces, against the enemies of the United States.

strategic vs. tactical. Strategic air operations are those undertaken against the essential power of an enemy to make war. Tactical air operations are those employed against an enemy force, the targets being the hostile forces or geographic positions essential to the hostile forces. In contrast, strategic targets are war-making facilities or installations such as key manufacturing systems, sources of fuel and raw material, critical stockpiles, power and transportation systems, communications, back-up concentrations or installations of armed forces such as central headquarters or major depots, long-range air installations not immediate to a battle area, and populations. Thus missile forces and air forces may be used "tactically" and "strategically," and missiles may be described as "tactical missiles" or "strategic missiles" according to their intended use.

subsonic. Speed less than that of sound. See **speed of sound.**

supersonic. Speed greater than that of sound. See **speed of sound.**

support base. A place from which logistic support is provided for a group of launch complexes and their control center.

swiveling engine. A rocket thrust chamber assembly that is attached to the missile structure through a gimbal mount, universal joint, or any other movable joint that permits the chamber to be swung through small angles, to use the thrust for steering the missile.

system phasing. Planning and adjusting the acquisition of all components of a weapon system to the acquisition of the item requiring the longest lead time for its procurement. Identifying and scheduling all action necessary to achieve a complete system by a specified, programed date.

systems engineering. The study and planning of a working ballistic missile system consisting of a large number of components and detailed parts that must be designed, developed, and assembled into such a system. Systems engineering is primarily concerned with the relationships of the various parts of the system to one another and to the over-all system performance. See "The Systems

Concept" in "Notes on Technical Aspects of Ballistic Missiles."

table of organization. A publication or table promulgated by the Air Force to direct the organizational structure and personnel for a standardized unit with a fixed mission and workload. Usually called and written "T/O."

tactical. See **strategic vs. tactical.**

Tarzon. See **Razon.**

telemetering. A system for taking measurements within a missile in flight and transmitting them by radio to a ground station, where the information received is used to evaluate the performance of the missile and its components. Telemetry measures and transmits a rate or a magnitude, as of velocity, pressure, or angle of attitude.

temperature gradient. Rate of change of temperature.

theodolite. A sighting and measuring telescopic instrument for obtaining readings of angles. Used to sight a missile in flight to determine its trajectory and point of impact.

theoretical gravity. The value of gravity at the earth's surface if the earth were a perfect sphere with no variation in mass to induce anomalies. See **gravity anomalies.**

thermal barrier. The zone of speed at which friction heat generated by rapid passage of an object through the air exceeds endurance compatible with the function of the object.

thermal load. Stresses imposed upon a missile structure because of expansion or contraction (or both) of certain structural elements by aerodynamic heating during flight and re-entry, by exposure to the heat of a rocket flame, or by cooling effects of liquid oxygen in the oxidizer system.

thermonuclear. Pertaining to nuclear reaction induced by heat, especially to nuclear fusion triggered by the intense heat and pressure of an atomic fission explosion.

thermonuclear weapon. Bomb, device, or warhead intended to explode by nuclear fusion. A hydrogen bomb. See **warhead.**

Thor. An Air Force liquid-rocket strategic ballistic missile designed for intermediate range, 1500 miles. Thor, the first strategic ballistic missile to go into operational use, is assigned to Strategic Air Command's 1st Missile Division for employment.

thrust. The driving force exerted on a missile by the jetting gases of its rocket engine. The thrust, or reaction force, exerted on the rocket structure is caused by the action of the pressure against the rocket engine combustion chamber and nozzle by the combustion gases jetting through the escape provided by the nozzle. These gases are produced by the burning of fuel in the rocket engine combustion chamber.

thrust cutoff point. The point in the missile's trajectory where the guidance system cuts off propulsive power at the desired altitude, speed, and direction. See **burnout.**

thrust-frontal area. A quantity used to evaluate engine performance and obtained from dividing the thrust output by the cross-section area of the engine.

thrust-weight ratio. A quantity used to evaluate engine performance and obtained from dividing the thrust output by the engine weight less fuel. If the pound is used as the unit of measure for thrust and weight, the result is pounds of thrust per pound of engine.

Titan. An Air Force intercontinental liquid-propellant, multistage ballistic missile under development. Titan is comparable to Atlas (see).

T/O. Table of organization (see).

trajectory tolerances. Trajectory tolerances, which should be considered in combination with systems tolerances, are those that affect propellant consumption. They include: (1) variations of mixture ratio (within maximum and minimum limits) of a rocket power plant as delivered by manufacturer, (2) variation of propellant-pump inlet pressure resulting from changes in the acceleration head of each fluid, and (3) variations of consumption by power-plant subsystems, such as the gas generators and the liquid-oxygen pressurization system, as well as variations of mixture ratio occurring during flight because of acceleration and attitude changes of the missile to make good a trajectory to selected target.

turbojet. A species of jet engine to which air is supplied by a turbine-driven air compressor, the turbine being driven by exhaust gases of the engine itself.

turbopump. A turbine-driven pump. Used for feeding propellant to the rocket engine. The turbine derives its power from hot gases, usually produced in a separate gas generator.

Unsatisfactory Report. A standard Air Force printed form for submitting a report of an unsatisfactory condition found, for example by maintenance personnel, in an item of equipment or a technical procedure.

UOC. Ultimate operational capability (as opposed to **IOC**, initial operational capability).

USAF. The United States Air Force.

V-1. The German World War II "Vengeance Weapon No. 1" was a winged robot bomb, a small pilotless, pulsejet monoplane with wooden wings attached to the bomb and conventional airframe and tail construction. It was the first operational "long-range" guided missile. As a terror weapon it had some success against London, first appearing in June 1944. Its slow speed of 400 mph and preset course made it vulnerable to fighters and to antiaircraft fire. The duration of its flight and its range (maximum 190 miles) were controlled by a windmill device in its nose to cut off power after a prescribed period of flight. The V-1 warhead weighed 1988 pounds.

V-2. The German World War II "Vengeance Weapon No. 2" was the first "long-range," rocket-propelled missile to be put in combat, the first missile landing in England in September 1944. The V-2 was a supersonic ballistic missile, launched vertically and automatically tilted on course soon after launching. It was a big missile, 46 feet, 11 inches tall and 5 feet, 5 inches in diameter, and its total weight at take-off was 14 tons, including a 1650-pound warhead. Maximum range was about 200 miles and top speed 3300 mph. Apogee of its parabolic trajectory was at height of 60 miles. The propellant was liquid oxygen and alcohol. Over 2000 V-2's were fired against London and 1600 against Antwerp.

vernier engines. Rocket engines of small thrust employed after the last stage (see) is shut down to make the final adjustment of velocity in order to fix the nose cone on its trajectory to target.

vertical deflection. The deflection of a true plumb line caused by undulations of the earth's crust or variation in earth mass. See **gravity anomalies.**

vulnerability. The susceptibility of a target to a damage agent.

WADC. Wright Air Development Center based at Wright-Patterson AF Base, Ohio, conducts development in aeronautical and related materials, propulsion, aerodynamics, applied human factors, self-contained navigation, guidance, reconnaissance, bombing-fire control, airborne electromagnetic radiation warfare, and aeronautical accessories. See **ARDC center.**

warhead. The part of the missile containing the charge intended to damage the enemy. The great effectiveness of a nuclear warhead comes from its ability to convert a small mass into an enormous amount of energy.

weapon system. The equipment, skills, and techniques forming together an instrument of combat, which usually—but not always—has an air vehicle, such as the B-52 bombardment airplane or the Thor missile, as its major operational element. A complete weapon system includes all related facilities, equipment, materials, services, and personnel required solely for operation of the major element so that as an instrument of combat it becomes a self-sufficient unit of striking power in its intended operational envionment.

weightlessness. The phenomenon of absence of weight or zerogravity is experienced by a pilot in a craft when the two forces of thrust and aerodynamic forces reacting on the craft vanish or cancel each other. The pilot may be in a craft moving in some orbit outside the earth's atmosphere in which the craft is coasting. In this case both thrust and aerodynamic forces are equal to 0. Consequently the pilot is in a weightless condition. The other situation of weightlessness occurs when thrust and aerodynamic forces cancel each other. This takes place when the propelling forces or thrust are equal to the drag forces acting on the craft. The craft in this instance is moving through the sensible atmosphere and is following some type of celestial trajectory. For a short duration, approximately 35 to 45 seconds according to present experiments, the pilot is in a weightless condition. A sustained condition of weightlessness, as experienced by crew members in space travel remote from an attracting celestial body or in an orbiting vehicle, is a physical and psychological hazard, unless gravity is simulated and weight is restored, by, for example, a constant acceleration of the spacecraft or rotation of the satellite to put a "floor" under the feet of the crew, resulting in "apparent gravity."

wind tunnel. A tunnel through which a stream of air is drawn at controlled speeds for aerodynamic tests and experimentation.

WRAMA. Warner-Robins Air Materiel Area. Located at Robins Air Force Base, near Macon, Georgia. See **AMA**.

WS-110. The B-70 bombardment aircraft (see).

X. Symbol for "experimental." When used as a prefix with the designation of a missile, it indicates that the designated item is an experimental model of the specified missile, *e.g.*, Lockheed X-17.

X-15. A rocket research aircraft with an inertial guidance system. The X-15 is expected to attain manned flight at altitudes as high as 300 miles and at speeds of mach 5 to mach 7 (in lower-altitude terms). Gross weight is about 16 tons.

Y. Symbol for "prototype." When used as a prefix with the designation of a missile, it indicates that the designated item has progressed beyond the experimental stage but is produced in limited numbers for service testing.

APPENDIX VI

Biographical Notes

LIEUTENANT COLONEL WILLIAM L. ANDERSON, is Deputy Director of Personnel, 1st Missile Division. After wartime service in the CBI theater, he has specialized in personnel work. In 1951–53 he was an assistant executive officer to the Assistant Secretary of the Air Force, and afterward was in the Directorate of Manpower and Organization, Headquarters USAF.

COLONEL ROBERT D. BOWERS, M.S., Nuclear Engineering, University of California, is Assistant for Plans, Air Force Ballistic Missile Division. He has also served in the War Plans Division, Headquarters USAF.

MAJOR ROY L. FERGUSON, JR., is Assistant for Weapon System 107A-1, AF Ballistic Missile Division. Previously he worked for three years on missile operational planning in Headquarters USAF.

MAJOR GENERAL BEN I. FUNK is Director, Ballistic Missiles Office, Headquarters Air Materiel Command. Much of his career has been on important assignments relating to Air Force equipment, procurement, and logistics.

LIEUTENANT COLONEL KENNETH F. GANTZ, Ph.D., University of Chicago, is Editor of *Air University Quarterly Review.*

COLONEL EDWARD N. HALL, M.S., California Institute of Technology, has been Director, Weapon System 315A (Thor), AF Ballistic Missile Division. Since the war he has contributed much to development of rocket power plants, leading to engines for the Atlas, Titan, and Thor missiles.

LIEUTENANT COLONEL RICHARD K. JACOBSON, M.S., Massachusetts Institute of Technology, is Chief, Test Office, Deputy Commander for Weapon Systems, Air Force Ballistic Missile Division. He has been engaged on missile and atomic projects since 1948.

MAJOR GENERAL CHARLES M. MCCORKLE, USMA, is Assistant Chief of Staff for Guided Missiles, Headquarters United States Air Force. During the war he commanded fighter groups in the Aleutians and Italy and was Chief of Staff, First Fighter Command, Mitchel Field. He is a graduate of the Armed Forces Staff College, Air War College, and National War College.

GENERAL THOMAS S. POWER is Commander in Chief, Strategic Air Command. In this capacity he is charged with the operational employment of ballistic missiles. His experience with strategic air operations dates from early World War II and with ballistic missiles from his 1954 assignment as Commander, Air Research and Development Command.

COLONEL CLAUDE E. PUTNAM, Chief of the Evaluation Staff, Air War College, has been associated with strategic air operations since early in World War II. He has previously served as Deputy Director of Plans, Headquarters Strategic Air Command and Commander, 818th Air Division, Strategic Air Command.

DR. DUANE ROLLER, Ph.D. in Physics, California Institute of Technology, is a member of the Space Technology Laboratories of the Ramo-Wooldridge Corporation. Associated with him in writing the "Notes on Technical Aspects of Ballistic Missiles" were Dr.

Charles T. Morrow, Ph.D., Acoustics and Communications, Harvard University; Reed P. Berry, M.S., Engineering, University of California at Los Angeles; and John W. Herrick, B.S., Aeronautics, B.S., Mechanical Engineering, Tri-State College. Dr. Roller is presently on leave from Ramo-Wooldridge to serve as visiting professor of physics at the new Harvey Mudd College of Science and Engineering.

MAJOR GENERAL BERNARD A. SCHRIEVER, M.S., Stanford University, is Commander, AF Ballistic Missile Division, and Deputy Commander for Ballistic Missiles of Air Research and Development Command. He was a test pilot in 1939 and flew sixty-three combat missions in the Southwest Pacific Theater of World War II. Since 1949 he has been in research and development and now has immediate control over the Air Force ballistic missile development program.

COLONEL HARVEY W. C. SHELTON, now studying at the Air War College, has been in Headquarters USAF with the Air Force atomic energy program and on the faculty of Air Command and Staff College, where he was responsible for the curriculum treatment of weapon systems under development.

COLONEL ALEXANDER SHERIDAN is a project officer on the Evaluation Staff, Air War College. With an extensive background in air transport assignments and in plans, Colonel Sheridan was recently project officer for the Intercontinental Ballistic Missile Force Study, examining missile reaction time and command arrangements.

MAJOR KENNETH A. SMITH is a student in the Air Command and Staff College. A World War II navigator, an oil company geologist in the interim before serving as a wing observer in the Korean War, he has for the past several years been an intelligence officer in Strategic Air Command.

COLONEL ALLEN W. STEPHENS is Chief of Staff, 1st Missile Division, Cooke Air Force Base. He has had many years' experience in assignments relating to military career incentives, including that of Deputy Staff Director with the Cordiner Committee.

LIEUTENANT COLONEL EDWARD A. SWANKE, is Chief, Test Facilities Division, Directorate of Installations, Air Force Ballistic Missile Division. He has been associated with Army and Air Force engineering since 1940.

GENERAL THOMAS D. WHITE, USMA, is Chief of Staff, United States Air Force. For four years preceding this appointment in 1957, he was Vice Chief of Staff, and for two years prior to that was Deputy Chief of Staff, Operations.